Private
Pilot
Manual

JEPPESEN
SANDERSON

JS314301A

INTRODUCTION

The new *Private Pilot Manual* is designed for pilot applicants who are training under FAR Part 141 in FAA approved schools. The manual and supplementary materials also meet the requirements of a home study course for pilot applicants who are seeking certification under FAR Part 61 and are not affiliated with an approved school.

The *Private Pilot Manual* is an authoritative textbook reference which is flexible, comprehensive, and well illustrated for easier study and understanding. Although this manual will produce good results when studied alone, the best results can be obtained when it is studied as an integral part of the total learning system within which it was designed. The textbook is the central component for academic study in the learning system. The Private Pilot Course contains several other complementary components for study and review of essential material.

1. Private Pilot Audiovisual Presentations review and reinforce the concepts presented in the manual. These motivating visual aids present essential subject areas in brilliant color and synchronized sound.
2. The *Private Pilot Workbook* contains comprehensive exercises which cover the material presented in the audiovisual course and in the manual. The workbook is designed for individual study and self-checking. The exercises also are necessary completion standards for the ground training lessons in the Training Syllabus.
3. The Private Pilot Stage Examination Set includes exam booklets containing questions over specific chapters of the manual. The exams are designed to evaluate the applicant's progress at various intervals throughout the course.
4. The Private Pilot Final Exam evaluates the applicant's comprehension of subject areas emphasized in the actual FAA written test. The exam booklet contains two exams with a common reference section and reflects the subject areas introduced in the new series of FAA exams. Answer keys and comprehensive critiques also are available.
5. The *Private Pilot Training Syllabus* provides a lesson-by-lesson guide for completion of the ground and flight training required under FAR Part 141. The Training Syllabus is required for all applicants who are enrolled in approved schools and also is beneficial for applicants seeking certification outside of approved schools.

The information presented in the Private Pilot Course provides the necessary framework for a successful training program. Applicants who complete this course of study under the guidance of a qualified instructor will be well prepared for the FAA written examination and flight test.

If you have questions or need explanations about any part of the course, we are prepared to offer assistance at any time. Just write:

Marketing Manager, Aviation Products
Jeppesen Sanderson, Inc.
55 Inverness Drive East
Englewood, Colorado 80112

TABLE OF CONTENTS

BEFORE BEGINNING YOUR STUDY

The private pilot trainee is required by regulation to obtain the following certificates and forms prior to receiving the private pilot certificate:

(1)   THIRD-CLASS MEDICAL CERTIFICATE — Issued by an FAA Medical Examiner when the applicant meets standards prescribed in Part 67 of the Federal Aviation Regulations. Names and addresses of FAA Medical Examiners may be obtained from your flight instructor, the airport operator, or your FAA General Aviation District Office. Medical Examiners issue student pilot certificates along with the medical certificates.

(2)   RADIOTELEPHONE OPERATOR'S PERMIT — Issued by the Federal Communications Commission. A pilot trainee must have this permit in his possession before operating an aircraft radio while solo. The application form for the permit is included in the Private Pilot Student Kit, or it can be obtained from the local airport dealer. The form is in a self-addressed postcard format.

(3)   FAA AIRMAN WRITTEN EXAMINATION REPORT FORM — Will be mailed to the pilot trainee by the FAA upon successful completion of the FAA Private Pilot Written Examination. A score of 70% is considered a passing grade. Written exams can be taken at the nearest General Aviation District Office.

After completion of a private pilot flight course, the student's flight instructor will assist in arranging an appointment with an examiner for the private pilot oral examination and flight test. A private pilot certificate will be issued by the FAA Examiner upon the trainee's successful completion of the private pilot oral examination and flight test and, upon submission by the trainee, of an Airman's Written Examination Report form with a 70% or above grade.

EXAM-O-GRAMS

Exam-O-Grams are brief and timely explanations of important aeronautical concepts which, in the past, have proven to be difficult areas for students on FAA Written Examinations. They are developed by the FAA on a continuing basis as the need arises, but they are not produced on a regular schedule. Subjects covered by past Exam-O-Grams are thoroughly discussed in this manual; however, if desired, the VFR Exam-O-Grams may be ordered from the FAA without charge from the following address.

Federal Aviation Administration
Flight Standards National Field Office
Examinations Branch
P.O. Box 25082
Oklahoma City, Oklahoma 73125

chapter 1

INTRODUCTION TO THE AIRPLANE

INTRODUCTION

This chapter will acquaint the student with the basic concepts of airplane design variation, structure, and the function of each major component. He will also become familiar with the dynamic nature of airflow and the dynamic and static forces acting on an airplane in flight. Additionally, this chapter will provide basic knowledge of the factors affecting aircraft performance.

SECTION A - THE AIRPLANE

VARIETIES OF AIRCRAFT

The FAA has developed guidelines which assist in differentiating between the vast array of aircraft. One method of classification is based on the manner in which an aircraft sustains itself while airborne. From this standpoint, aircraft are divided into the four following categories:

1. Lighter-than-air.
2. Gliders.
3. Rotorcraft.
4. Airplane.

LIGHTER-THAN-AIR

Historically, *balloons* were the first aircraft that enabled man to break the bond that had held him to earth. Today, the balloon survives principally for sport, and the dangerously flammable hydrogen, used previously to provide lifting power, has been replaced by hot air. (See Fig. 1-1.)

Another variety of lighter-than-air craft is the *blimp*. (See Fig. 1-2.) A rigid keel runs along the bottom of the gas envelope, and to this keel a control car or cabin is attached. Generally, twin

Fig. 1-1. Balloon

Fig. 1-2. Blimp

powerplants are used, one on each side of the control car.

A third variation of lighter-than-air craft was the *dirigible* or Zeppelin. (See Fig. 1-3.) These giant airships differed from the blimp in that they had a lightweight aluminum framework.

Fig. 1-4. Sailplane

ling the sailplane to achieve great altitudes and long duration flights.

ROTORCRAFT

Rotorcraft may be subdivided into *gyroplanes* which attain thrust with a pusher-type propeller and lift with a free-wheeling rotor, and *helicopters* on which the rotor is powered in order to achieve lift. (See Fig. 1-5.)

AIRPLANES

By far, the most important type of aircraft in terms of its numbers, economic contributions, and sociological impact is the airplane.

As with other types of aircraft, airplanes may be classified on the basis of certain characteristics. In the case of airplanes, this breakdown is made on the basis

Fig. 1-3. Dirigible with Lightweight Internal Framework

GLIDERS

The type of *glider* most prominent today is the high-performance sailplane. (See Fig. 1-4.) This type of craft possesses excellent aerodynamic characteristics and has enjoyed great popularity in a sport which allows the pilot to pit his knowledge of air currents and skill in control-

GYROPLANE

HELICOPTER

Fig. 1-5. Gyroplane and Helicopter

of their intended use, number of engines, type of landing gear, and the location and configuration of their wings. As shown in figure 1-6, single-engine land, single-engine sea, multi-engine land, and multi-engine sea airplanes denote a more detailed classification.

Fig. 1-6. Airplanes

AIRPLANE COMPONENTS

The major component parts of an airplane are: (See Fig. 1-7.)

1. Wings.
2. Fuselage or body.
3. Tail assembly or empennage.
4. Landing gear.
5. Powerplant.

WINGS

WING CONFIGURATION AND LOCATION

A casual walk around any large airport will show that most airplanes are *monoplanes*, or airplanes with one wing. (See Figs. 1-8 and 1-9.) Airplanes with two wings, called *biplanes*, are likely to be agricultural aircraft, restored antiques, or sport airplanes designed and built by the homebuilder. As shown in figure 1-10, wings can take various shapes and may be located on the fuselage in different positions.

WING CONSTRUCTION

Many high-wing airplanes have external braces or wing struts which transmit the flight and landing loads through the struts to the main fuselage structure. A few high-wing and most low-wing airplanes, on the other hand, have a *full-cantilever* wing designed to carry the loads without external bracing or struts.

Wings are designed to be extremely strong and, at the same time, lightweight. *Spars* run the length of the wing from wing root to wingtip and bear the major portion of bending loads. Bending or twisting loads are transferred to the metal skin and absorbed by tension or compression of the skin. *Ribs* maintain the shape of the wing and stiffen the skin. Additional resistance to buckling-under loads is provided by parts known as *stringers* and *formers*. In almost all aircraft, some of the space inside the wing is occupied by fuel tanks. (See Fig. 1-11.)

COMPONENT PARTS

Flaps and *ailerons* are hinged along the trailing edge of most airplane wings. (See Fig. 1-11.) The ailerons make up the outboard segment of the wings' trailing edges and move in opposite directions in order to make the aircraft roll or bank. The flaps move together and are used primarily during the takeoff and landing phase of a flight.

FUSELAGE

The *fuselage*, or body, of the airplane provides an attachment point for the wing, tail assembly, landing gear, and powerplant. In addition, it provides space for the crew and passengers and houses the various controls and instruments required for flight.

Fuselages are sometimes categorized according to the type of construction employed. In the *truss-type* construction, the forces of compression, tension, and shear are absorbed by a framework of steel tubing. (See Fig. 1-12.) The *semimonocoque* type is an alternate method

Fig. 1-7. Airplane Components

Fig. 1-8. Typical Monoplane in Low-Wing Configuration

Fig. 1-9. Typical Monoplane in High-Wing Configuration

HIGH WING-EXTERNALLY BRACED

SWEPTBACK WING

LOW WING

TAPERED TRAILING EDGE WING

DOUBLE TAPERED WING

HIGH WING-GULL

DELTA WING

MID WING

ELLIPTICAL WING

RECTANGULAR WING

HIGH WING-FULL CANTILEVER

TAPERED LEADING EDGE WING

LOW WING-INVERTED GULL CONFIGURATION

Fig. 1-10. Various Wing Shapes and Locations

FUEL TANK

(HIGH LIFT DEVICE) FLAP

AILERON

STRINGER

RIB

SKIN

SPAR

TIP FAIRING

Fig. 1-11. Wing Components

WELDED STEEL TUBING   SEMI-MONOCOQUE

SKIN
FORMERS

STRINGERS
BULKHEAD

Fig. 1-12. Two Methods Employed in Fuselage Construction

of construction. This means that the skin, made of stamped and formed sheets of aluminum alloy, carries a major portion of the stresses. A part of the structural strength also lies in internal members such as the floor, bulkheads, stringers, formers, and stiffeners.

EMPENNAGE

The *empennage* most often consists of a fixed vertical stabilizer, attached movable rudder, horizontal stabilizer, and hinged movable elevator. (See Fig. 1-13.) Some airplanes have a pivoting one-piece horizontal stabilizer which needs no elevator. A horizontal surface designed in this manner is called a stabilator.

TRIM TABS

Most airplanes have a small hinged section on the elevator called the *trim tab*. The trim tab is connected by cables to a control wheel in the cabin and is used to relieve control pressures at any desired flight attitude, thus helping to prevent pilot fatigue.

The direct effect of a trim tab is to exert pressure on the control surface to which it is attached. Figure 1-14 shows an elevator trim tab in the down position, thus

exposing it to the pressures of the slipstream. This forces the elevator up, and the nose of the airplane rises. More complex airplanes may also have trim tabs on the rudder and the ailerons.

LANDING GEAR

Even though the airplane is basically designed to fly, provisions must be made for ground operations such as taxiing, takeoff, and landing. The landing gear of an airplane may be of the so-called *conventional* type which incorporates two main wheels and a tailwheel (see Fig. 1-15), or it may be of the *tricycle* type with two main wheels and a steerable nosewheel (see Fig. 1-16). The wheels may be fixed in position, or by utilizing a retraction mechanism, they may be withdrawn into the wings or fuselage thereby effecting a great reduction in aerodynamic drag. (See Fig. 1-17.)

In order to absorb landing shocks, the wheels of most airplanes are attached to *oleo struts*. (See Fig. 1-18.) The oleo struts make use of confined air and oil in order to absorb impacts. Other aircraft may have a spring steel landing gear, and a few aircraft use shock-absorbing biscuits, shock cords, and torsion bar systems.

VERTICAL STABILIZER (FIN)   RUDDER   HORIZONTAL STABILIZER AND ELEVATOR

ELEVATOR

STABILATOR

HORIZONTAL STABILIZER

Fig. 1-13. Components of the Tail Assembly or Empennage

Fig. 1-14. Function of the Elevator Trim Tab

Fig. 1-17. Airplane with Landing Gear Retracted

Fig. 1-15. Typical Conventional Landing Gear Installation

Fig. 1-16. Modern Tricycle-Geared Airplane

The utility of the airplane has been greatly extended through the adaptation of specialized types of landing gears. Figure 1-19 illustrates the distinctive landing gears provided for skiplanes, floatplanes, and amphibious airplanes. Pilots utilizing ski-equipped airplanes can operate from frozen lakes, glaciers, and snowbound airports.

Fig. 1-18. Airplane Landing Gear Shock Struts

FLOATS

SKIS

AMPHIBIAN

Fig. 1-19. Special Landing Gear

BRAKES

The brakes may be considered as components of the landing gear. Small general aviation aircraft utilize a simple self-contained hydraulic system to apply braking action.

On some aircraft, the brakes on the left and right wheels are equipped with individual hydraulic brakes which are operated by applying toe pressure to the rudder pedals. The rotation of the pedals ac-

tuates the brake cylinders, resulting in brake fluid being forced through the brake lines to the brakes, where a braking action is applied to the main landing gear wheels. A separate handle is used to set the brakes for parking. (See Fig. 1-20.) Steering is accomplished by a mechanical linkage from the rudder pedals to the nose- or tailwheels.

On some aircraft, the brakes on the left and right main wheels are applied simul-

PARKING BRAKE HANDLE

TOPS OF PEDALS
ACT AS TOE BRAKES

LEFT
RUDDER
PEDAL

RIGHT
RUDDER
PEDAL

SPRING

SPRING

BRAKE
HOUSING

BRAKE
PISTON

BRAKE
CYLINDER

VENT

BRAKE
RETURN
SPRING

RESERVOIR
CAVITY

BRAKE
LININGS

PISTON
CHECK VALVE

LEFT MAIN
LANDING
WHEEL

BRAKE
DISC

RIGHT
MAIN
LANDING
WHEEL

MASTER CYLINDER
DETAIL

Fig. 1-20. Typical Individual Hydraulic Brake System

Fig. 1-21. Typical Hand Brake System

taneously by means of a hand brake. (See Fig. 1-21.) This type of system is primarily designed for deceleration and parking operations. Steering is accomplished by a mechanical linkage from the rudder pedals to the nose- or tailwheels.

THE POWERPLANT

The powerplant may consist of an engine-propeller combination or, in the case of jet propulsion, the engine itself is considered the powerplant. A commonly used powerplant is the gasoline-powered internal combustion engine.

In single-engine aircraft, an engine mount holds the powerplant to a sealed firewall at the front of the cabin section. (See Fig. 1-22.) The cowling is used to enclose the engine and serves several additional purposes. The cowling:

1. Shrouds the engine to provide engine cooling by ducting the cooling air around the engine cylinders.

2. Streamlines the front of the airplane so that the on-rushing air will pass the nose of the airplane with a minimum of drag and turbulence.

Fig. 1-22. Details of Engine Compartment

3. Protects the engine and accessories from rain and snow when the aircraft is parked.

4. Enhances the appearance of the airplane.

PROPELLERS

In most cases, the propeller is mounted directly on the crankshaft which is driven by the moving pistons as they go through their power cycle. Each blade of the propeller is shaped like a small airfoil or wing. (See Fig. 1-23.) These blades are "twisted" to insure that the blades of the propeller "bite" into the air at the proper angle and provide forward lift, much like the wing provides vertical lift. In a sense, then, the propeller becomes a revolving wing. The path of the propeller on a cruising airplane is shown in figure 1-24.

Details of powerplants and propellers are discussed in Chapter 2.

AIRFOIL OR REVOLVING WING

Fig. 1-23. The Propeller

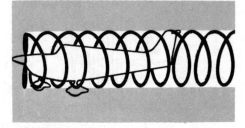

Fig. 1-24. The Path of the Propeller

SECTION B - AERODYNAMICS

Once the aircraft leaves the ground, it is supported in the air by aerodynamic forces. An examination of the forces acting upon an airplane and the application of the principles upon which these forces are based follows.

BERNOULLI'S PRINCIPLE

One of the most significant physical laws that led to the creation of the airfoil is the *Bernoulli Principle*, which states the relationship between pressure, fluid flow velocity, and the potential energy of fluids (liquids and gases). This principle, discovered by Daniel Bernoulli (1700-1782), a Swiss scientist, states that: "As the velocity of the fluid increases, the pressure in the fluid decreases;" and conversely, "as the velocity of the fluid decreases, the pressure in the fluid increases."

An operating example of Bernoulli's Principle is the *venturi tube.* (See Fig. 1-25.) This device is a tube which is narrower in the middle than at the ends. As air passes through the tube, it speeds up as it reaches the narrow portion and slows down again as it passes the restriction.

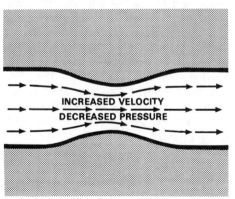

INCREASED VELOCITY

DECREASED PRESSURE

*Fig. 1-25. Flow of Air Through
a Venturi Tube*

The previous statement can be explained as follows: if the air flowing through the entrance to the tube has 1,000 molecules per inch in the tube and is moving at a rate of one inch per second, there are 1,000 molecules flowing through the tube each second. Assuming that the area of the narrow part of the tubing is one-half that of the rest of the tube, the molecules in the air must speed up to get 1,000 molecules per second through this restricted area. With one-half the area, the speed must be twice that in the rest of the tube to permit the same volume of air to pass through the restriction.

More energy is imparted to the molecules as they accelerate. This leaves less energy to exert pressure and the pressure thus decreases. The throat in a carburetor, as described in Chapter 2, is an application of the venturi principle.

AIRFOILS

The principles applied to the venturi are also utilized to create lift for an airplane. However, in lieu of a venturi, a wing with an airfoil shape is used to create a pressure differential in the air.

An *airfoil* is any shape which is designed to produce lift. Although the wing is the primary part of the airplane that produces lift, other airfoils find application as propeller blades and tail surfaces. An airfoil has a leading edge, a trailing edge, a chord, and camber as shown in figure 1-26.

The *leading edge* is the part of the airfoil that first meets the oncoming air. The *trailing edge* is the aft end of the airfoil where the airflow over the upper surface joins the airflow over the lower surface.

The *chord line* is an imaginary straight line drawn from the leading edge to the trailing edge. This line has significance only in determining the angle of attack of an airfoil and in determining wing area.

The *camber* of an airfoil is the curvature of its upper (upper camber) and lower (lower camber) surfaces.

Fig. 1-26. Airfoil Terminology

The *relative wind* is the wind moving past the airfoil. The direction of this wind is relative to the attitude or position of the airfoil and it is always parallel to the flight path of the aircraft. (See Fig. 1-27.) The velocity of the relative wind is the speed of the airfoil through the air.

The *angle of attack* is the angle formed by the chord of the airfoil and the direction of the relative wind. The pitch attitude of the airfoil and the angle of attack are the same only in level flight. In other flight conditions, they are different values. (See Fig. 1-27.)

THE FOUR FORCES

An aircraft in straight-and-level flight is acted upon by four forces: lift, gravity, thrust, and drag. *Lift* is the upward acting force; *gravity*, or weight, is the downward acting force; *thrust* acts in a forward direction; and *drag* is the backward, or retarding force produced by air resistance. (See Fig. 1-28.)

Lift opposes weight and thrust opposes drag. When an aircraft is in straight-and-level flight, the opposing forces balance each other; lift equals weight and thrust equals drag. Any inequality between thrust and drag, while maintaining straight-and-level flight, will result in acceleration or deceleration until the two forces again become balanced.

LIFT

According to the Bernoulli Principle, there is an acceleration or increase in the velocity of air as the air flows around an airfoil shape; therefore, there is an acceleration of the relative wind as it flows above and below the surface of the airplane wing. Because the camber of the upper wing surface is greater than that of the lower surface, air flowing above the wing will be accelerated more than air flowing beneath the wing. The Bernoulli Principle also states that an increase in the velocity of a fluid, such as air, results in a decrease of pressure with-

Fig. 1-27. Angle of Attack Depends Only on Relative Wind; Not on Pitch Angle

Fig. 1-28. The Four Forces Acting on an Aircraft in Straight-and-Level Flight

in that fluid. As a result, the reduction in air pressure above the wing will be greater than the pressure reduction along the lower wing surface. This difference of pressure accounts for the upward force called lift. (See Fig. 1-29.)

At *high angles of attack*, an additional force is derived from the impact of air against the lower surface of the wing because it is inclined to the relative wind. This principle may be observed by putting a hand or flat surface out of the window of a fast-moving car. The impact of the air on the bottom surface when it is inclined sharply upward creates a lifting force that is easily sensed. (See Fig. 1-30.)

Even at high angles of attack, the lift generated by the impact of air on the bottom surface of the wing amounts to only a fraction of the lifting force needed to sustain the aircraft in flight. More than 75% of the lift is caused by the lower pressure above the airfoil. The wing is

not so much pushed up from below by excess air pressure as pulled up from above by a suction force.

Lift can be increased in two ways; by increasing the forward speed of the airplane or by increasing the angle of attack. The pilot can increase the forward speed of the aircraft by applying more power. This increases the speed of the relative wind over the airfoil.

THE STALL AND ITS CAUSE

Increasing the angle of attack will increase lift up to a point. As the airfoil is inclined, the air flowing over the top of the airfoil is diverted over a greater distance resulting in an even greater increase in air velocity and more lift.

However, as the airfoil is given a greater angle of attack relative to oncoming air, it becomes more difficult for the air to flow smoothly across the top of the wing. Thus, it starts to separate from the wing and enters a burbling or turbulent pattern. The angle at which airflow separation and turbulence occurs on the upper wing surface is called the *critical angle of attack*. This turbulence results in a loss of lift in the area of the wing where it is taking place.

The separation point starts near the trailing edge of the wing and progresses forward as the angle of attack is increased. (See Fig. 1-31.) Finally, the separation

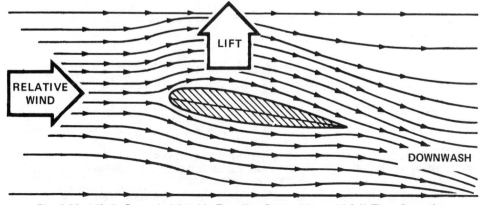

Fig. 1-29. Lift is Generated by Air Traveling Faster Above Airfoil Than Beneath

Fig. 1-30. At High Angles of Attack, Part of Lifting Force is Obtained
From Air Deflected Downward

point moves so far forward that most of the wing loses its lift and a *stall condition* occurs.

FACTORS AFFECTING THE STALL SPEED

Weight

As the weight of the airplane is increased, the stall speed increases. Because of the greater weight, a higher angle of attack must be maintained to produce the extra lift required to support the additional weight; therefore, the critical angle of attack will be reached at a *higher* airspeed when the aircraft is loaded to maximum takeoff weight than when a lighter load is carried.

Flaps

The stall speed chart, shown in figure 1-32, illustrates how the use of flaps results in a reduction in stall speed. Notice that there is a progressive reduction in stall speed in level flight from 47 knots with the flaps up to 41 knots with the flaps extended 40°.

Angle of Bank

Figure 1-33A illustrates the relationship between angle of bank and stall speed. Note that there is a progressive increase in stall speed as the angle of bank is increased from zero. The stall speed increases due to the additional load factor or weight supported by the wings. As load factor increases, the total lift must also increase to maintain level flight. This additional lift is generated by increasing the angle of attack. Therefore, in a turn, the critical, or stall, angle of attack is reached at a higher airspeed than in level flight. For example, the stall speed is approximately 40% greater in a 60° bank turn than when the aircraft is in straight-and-level flight. (See Fig. 1-33A, item 1.)

SEPARATION POINT STARTS
NEAR TRAILING EDGE

SEPARATION POINT MOVES
FORWARD AS ANGLE OF
ATTACK IS INCREASED

BURBLE   STALL

Fig. 1-31. Stall Occurs When Angle of Attack is Increased Too Much

STALL SPEEDS, POWER OFF MOST FORWARD CENTER OF GRAVITY				
CONDITION	ANGLE OF BANK			
	0°	30°	45°	60°
FLAPS UP	47	51	56	66
FLAPS 10°	44	47	52	62
FLAPS 40°	41	44	49	58
WEIGHT—2300 LBS		SPEEDS ARE KNOTS, IAS		

Fig. 1-32. Effect of Flaps

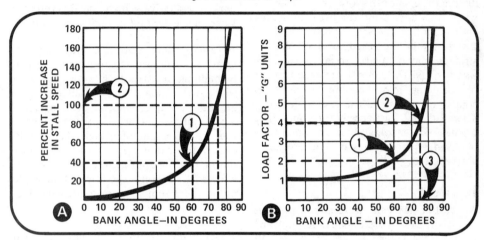

Fig. 1-33. Stall Speed and Load

Center of Gravity Location (Weight Distribution)

If the weight distribution of the aircraft is located farther forward (forward CG), additional down force on the tail must be developed through elevator back pressure to produce a critical angle of attack. If the elevators are already in the full-up position, the additional aerodynamic force must be generated by increasing airflow over the horizontal tail surfaces. To do this, the airspeed must be greater; therefore, the *stall speed increases.*

Conversely, the farther aft the weight distribution, the *lower* the stall speed. The pilot should not interpret this to mean that it is desirable to have a CG which is aft of limits. The problems involved in stability and stall recovery

will far outweigh any advantages obtained by the decrease in stall speed.

Load Factor

Load factor is the ratio of the load supported by the wings to the actual weight of the aircraft and its contents. With the bank required to produce a load factor of two G's (twice the force of gravity), the wings support twice the weight of the aircraft; at a load factor of four G's, they support four times the weight of the aircraft. (See Fig. 1-33B, items 1 and 2.)

Airplanes certificated by the FAA in the *normal category* are required to have a minimum limit load factor of 3.8. The limit load factor is that load factor that an aircraft can sustain without incurring permanent structural damage. Note, on load factor charts, that this limit load factor is attained in a level, banked turn of approximately 75° (item 3). At this angle of bank, the stall speed is also approximately 100% greater than the value for straight-and-level flight. (See Fig. 1-33A, item 2.)

Frost, Snow, and Ice

Even a light accumulation of frost, snow, or ice on the wings can cause a significant increase in stall speed. The accumulation disrupts the smooth flow of air over the wing, thus decreasing the lift it produces and increasing the stall speed. The stall speed may be increased so much that an airplane may be unable to attain the necessary speed to take off or, even though the airplane may become airborne, it could be so close to the stall speed that it would not be possible to maintain flight. Frost, snow, and ice should always be removed from the wings before flight is attempted.

Turbulence

Air turbulence can cause large, momentary increases in stall speed. An upward vertical gust causes an abrupt change in the direction of the relative wind and the angle of attack. It is this abrupt increase in angle of attack which can produce a stall. Pilots making landing approaches under turbulent conditions generally maintain an approach speed somewhat higher than the normal approach speed in order to guard against a stall.

MISCONCEPTIONS REGARDING STALLS

Some persons believe that stalls occur only at relatively low airspeeds; however, this is not true. An airplane can be stalled *at any airspeed*. All that is necessary is to exceed the critical angle of attack. This can be done at any airspeed if the pilot applies abrupt or excessive back pressure on the elevator control. The stall that occurs at a relatively high speed is referred to as an *accelerated* or *high-speed stall*.

Another misconception is that it is necessary for the airplane to have a relatively high pitch attitude in order for it to stall. An airplane can be stalled *in any attitude*; level, banked, or even inverted. Again, all that is necessary is to exceed the critical angle of attack. This could occur, for example, in a level attitude during landing approach if the airspeed is allowed to become too low and the angle of attack becomes too great. (See Fig. 1-34.)

Another misconception is that the speed of the airplane over the ground, or ground speed, is related to the stall speed. For example, this question was posed to a group of student pilots: "If an airplane's stalling speed was 60 m.p.h. and you are

Fig. 1-34. Stall Can Occur in Level Attitude

flying at an airspeed of 70 m.p.h. into a 30 m.p.h. wind, what would happen if you maintained this airspeed of 70 m.p.h., but turned downwind?" A number of the students said the airplane would stall; however, this is not correct. *Airspeed* is the only speed which is of any significance in aerodynamics. Once it is off the ground, an airplane "feels" nothing but its own speed through the air. Its stall speed is not affected by what the airplane's speed happens to be in relation to the ground. The airplane in flight "feels" no wind; it simply proceeds through the air mass operating with the same mechanical efficiency upwind, downwind, crosswind, or in no wind at all.

STALL RECOVERY

When the wing stalls, the airplane descends since insufficient lift is being generated to hold the aircraft aloft. The pilot can recover from a stall condition by one of two methods:

1. By lowering the nose of the aircraft. This decreases the angle of attack of the wings and allows the airflow over the wings to smooth out again.
2. By accelerating the aircraft. This is done by the application of more engine power. However, if the aircraft is moving under full power when the stall occurs, the only way to recover is to lower the nose.

As noted above, lift is affected by the angle of attack of the airfoil with respect to the relative wind. To hold the airfoil in a particular position requires an external aerodynamic force. Through the use of elevators or a stabilator, the pilot can control the angle of attack. The pilot holds the surface in the position that causes the airflow over the tail surfaces to exert the required amount of force to hold the wings in the desired attitude.

DESIGN OF THE WING

The shape of the wing is very important for the type of operation that the aircraft is designed to accomplish. The shape of the airfoil selected is determined by the primary function of the airplane. If the aircraft is designed for slow speed, a thick

airfoil is used; for high speed aircraft, a thin airfoil is utilized.

Planform

Planform is the shape of the wing as seen from directly above or below. The relationship between the length and the width of a wing is called the *aspect ratio.* It is computed by dividing the span (distance from wingtip to wingtip) by the average chord of the wing. (See Fig. 1-35.) The average chord is called the mean aerodynamic chord (MAC).

In general, the higher the aspect ratio, the more efficient the wing. A long narrow wing will create more lift per square foot of area than a short wide wing. The aspect ratios on gliders can be as great as 20 to one. The average aspect ratio of general aviation aircraft is approximately six to one.

The wingtip is the least efficient portion of the wing because the air under the wing rolls from beneath the wingtip into the low pressure area above the upper surface of the wing. This rolling air causes a swirl, or vortex, at the tip of the wing and decreases the amount of smooth air which creates lift. (See Fig. 1-36.) Thus, a narrow chord wing has less wing surface in the disturbed vortex area and has less loss of lift than a wide chord wing.

The swirling air trailing behind the wingtips is called wake turbulence. A discussion of the operational aspects of flight in areas where wake turbulence from large aircraft is most often encountered is included at the end of Section C of this Chapter.

The advantages and disadvantages of the various wing planform shapes shown previously in figure 1-10 are noted below:

1. STRAIGHT WING — excellent stall characteristics. Most economical to build. Inefficient from structural, weight, and drag standpoints.
2. TAPERED WING — efficient from structural, weight, and drag standpoints. Stall characteristics are not as good as straight wing.

ASPECT RATIO = 4
WING AREA = 144 SQ. FT.

6 FT. CHORD

24 FT. SPAN

ASPECT RATIO = 9
WING AREA = 144 SQ. FT.

4 FT. CHORD

36 FT. SPAN

ASPECT RATIO = 9
WING AREA = 144 SQ. FT.

4 FT. AVER. CHORD

36 FT. SPAN

$$\text{ASPECT RATIO} = \frac{\text{SPAN}}{\text{AVER. CHORD}}$$

Fig. 1-35. Aspect Ratio

Fig. 1-36. Wingtip Vortex

3. ELLIPTICAL WING — most efficient from structural, weight, and drag standpoints. Stall characteristics are not as good as straight wing and wing is more expensive to build than tapered wing.

4. SWEPTBACK AND DELTA WINGS — efficient at high speeds near the speed of sound, but inefficient at approach and landing speeds.

Incidence

The angle of incidence is the name given to the angle between the wing chord line and the airplane's longitudinal axis. (See Fig. 1-37.) Choosing the right angle of incidence in designing the airplane can improve flight visibility over the nose and reduce drag in cruising flight. Most airplanes have a slight positive angle of incidence so that the wing has a positive angle of attack when the fuselage is perfectly level, as in cruising flight.

Washout or Twist

To provide positive aileron control throughout the stall, wing twist is often built into the wing. (See Fig. 1-38.) In this configuration, the wingtip has a lower angle of incidence than the wing root (usually two or three degrees). This results in the wingtips having a lower angle of attack than the root during the approach to a stall. Thus, the ailerons and the wingtip will still be flying and providing control when the wing root has stalled. This also produces a more gentle stall since the wing does not stall all at once.

Stall Strips

Stall strips are sometimes employed to make the wing root stall first. As the

Fig. 1-37. Angle of Incidence

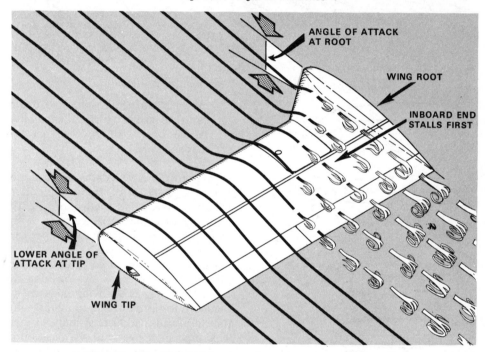

Fig. 1-38. Wing Twist Maintains Aileron Control During the Stall

angle of attack increases, these strips break up the airflow and start the stall at the root. (See Fig. 1-39.)

Spanwise Airfoil Variation

Some wings employ a high-speed airfoil at the root and a low-speed type at the tip to keep the wingtips from stalling. The low-speed airfoil can fly at higher angles of attack than the high-speed root section. Thus, the root stalls first.

WING FLAPS

As noted previously, increasing the camber of the wing increases lift. A de-

vice used to change the camber is the *flap*. It is a movable device which results in the turning down of the trailing edge of the wing. Some of the more common types of flaps are: (See Fig. 1-40.)

1. PLAIN FLAP — This device is hinged to the trailing edge of the wing and is the simplest method of changing the camber of an airfoil. In the retracted position, the flap streamlines and adds to the area of the wing surface.

2. SLOTTED FLAP — This type of device moves aft and down when extended. A slot is formed between the

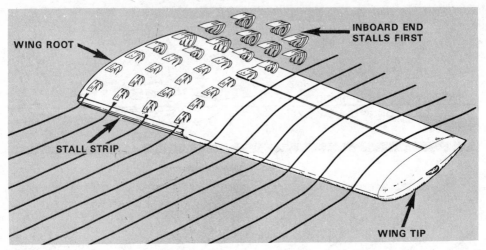

Fig. 1-39. Stall Strips Cause Stall to Begin at Wing Root

Fig. 1-40. Most Common Types of Wing Flaps

wing and flap permitting a smooth flow of air between the two components.

3. SPLIT FLAP — This is a flat surface hinged to, or set into, the lower side of the trailing edge of the wing. The shape of the upper surface of the wing is unchanged when the split flap is lowered. This type of device creates more drag than the plain flap because of its turbulent wake.

4. THE FOWLER FLAP — This mechanism moves backward on rollers in a track and then is rotated downward to provide high lift capability. When down, this device increases lift and wing area.

Flaps normally have a deflection range of from 0° to 40° from the chord of the wing. The deflection of the flap increases the upper camber of the wing, thus increasing the negative pressure on top of the wing and allowing more positive pressure to build up underneath. Thus, lift is *increased* by lowering the flaps. However, as the wing flaps are extended into the airstream to increase lift, they also cause additional induced drag. This drag increases with the position of the flaps — the greater the flap deflection, the greater the drag.

Pilots make use of the lift-to-drag ratio generated by wing flaps in several flight operations. For example, during takeoff or climb over obstacles, the pilot desires high lift with as little drag as possible. To accomplish this, wing flaps are usually extended to one-fourth or one-half the flap travel. This permits additional lift to be obtained with a minimum of additional drag.

Beyond the half-flap position, although it is true that wing flaps produce more lift with deflection, the drag increases to the extent that the flaps are acting more as air brakes than lifting devices. It is because of this braking effect that more than one-half flap travel is not used in takeoff or in operations where high lift with low drag is desired.

The braking effect of the flaps in the full-flap position is very advantageous for landing, however. The landing flight path, without flaps, is very shallow. When landing over obstacles, this causes the aircraft to land further down the field. With the air-brake effect of full flaps, the aircraft descends at a much steeper angle. This permits landing closer to the approach end of the runway. The landing speed, with flaps, is slower during the touchdown, and the aircraft is easier to stop.

GRAVITY

Gravity is the force that lift has to overcome for the airplane to fly and amounts to nothing more than the weight of the loaded airplane.

THRUST

Forward motion is essential for the flight of all fixed-wing airplanes. This force, called *thrust*, is obtained through the use of a propeller or jet engine. During straight-and-level flight at a constant airspeed, thrust and drag are equal. When the thrust is increased by increasing engine power, thrust momentarily exceeds drag, and the airspeed increases. The increase in airspeed causes a corresponding increase in drag. Airspeed, however, does not increase at the same rate as drag. As airspeed is increased, drag increases at a much *faster* rate. At a new higher airspeed, thrust and drag forces again become equalized and speed again becomes constant.

For the airplane to remain in steady flight, equilibrium must be maintained; lift must be equal to airplane weight, and powerplant thrust must be equal to airplane drag. Thus, airplane drag determines the thrust required to maintain level flight.

DRAG

Drag may be subdivided into induced drag and parasite drag. *Induced drag* is simply that drag which is created in the process of developing lift. Increasing the angle of attack or applying flaps to increase lift are two actions which will increase induced drag. (See Fig. 1-41.)

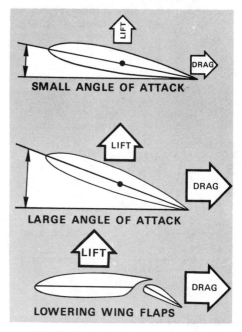

Fig. 1-41. Increasing Induced Drag

In addition to the induced drag caused by the development of lift, there is *parasite drag* due to skin friction and form. Parasite drag is present any time the airplane is moving through the atmosphere, even in a zero lift condition. Components of the airplane, such as the wings, fuselage, tail, and landing gear, contribute to the drag because of their own form. Additionally, any loss of momentum of the airstream due to cowl openings for powerplant cooling, or gaps such as between the wing and aileron, creates additional parasite drag. The sum of all the drag due to form, friction, leakage, momentum losses, and interference is termed *total parasite drag*, since none of these factors are directly associated with the development of lift.

The total drag of the aircraft in flight is the sum of the *induced* and *parasite* drag. Figure 1-42 illustrates the variation of drag with speed for a given aircraft in level flight, at a particular weight, configuration, and altitude. Note that parasite drag increases with speed, while induced drag decreases with speed. The total drag of the aircraft shows the predominant influence of *induced drag at low speeds* and *parasite drag at high speeds*.

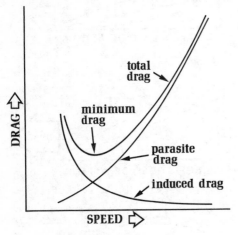

Fig. 1-42. Effect of Speed on Drag

GROUND EFFECT

When the airplane wing operates within a wingspan distance above the ground, induced drag is significantly reduced. Within this height above the ground, the strength of wingtip vortices and the wing downwash is substantially reduced, since these forces are restricted in downward movement.

Therefore, as the aircraft nears the ground, drag effects are reduced rapidly; just before touchdown drag can be decreased as much as 40%. The low-wing airplane is more subject to ground effect than mid- or high-wing airplanes because the wing is closer to the ground.

LIFT-TO-DRAG RATIO

The best power-off glide ratio is obtained at the best lift-to-drag ratio (the lowest point on the *total drag* curve). For example, if an airplane in a glide has a lift-to-drag ratio of 15:1 (15 times as much lift as drag), each mile of altitude can be traded for 15 miles of horizontal distance. To obtain this glide performance, the airplane should be flown at the angle of attack which yields the best lift-to-drag ratio. This is usually expressed in terms of a *best angle-of-glide* airspeed which can be found in the pilot's operating handbook for the aircraft.

THE THREE AXES

There is one point in the aircraft, regardless of its attitude, about which it can be balanced perfectly. This point is the center of the aircraft's total weight and is called *center of gravity*, or "CG." The location of this point varies with the loading of the aircraft. For example, the CG is located further forward in an aircraft loaded with two persons in the front seats than it would be with both front and rear seats occupied.

All movements of the airplane in flight rotate around the center of gravity. These movements are made about one or more of three axes of rotation. These axes are called vertical, lateral, and longitudinal, and all pass through the airplane's center of gravity. (See Fig. 1-43.)

An axis is defined as a line passing through a body about which the body rotates. A turning maneuver rotates the aircraft about the *vertical axis*; climbing and diving produce movement around the *lateral axis*; and banking right or left rotates the aircraft around the *longitudinal axis*.

The control surfaces produce motion about each of these axes. Although rotation about the lateral or pitch axis is affected by several factors, the control of pitch is primarily the function of the *elevator* or *stabilator*. This surface is con-

AILERONS FOR ROLL CONTROL

ELEVATOR FOR PITCH CONTROL

RUDDER FOR YAW CONTROL

LONGITUDINAL (ROLL) AXIS

LATERAL (PITCH) AXIS

VERTICAL (YAW) AXIS

Fig. 1-43. The Three Axes

trolled by fore and aft movement of the control wheel or stick. When forward pressure is applied to the control wheel, the elevators or stabilator move downward, producing an upward force on the horizontal tail. This raises the tail, and therefore lowers the nose. When back pressure is applied to the wheel, the elevators move upward, resulting in a downward tail movement. (See Fig. 1-44.)

The *ailerons* create movement known as *roll* about the longitudinal axis. The ailerons are moved by rotating the control wheel clockwise or counterclockwise. A downward deflected aileron produces additional lift, and the wing to which it is

attached rises. The wing with the aileron deflected upward produces less lift and descends. (See Fig. 1-45.)

Once the ailerons have been properly positioned, the pilot returns the control wheel to a neutral position. The aircraft then continues to bank until the pilot applies opposite control pressure to take the aircraft out of the bank.

Increasing the lift, though, also increases the drag. The wing with the lowered aileron will generate *both* greater lift and greater drag. The aircraft will yaw in the direction of the wing with the lowered aileron, which is the direction opposite

ACTION OF THE ELEVATORS MOVES THE AIRPLANE ON ITS LATERAL AXIS

RAISING ELEVATOR FORCES TAIL DOWN AND THE NOSE RISES

NEUTRAL LIFT

LOWERING ELEVATOR FORCES TAIL UP AND THE NOSE DROPS

Fig. 1-44. Effect of Elevators

NORMAL LIFT

LOWERING AILERON INCREASES
LIFT AND RAISES WING

RAISING AILERON DECREASES
LIFT AND LOWERS WING

ACTION OF AILERONS MOVES THE PLANE
ON ITS LONGITUDINAL AXIS

Fig. 1-45. Effect of Ailerons

the turn being performed. This tendency is called *adverse yaw.*

Movement about the vertical axis is referred to as *yaw.* The *rudder* is a movable control surface on the fin and is responsible for rotation or control around the vertical axis. Movement of the rud-

der is to the left and to the right and is controlled by pressure on the rudder pedals mounted on the floor of the cabin.

Pressure applied to the right rudder pedal displaces the rudder to the right. This increases the camber on the left side of the vertical tail components, creating a low-pressure area on the left side and a high-pressure area on the right side of the tail. (See Fig. 1-46.) The resulting pressures cause the tail to move left and the nose of the aircraft to move right.

Applying pressure to the left rudder pedal provides an opposite reaction. Left pedal movement displaces the rudder to the left. A low-pressure area forms on the right side of the tail and a high-pressure area on the left side. The tail moves to the right and the nose of the airplane moves left.

The rudder is used initially in a turn to overcome adverse yaw. During any flight training maneuver, the student learns that, after a turn is established, the rudder is neutralized to maintain the desired turn.

MOVING RUDDER TO THE LEFT
FORCES TAIL TO THE RIGHT

NEUTRAL

MOVING RUDDER TO THE RIGHT
FORCES TAIL TO LEFT

ACTION OF THE RUDDER
MOVES PLANE ON ITS
VERTICAL AXIS

RUDDER

Fig. 1-46. Effect of Rudders

AIRCRAFT STABILITY

An airplane in flight is constantly affected by minor control pressures and outside forces that move it from the desired flight attitude. The tendencies of an airplane, once it is disturbed from an attitude, depend upon the type of stability designed into the airplane.

Stability refers to the characteristic that causes an aircraft to tend to return to, stay at, or move farther from its original attitude after it has been displaced. *Positive static stability* refers to the initial tendency to return to the original attitude. An aircraft that has *positive dynamic stability*, on the other hand, will have the tendency to return to the original attitude through a series of decreasing oscillations.

An aircraft that tends to stay in an attitude in which it is placed has *neutral static stability*. On the other hand, an aircraft that tends to return to the original attitude (responds to positive static stability) but overshoots and continues to perform oscillations of equal magnitude has *neutral dynamic stability*.

An aircraft that has *negative static stability* will constantly change from one attitude to another and will require the continuous use of controls to maintain a particular attitude. *Negative dynamic stability* is the tendency of an aircraft to deviate farther and farther from the original attitude through a series of oscillations of increasing magnitude. Of course, no aircraft possessing this characteristic may be certified.

An example of the different types of stability can be seen by raising the wing of an airplane while in flight. In a modern aircraft, the resulting tendency of the wing will be to return to a level attitude, thereby exhibiting positive static and positive dynamic stability. Neutral stability would have caused the airplane to stay in a wing-high attitude. Conversely, negative stability would have caused the wing to progress farther from a wings-level attitude through a series of oscillations of increasing magnitude.

LONGITUDINAL STABILITY

If an aircraft is stable about its lateral axis, it will not pitch up or down unless some force raises or lowers the nose of the aircraft. If the aircraft is statically stable about its lateral axis, it will resist any force which might cause it to pitch, and it will return to level flight when the force is removed. This resistance to pitch-up and pitch-down motion is called *longitudinal stability* because the airplane is stable *along* the longitudinal axis. Of the three types of stability of an aircraft in flight, this type is the most important.

To obtain longitudinal stability, the aircraft is designed so that it is slightly nose-heavy. During normal flight, the aircraft has a continuous tendency to descend. However, this tendency is offset by the horizontal tail surfaces (stabilizer) being set at a negative angle of attack. This position produces a downward, or negative, lift so the downward force on the tail exactly counteracts the nose heaviness at a predetermined aircraft speed. (See Fig. 1-47.)

When power is reduced to idle, the airplane loses speed due to lack of thrust. Thus, the speed of the air over the tail decreases, resulting in less downward force on the tail. This permits the nose to drop and allows gravity to act as a thrust force.

As the airplane dives, its airspeed increases. This, in turn, provides a downward force on the tail that pushes the tail down and the nose up, causing the aircraft to go into a climb. As the climb continues, the speed again decreases, and the downward force on the tail decreases gradually until the nose drops once more. This time, if the aircraft is dynamically stable, the nose does not drop as far as it did the first time, and the aircraft enters a much shallower dive. The speed increases until the aircraft

CENTER
OF
LIFT

CENTER
OF
GRAVITY

NEGATIVE ANGLE OF ATTACK (EXAGGERATED IN THIS ILLUSTRATION) CREATES DOWN PRESSURE ON THE HORIZONTAL STABILIZER DURING CRUISE FLIGHT SUFFICIENT IN AMOUNT TO OFFSET NOSE HEAVINESS.

Fig. 1-47. Longitudinally Stable Aircraft is Slightly Nose Heavy

goes into a shallower climb, as before. After several such oscillations, the aircraft will finally settle down to a speed at which the downward force on the tail exactly offsets the tendency of the aircraft to dive. The aircraft can then make a smooth glide down, regardless of whether the power is on or off.

When an aircraft is balanced so that the center of gravity is *behind* the center of lift, the aircraft is tail-heavy and has a tendency to climb. This climbing tendency may be offset only by increasing the lift on the horizontal tail surfaces to produce a positive lift or upward force.

If the throttle is retarded when the airplane is in a tail-heavy condition, the lifting force developed by the tail is decreased because of the loss of thrust. As a result, the aircraft becomes tail-heavy and starts to climb. Since there is nothing to check this climbing tendency, the aircraft continues to climb until it stalls.

If the same aircraft is put into a dive with the controls released, the lift on the tail becomes greater and greater as the speed increases. This, in turn, forces the nose of the aircraft down and causes the aircraft to dive more

and more steeply, until it finally may go partly on its back.

Most airplanes in use today have good longitudinal stability and have sufficient trim tab control to correct for almost any condition of loading.

LATERAL STABILITY

If an aircraft is stable about the longitudinal axis, the wingtips will hold their positions in level flight unless some force is applied to displace them. Any force causing the wings to roll will be resisted, and the wings will return to straight-and-level flight once the force is removed. The most common design factor for providing lateral stability is *dihedral*. Dihedral is the upward angle of an airplane's wings with respect to the horizontal. (See Fig. 1-48.) Low-wing airplanes have more dihedral than high-wing airplanes because the center of gravity is above the wing in a low-wing airplane. When the center of gravity is below the wing, such as in a high-wing airplane, it has a lateral stabilizing effect and very little dihedral is required.

When an aircraft with dihedral rolls so that one wing is lower than the other, the lower wing will have more effective lift

Fig. 1-48. Dihedral Assists
Lateral Stability

than the raised wing because it is not tilted from the horizontal as much. The imbalance in lift tends to raise the lower wing and restore level flight.

Sweepback (see Fig. 1-49) has a lateral stabilizing effect also. When an aircraft with sweepback wings begins to slip, the leading edge of the low wing meets the relative wind more nearly perpendicular than the up wing. This results in more lift on the low wing which causes a restoring force to return the wing to a level position.

Fig. 1-49. Sweepback

Sweepback also contributes to directional stability. If a sweepback wing momentarily yaws because of turbulence or rudder application, the wing which moves forward has the relative wind more perpendicular to the leading edge. This increases the airspeed over the forward wing and consequently decreases the airspeed over the wing which yawed back-

ward. Increased airspeed supplies additional drag while decreased airspeed lessens drag. The increased drag on the forward wing pulls it back while the opposite reaction occurs to the trailing wing. For this reason, both wings will tend to return to their original position automatically correcting the airplane's direction.

DIRECTIONAL STABILITY

Directional stability tends to keep the aircraft flying in a straight direction. An aircraft acts something like a weathervane. If it swings away from its course by rotating about its vertical axis (yawing), the force of the air on the vertical tail surfaces tends to swing it back to its original line of flight. Here again, the location of the center of gravity is important. The area of the side of the airplane behind the center of gravity must be greater than the side area in front of the center of gravity in order to prevent yaw, because, if there were more side area in front of the center of gravity, any tendency of the aircraft to rotate about its vertical axis would then tend to turn the aircraft around. Directional stability, again, is the result of aircraft design. Adequate vertical stabilizer surface provides the necessary directional stability. (See Fig. 1-50.)

TURNING EFFECTS

There are several factors inherent in airplane design that result in a turning tendency. These include the *torque reaction* of the engine, *gyroscopic precession*, *asymmetrical thrust* from the propeller, and *slipstream rotation*.

TORQUE

Except for some twin-engine aircraft, propellers rotate clockwise as seen from the pilot's seat. The torque reaction from the spinning propeller causes the airplane to tend to rotate counterclockwise. (See Fig. 1-51.)

To minimize pilot effort, aircraft are adjusted, or rigged, to compensate for torque in cruising flight. In addition,

SIDE AREA AHEAD OF C.G.

SIDE AREA BEHIND C.G.

VERTICAL STABILIZER CONTRIBUTES TO DIRECTIONAL STABILITY

C.G.

Fig. 1-50. Directional Stability

ACTION

THE TORQUE OF A PROPELLER TURNING CLOCKWISE CAUSES THE AIRPLANE TO ROLL COUNTERCLOCKWISE

REACTION

Fig. 1-51. Torque Effect

pilot-adjustable aileron trim tabs often are utilized in high performance aircraft, to correct the torque effects of various power settings.

PRECESSION

The turning propeller on an airplane possesses characteristics of a gyroscope. One of the properties of gyroscopic action is precession. *Gyroscopic precession* can be explained as the resultant action or deflection of the spinning object when a force is applied to this object. The reaction to a force applied to a gyro acts approximately 90° in the direction of rotation from the point where the force is applied. Therefore, if an airplane is rapidly moved from a nose-high pitch attitude to a nose-low pitch attitude, gyroscopic precession will create a tendency

for the nose to yaw to the left. The left-turning force is quite apparent in tailwheel type airplanes as the tail is raised on the takeoff roll. (See Fig. 1-52.)

ASYMMETRICAL THRUST

In a propeller-driven airplane at a high angle of attack, asymmetrical thrust is created because the descending propeller blade on the right side of the engine has a greater angle of attack than the ascending blade on the left. This produces greater thrust from the right side of the propeller resulting in a left yaw known as *P-factor*. (See Fig. 1-53.) It should be remembered that P-factor creates a left-turning tendency *only* when the airplane is flying with a positive angle of attack. P-factor is not prevalent in level cruise flight since both propeller blades

Fig. 1-52. Gyroscopic Effect

NOSE HIGH ATTITUDE

FLIGHT PATH

ASCENDING LEFT BLADE

DESCENDING RIGHT BLADE

"P" FACTOR

THRUST

THRUST

Fig. 1-53. "P"-Factor

are at the same angle of attack, producing *equal* thrust.

SPIRALLING SLIPSTREAM

The propeller also induces a slipstream rotation which causes a change in flow direction across the vertical stabilizer. Due to the direction of propeller rotation, the slipstream strikes the left surface of the vertical fin causing the airplane to yaw left. (See Fig. 1-54.) Some airplane manufacturers correct this problem by offsetting the rudder, thereby allowing the airplane to fly a straight path.

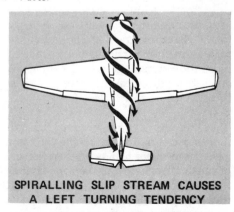

SPIRALLING SLIP STREAM CAUSES A LEFT TURNING TENDENCY

Fig. 1-54. Slipstream Effect

WHY THE AIRCRAFT TURNS

Turns are made by inclining the lift of the wings to one side to produce a force which turns the aircraft. The lift force can be subdivided and represented as two forces: one acting vertically and one acting horizontally. (See Fig. 1-55.) The horizontal force is the part that makes the aircraft turn, while the vertical force is the part that overcomes gravity.

Fig. 1-55. Lift has Vertical and Horizontal Components in a Turn

In a level turn, there are pairs of opposing forces in balance. The centrifugal force acting on the aircraft is opposite and equal to the turning force. The vertical part of the lift is equal and opposite to the force of gravity. The combined centrifugal force and gravity force is called the resultant force and is equal and opposite to the total lift force. (See Fig. 1-56.)

The arrangement of forces on the aircraft in a turn can be likened to the forces on a bucket of water being swung at the end of a rope. The strain on the rope holding the bucket is the same as the total lift force supporting the aircraft. (See Fig. 1-57.)

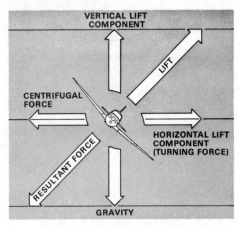

Fig. 1-56. Forces Balance in a Coordinated Turn

Centrifugal force, which tends to swing the bucket away from the hand, and the gravity force combine to form the resultant force or load-factor force which makes the bucket feel heavier than when the bucket is at rest. It is this same resultant force that holds the water in the

Fig. 1-57. Forces on an Aircraft

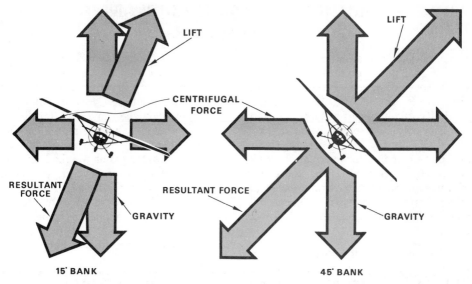

Fig. 1-58. The Steeper the Bank, the Greater the Load Factor

bucket with no tendency for the water to spill over the sides.

In a properly executed turn, the pilot feels heavier in a manner similar to the water in the bucket. The pilot does not experience any side forces like those felt when an automobile follows a curve on a highway.

The steeper the bank, the greater the total lift needed and the greater the force required to make the airplane turn. This also means that the centrifugal force and the gravitational force combine to make a greater resultant force and higher load factor and to make the pilot feel heavier in the seat. (See Fig. 1-58.)

Figure 1-33B illustrates the load factors imposed for various degrees of bank. For example, 60° of bank would produce a load factor of two "G's," thus making the effective weight of the aircraft twice its normal weight. If the aircraft weighs 2,000 pounds in straight-and-level flight, a level 60° bank turn would make the effective weight of the aircraft 4,000 pounds.

In level flight, the total lift force is equal to gravity, as shown in figure 1-59. When the aircraft is banked, the total lift is diverted. Since the total lift is still equal

to gravity, not enough lift is acting vertically to counteract gravity and the aircraft descends. In order to maintain altitude in a turn, the total lift must be increased until enough lift will act vertically to counteract gravity. This is done by increasing the angle of attack by raising the nose with back pressure on the control wheel.

In summary, the aircraft in flight is subjected to many forces, some of which act together, while others act in opposition. In order to master the art and science of flight, the pilot must develop a familiarity and working knowledge of the interplay of forces acting on the airplane.

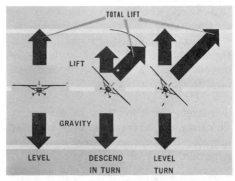

Fig. 1-59. Lift Must be Increased to Keep Aircraft From Descending in a Turn

SECTION C - BASIC AIRPLANE PERFORMANCE

The *performance* of an aircraft is gauged by how well it accomplishes the job for which it was designed — whether it was designed for speed, utility, or maneuverability. A high-performance aircraft can accelerate and climb more quickly and fly faster than one with relatively low performance. However, an aircraft specifically designed for short-field landings and takeoffs may have excellent takeoff and landing performance, but may not have exceptional acceleration or speed.

Atmospheric conditions greatly influence aircraft performance. A well-informed pilot knows how to obtain and interpret the published performance information and how to operate the aircraft within the performance capabilities imposed by aircraft design and atmospheric conditions.

EFFECTS OF TEMPERATURE AND ALTITUDE

The density of the air on a given day largely determines aircraft performance, since lift and drag are directly affected. As the air density increases, lift and drag increase; as the air density decreases, lift and drag decrease.

Air density is affected by three major factors: pressure, temperature, and humidity. For example, at an altitude of 18,000 feet, the air pressure measures approximately 15 inches of mercury (in. Hg) as compared to approximately 30 in. Hg at sea level. (See Fig. 1-60.) (Inches of mercury is a common unit of measurement for barometric pressure in the United States.) As pressure decreases, air density also decreases. Therefore, an aircraft requires a longer takeoff distance at higher elevation airports than at sea level airports.

Because air expands when heated, warm air is less dense than cool air. A cubic foot of air on a hot day will contain fewer air molecules than that same cubic foot on a cooler day. Therefore, when other conditions (such as pressure and humidity) remain the same, an aircraft will require a longer takeoff run on a hot day than on a cool day. Likewise, because air containing water vapor weighs less than an equal amount of dry air, moist air (high relative humidity) is less dense than dry air (low relative humidity). Thus, if other conditions remain the same, an aircraft will require a longer takeoff run on a humid day than on a dry day.

Fig. 1-60. Pressure Decreases With Altitude

DENSITY ALTITUDE AND AIRCRAFT PERFORMANCE

Density altitude is a measure of air density that is often used to determine aircraft performance. Under non-standard conditions of temperature and pressure at a given airport, density altitude will differ from the airport elevation. As air density decreases (i.e., air becomes thinner), density altitude increases, and vice versa. Low atmospheric pressure, high temperature, and high humidity all result in a decrease in air density and a corresponding increase in density altitude.

In computing density altitude, the small effect of humidity is usually disregarded. Thus, air temperature and pressure are the two variables considered in most aircraft performance computations.

Density altitude, as it relates to changing temperatures, can be easily misunderstood. High density altitude does not mean that the air has a high density, but rather, the air has a low density as associated with high altitude in the standard atmosphere. On a hot day, the density altitude at a particular airport may be 2,000 or 3,000 feet higher than the elevation of that field. As a direct consequence, an aircraft operating in this area will perform as though it were flying at the higher altitude.

With an increase in density altitude, the engine horsepower decreases (unless it is a turbocharged engine) since the actual amount of air to support combustion in the engine has decreased. In addition, both the wing and the propeller lose lifting efficiency in the thinner air.

DENSITY ALTITUDE COMPUTATION

One way of determining density altitude for a specific temperature and pressure is with a density altitude graph, as shown in figure 1-61. To explain the use of this graph, a sample problem will be worked using a pressure altitude of 6,000 feet and an outside air temperature of +30°C. (See Fig. 1-61.)

1. First, locate the vertical line which represents the outside air temperature (+30°C) by referring to the scale at the bottom of the graph (Point A).

2. Then, proceed vertically along the +30°C temperature line until the 6,000-foot pressure altitude line is intersected (Point B).

Fig. 1-61. Density Altitude Graph

NOTE: Pressure altitude is determined by setting the altimeter to 29.92 in. Hg and reading the indicated altitude.

3. Proceed horizontally from Point B to the left edge of the graph and read density altitude at Point C. The solution to this problem is 9,000 feet density altitude.

To determine density altitude when the pressure altitude and outside air temperature values do not fall on the printed grid lines, it is necessary to interpolate between lines. In this example, pressure altitude is 3,500 feet and the outside air temperature is +42°C. This problem is solved as follows:

1. Locate +42°C at Point D. Since each vertical line on this graph is equal to 5°, this point is two-fifths the distance between +40° and the next graduation to the right, 45°.
2. Proceed vertically up from Point D until reaching 3,500 feet pressure altitude (Point E). Since the pressure altitude lines are drawn at 1,000-foot intervals, 3,500 feet would be midway between the 3,000-foot and 4,000-foot pressure altitude lines.
3. Moving horizontally to the left edge of the chart, read the density altitude at Point F. Since this point is halfway between the 7,000-foot and 8,000-foot graduations, the density altitude is 7,500 feet.

An alternate method of determining density altitude is to use the flight computer. (Refer to Chapter 10, Page 10-6.)

TAKEOFF PERFORMANCE

Takeoff performance depends mainly upon factors that can be measured or calculated in advance, such as density altitude, pressure altitude, temperature, wind, aircraft weight, and runway gradient or surface. With these factors, an accurate estimate of takeoff performance can be obtained by using the takeoff performance charts or tables in the pilot's operating handbook.

DENSITY ALTITUDE, PRESSURE ALTITUDE, AND TEMPERATURE

The performance charts for older model aircraft are based on density altitude. Therefore, one of the methods for calculating density altitude described in previous paragraphs must be followed before using these charts. In contrast, pressure altitude and temperature values can be obtained directly from charts designed for newer model aircraft.

WIND

Wind direction and velocity affect takeoff performance. For example, a headwind shortens the takeoff run, while crosswinds, and especially tailwinds, lengthen the takeoff roll and reduce the subsequent angle of climb. Decreased controllability and takeoff performance can make crosswind takeoffs undesirable and downwind takeoffs hazardous.

AIRCRAFT WEIGHT

The weight of an aircraft on takeoff also affects length of the takeoff roll and climb performance. Takeoff performance charts for light aircraft are based on maximum takeoff weight, so operations at lower weight offer a bonus of shorter takeoff distances and better climb performance.

RUNWAY GRADIENT AND SURFACE

Runway gradient refers to the uphill or downhill slope of a runway. An uphill runway decreases airplane acceleration, thereby increasing the takeoff distance. A downhill slope, on the other hand, will help decrease takeoff distance. In addition, the surface covering the runway can vary runway length requirements. Soft, muddy, or rough fields can increase runway requirements, and in extreme cases, may make a takeoff impossible.

TURBULENCE

Turbulence caused by high winds or other atmospheric conditions in the vicinity of an airport, can decrease takeoff maneuverability and climb performance. Essentially, this is because turbulence can increase the possibility of a stall. Therefore, increased climb speeds must be maintained in rough air.

HUMIDITY

Although not a factor normally included in takeoff performance computations, high humidity will increase takeoff distance and decrease climb performance. An unusually hot and humid day is cause for the pilot to exercise additional caution prior to attempting a marginal takeoff.

TAKEOFF PERFORMANCE CHARTS

The performance charts published for specific aircraft describe or predict the way in which the airplane should perform under a given set of conditions. These charts are published in either tabular or graph form.

Pilots should consult performance charts any time there is doubt about the airplane's capability, whether it be due to the length and/or condition of the runway, the high density altitude, or a lack of familiarity with the equipment being flown. In addition, Federal Aviation Regulations require that a pilot know the takeoff and landing distances his aircraft requires for each operation he conducts.

As an added safety measure, he should consider the performance of his airplane less than that predicted by the performance charts. For example, a pilot flying an older airplane, slightly out of rig and equipped with several protruding radio antennas, will find it difficult to meet

TAKEOFF DISTANCE

CONDITIONS:
Flaps Up
Full Throttle Prior to Brake Release
Paved, Level, Dry Runway
Zero Wind

NOTES:
1. Maximum performance technique.
2. Prior to takeoff from fields above 5000 feet elevation, the mixture should be leaned to give maximum RPM in a full throttle, static runup.
3. Decrease distances 10% for each 9 knots headwind. For operation with tailwinds up to 10 knots, increase distances by 10% for each 2 knots.
4. Where distance value has been deleted, climb performance after lift-off is less than 150 fpm at takeoff speed.
5. For operation on a dry, grass runway, increase distances by 15% of the "ground roll" figure.

WEIGHT LBS	TAKEOFF SPEED KIAS		PRESS ALT FT	0°C		10°C		20°C		30°C		40°C	
	LIFT OFF	AT 50 FT		GRND ROLL	TOTAL TO CLEAR 50 FT OBS	GRND ROLL	TOTAL TO CLEAR 50 FT OBS	GRND ROLL	TOTAL TO CLEAR 50 FT OBS	GRND ROLL	TOTAL TO CLEAR 50 FT OBS	GRND ROLL	TOTAL TO CLEAR 50 FT OBS
1600	53	60	S.L.	655	1245	710	1335	765	1435	820	1540	880	1650
			1000	720	1365	775	1465	835	1575	900	1690	970	1815
			2000	790	1500	855	1615	920	1735	990	1865	1065	2005
			3000	870	1650	935	1780	1010	1915	1090	2065	1170	2225
			4000	955	1820	1030	1965	1115	2125	1200	2290	1290	2475
			5000	1050	2015	1140	2185	1230	2360	1325	2555	1430	2770
			6000	1160	2245	1255	2435	1360	2640	1465	2870	1580	3120
			7000	1285	2510	1390	2730	1505	2970	1625	3240	---	---
			8000	1420	2820	1540	3080	1670	3370	---	---	---	---

Fig. 1-62. Takeoff Distance Chart

the performance specifications indicated on the charts. A careful pilot always leaves a respectable margin of safety between expected and required performance.

TAKEOFF PERFORMANCE TABLES

The takeoff performance table should be used for flight planning purposes, especially when a takeoff is contemplated at a high altitude airport or on an airstrip of marginal length. For example, referring to the chart shown in figure 1-62, the pilot can determine the ground roll and distance to clear a 50-foot obstacle under the following conditions:

```
Runway surface ... Paved, level, dry
Aircraft weight .......... 1,600 lbs.
Wind ..................... Calm
Pressure altitude ........ Sea level
Temperature .............. 20°C
Takeoff speed @ 50 ft ..... 60 KIAS
```

By looking at the sea level data at 20° Celsius, the pilot finds that the ground roll required is 765 feet and the distance required to clear a 50-foot obstacle is 1,435 feet. It should be noted that, as the pressure altitude increases, the runway length requirements also increase until the takeoff roll has almost doubled at the 7,000-foot level when compared to the sea level value.

The optimum use of performance tables requires a pilot to take into account the various factors used in determining performance data. For instance, as noted at the top of the chart, the values in figure 1-62 were calculated with the flaps up and on a paved, level, dry runway. In addition, note 3 states that distance must be decreased by 10 percent for each nine knots of headwind. Note 5 shows that distance increases by 15 percent of the ground roll figure for operations on dry, grass runways.

Factors affecting takeoff performance that are not found on this chart include humidity, runway gradient, and turbulence. In addition, pilot technique plus the age and condition of the airplane can greatly affect these figures.

INTERPOLATION

Interpolation is the process of determining values for conditions which may not be shown directly on a performance chart. In order to help the pilot understand the process of interpolation, a sample problem is presented using the performance table in figure 1-62.

For the sample problem, a takeoff is planned from a paved, level, dry runway at an airport with a pressure altitude of 5,500 feet and a temperature of 20° Celsius. Since the table shows the takeoff ground roll for 5,000 feet and 6,000 feet, interpolation must be used to determine the ground roll at 5,500 feet. In the problem, the pilot determines that 5,500 feet is one-half the distance between 5,000 and 6,000 feet. Therefore, the difference between the two ground rolls can be divided by one-half and added to the 5,000-foot value. This procedure provides the ground roll at 5,500 feet. The following calculations explain this interpolation, which results in a ground roll of 1,295 feet.

```
Ground roll @ 5,000 ft. ..... 1,230 ft.
Ground roll @ 6,000 ft. ..... 1,360 ft.
1,360 ft. − 1,230 ft. ........ 130 ft.
130 ft. × ½ ................. 65 ft.
1,230 ft. + 65 ft .......... 1,295 ft.
```

TAKEOFF PERFORMANCE GRAPHS

Takeoff performance information may also be published in graph form, as illustrated in figure 1-63. Using this graph, takeoff distance over a 50-foot obstacle can be figured.

Fig. 1-63. Takeoff Performance Graph

Here's a sample problem. Assume the temperature is 21° Celsius, the pressure altitude is 1,000 feet, the wind is calm, and the takeoff must be made over a 50-foot obstacle. The following steps can be used to find the ground roll and distance to clear the obstacle.

1. Enter the graph at 21° Celsius (Point A) and move upward to the pressure altitude of 1,000 feet (point B).

2. Move horizontally to the right until intersecting the ground roll line (Point C).

3. Drop vertically to the bottom of the graph (Point D) to read the ground roll distance of approximately 900 feet.

4. To determine the distance to clear a 50-foot obstacle, continue horizontally from Point C to the 50-foot obstacle line at Point E.

5. Move vertically down to the bottom line of the graph (Point F) and note that it will take approximately 1,450 feet to clear a 50-foot obstacle under these conditions.

THE DENALT COMPUTER

The DENALT (density altitude) computer comprises a handy additional method to compute takeoff distance and rate of climb. This computer is produced by the U.S. Government and can be purchased from the Superintendent of Documents, U.S. Government Printing Office, Washington, D.C. 20402. The computer shown in figure 1-64 is designed specifically for use with fixed-pitch propeller airplanes. Another computer, similar in format and use, is produced for variable-pitch propeller airplanes. If a computer is ordered, the desired type, fixed-pitch or variable-pitch, should be specified.

As an example of use of the DENALT computer, assume the following conditions:

Given:
1. Surface temperature — +80°F
2. Airport pressure altitude — 4,000 feet
3. Takeoff distance under sea level standard conditions — 1,700 feet

Find:
    Corrected takeoff distances.

Fig. 1-64. The Denalt Computer

Solution:

1. Set 80°F in the AIR TEMP window as shown in figure 1-64, item 1.
2. Note that a takeoff factor of 2.0 is located opposite the pressure altitude of 4,000 feet. (See Fig. 1-64, item 2.)
3. Multiply the takeoff distance on a standard day at sea level by the takeoff factor of 2.0 to find the correct takeoff distance of 3,400 feet.

Note that the other portion of the DENALT computer is used to calculate the corrected rate of climb using procedures similar to those just outlined.

CLIMB PERFORMANCE

Most of the factors affecting takeoff performance also affect the subsequent climb capability of an aircraft. In addition, turbulent air, variable piloting techniques, and the condition and age of the aircraft, can all result in a different rate of climb than that specified in the pilot's operating handbook.

There are three climb airspeeds with which pilots should become familiar in order to obtain the best performance from their aircraft: best rate-of-climb airspeed, best angle-of-climb airspeed, and normal climb airspeed.

BEST RATE-OF-CLIMB AIRSPEED

An airplane operated at the *best rate-of-climb speed* will obtain the *greatest gain in altitude over a given time period.* (See Fig. 1-65.) This speed is normally used during the climb after all obstacles have been cleared and is usually maintained until leaving the traffic pattern. Best rate-of-climb speed is also useful when a climb over higher terrain is required, since this speed will allow the pilot to climb to a terrain clearance altitude in the shortest period of time.

The best rate-of-climb airspeed decreases with an increase in altitude. Prolonged operation at this speed in some airplane types can produce high engine temperatures, especially on days when the outside air temperature is high. Pilots must closely monitor the oil and cylinder head temperature gauges any time a steep climb is used for a long period of time.

BEST ANGLE-OF-CLIMB AIRSPEED

The *best angle-of-climb airspeed* yields the *greatest gain in altitude over a given*

BEST **RATE-OF-CLIMB** AIRSPEED

GREATEST ALTITUDE GAINED
OVER A GIVEN TIME PERIOD

BEST **ANGLE-OF-CLIMB** AIRSPEED

GREATEST GAIN IN ALTITUDE
OVER DISTANCE TRAVELLED

Fig. 1-65. Best Rate-of-Climb and Best Angle-of-Climb Airspeeds distance. To help distinguish between best rate and best angle airspeed, one can think of best rate-of-climb performance expressed in altitude gained per minute, and best angle-of-climb performance as expressed in altitude gained per horizontal distance traveled. (See Fig. 1-65.)

The best angle-of-climb airspeed is used after liftoff to clear obstacles that may be at the end of the runway. Since this airspeed is relatively low and full power is used for obstacle clearance, it is recommended that the best angle-of-climb speed be maintained only for short time intervals to prevent engine overheating. Once an obstacle is cleared, the nose of the airplane should be lowered to increase the airspeed to at least the best rate-of-climb airspeed. The airspeed recommended for best angle-of-climb *increases* with altitude.

NORMAL CLIMB SPEED

Pilot's operating handbooks will usually specify a *normal* or *cruise climb airspeed* to be used for prolonged time periods. While the normal climb airspeed certainly does not produce the climb rate associated with the best rate-of-climb airspeed, it does provide adequate performance for most operations while insuring adequate engine cooling and improved "over the nose" visibility.

Unless high terrain must be crossed shortly after takeoff, the pilot should climb at the normal climb speed after departing the airport traffic pattern. Not only will this enhance engine cooling, but it also will provide better cross-country speeds, cutting down the total time en route to the destination.

CLIMB PERFORMANCE TABLES

Climb performance tables are included in the pilot's operating handbook to provide an idea of the approximate performance that can be expected under various conditions. It should be remembered, however, that several conditions affecting climb performance are not taken into consideration on these tables and the pilot must adjust climb requirements and expectations accordingly.

The climb performance table, shown in figure 1-66, illustrates that, at sea level, with an outside air temperature of 0° Celsius, a weight of 1,600 pounds, and the best rate-of-climb airspeed of 68 knots indicated airspeed, the pilot can expect a rate of climb of 710 feet per minute. In addition, note that the climb airspeed decreases as the altitude increases, and that the rate of climb decreases with an increase in altitude or temperature. As shown to the left of the table, the climb performance values were calculated with flaps up and full throttle.

RATE OF CLIMB

CONDITIONS: Flaps Up Full Throttle	WEIGHT LBS	PRESS ALT FT	CLIMB SPEED KIAS	RATE OF CLIMB - FPM			
				-20°C	0°C	20°C	40°C
	1600	S.L.	68	770	710	655	595
		2000	67	675	615	560	500
		4000	65	580	520	465	405
		6000	64	485	430	375	310
		8000	63	390	335	280	215
		10,000	62	295	240	185	- - -
		12,000	61	200	150	- - -	- - -

Fig. 1-66. Rate-of-Climb Table

CLIMB PERFORMANCE GRAPHS

Climb performance also may be presented in the form of graphs, as illustrated in figure 1-67. Here's a sample problem. Assume the airplane weight is 3,400 pounds, the pressure altitude is 7,000 feet, and the temperature is 8° Celsius.

1. Enter the graph at 8° Celsius (Point A) and move vertically to the pressure altitude of 7,000 feet (Point B).
2. From this point, move horizontally to the right to the appropriate airplane weight line (Point C).

3. Proceed straight down to the bottom edge of the graph to read the rate of climb of 600 feet per minute (Point D).

MISCONCEPTIONS REGARDING WIND AND CLIMB PERFORMANCE

One of the least understood areas of aeronautical knowledge is the effect of wind on airspeed and climb performance. One pilot who stalled an aircraft shortly after takeoff attributed the stall to a turn downwind which decreased the airspeed over the wings resulting in a

Fig. 1-67. Takeoff Climb Performance Graph

loss of lift. This, of course, could not have been the cause since airspeed is not determined by atmospheric wind direction or velocity. Airspeed, rather, is the speed at which the airplane is moving through the atmosphere and is unaffected by the wind. Atmospheric wind affects only the ground speed, or speed at which the airplane is traveling over the earth's surface. Because of this, the only climb performance affected by atmospheric wind is the *angle of climb*, or gain in altitude over a given distance.

A pilot making a downwind turn will retain the *same* rate of climb; however, the ground speed will increase, resulting in less altitude gained for the distance traveled.

During turns close to the ground where the pilot can visually judge altitude, it may seem that a downwind turn has actually resulted in a loss of lift and a decrease in climb rate. This is just an illusion, however, due to the decrease in angle of climb. Although rate of climb remains the same, the decrease in climb

angle could, in some cases, be hazardous — not because it produces a stall, but because of the decrease in obstacle clearance capability.

CRUISE PERFORMANCE

The manufacturers of today's light airplanes provide cruise performance tables or graphs to indicate rate of fuel consumption, true airspeed, range, and endurance at different altitudes and power settings. These charts may be relatively simple or quite sophisticated but, in either case, it is important to remember that the performance data are based on specific conditions of fuel/air mixture, atmospheric temperature and pressure, aircraft weight, and wind.

Any deviation from the specific information upon which the chart computations are based will affect the accuracy of some or all of the results. For example, many cruise performance charts are based on zero wind and standard atmospheric conditions. However, during actual operations, these

CRUISE PERFORMANCE

CONDITIONS:
Recommended Lean Mixture
1600 Pounds
Flaps Up

ALTITUDE	RPM	20°C BELOW STANDARD TEMP			STANDARD TEMPERATURE			20°C ABOVE STANDARD TEMP		
		% BHP	KTAS	GPH	% BHP	KTAS	GPH	% BHP	KTAS	GPH
2000	2650	- - -	- - -	- - -	78	103	5.9	72	102	5.4
	2600	80	102	6.0	73	101	5.5	68	100	5.1
	2500	70	97	5.3	65	96	4.9	60	95	4.6
	2400	62	92	4.7	57	91	4.3	53	91	4.1
	2300	54	87	4.1	50	87	3.9	47	86	3.7
	2200	47	83	3.7	44	82	3.5	42	81	3.3
4000	2700	- - -	- - -	- - -	78	105	5.8	72	104	5.4
	2600	75	101	5.6	69	100	5.2	64	99	4.8
	2500	66	96	5.0	61	95	4.6	57	95	4.3
	2400	58	91	4.4	54	91	4.1	50	90	3.9
	2300	51	87	3.9	48	86	3.7	45	85	3.5
	2200	45	82	3.5	42	81	3.3	40	80	3.2
6000	2750	- - -	- - -	- - -	77	107	5.8	71	105	5.3
	2700	79	105	5.9	73	104	5.4	67	103	5.1
	2600	70	100	5.2	64	99	4.8	60	98	4.5
	2500	62	95	4.7	57	95	4.3	53	94	4.1
	2400	54	91	4.2	51	90	3.9	48	89	3.7
	2300	48	86	3.7	45	85	3.5	42	84	3.4

Fig. 1-68. Cruise Performance Table

conditions seldom prevail. It should be noted that wind has a very significant effect on the distance an aircraft can fly, but no effect on its rate of fuel consumption or the total time it can remain aloft.

CRUISE PERFORMANCE TABLES

A table similar to the one shown in figure 1-68 is used in many pilot's operating handbooks. This table is for an airplane with a fixed-pitch propeller. Therefore, for every pressure altitude shown, the power settings are expressed in r.p.m. The percent of brake horsepower, true airspeed, and fuel consumption correspond to a specific pressure altitude, r.p.m. setting, and temperature range.

Analysis of the table will show that the fuel consumption for any selected percent of brake horsepower (%BHP) is always about the same, regardless of altitude. Range, however, improves

somewhat with altitude because of increased true airspeed. (Effects of altitude on true airspeed are discussed in Chapter 2.) The chart also shows that, as altitude increases, r.p.m. must be increased to maintain the selected %BHP. Since air becomes less dense as altitude increases, the engine must turn more revolutions per minute to produce the same power.

As seen from the table, an airplane flying at a pressure altitude of 6,000 feet with a standard temperature, a power setting of 2,600 r.p.m., and 64% brake horsepower should obtain approximately 99 knots true airspeed and a fuel consumption rate of 4.8 gallons per hour.

CRUISE PERFORMANCE GRAPHS

Some pilot's operating handbooks use cruise performance graphs instead of tables. In the range graph shown in figure 1-69, the pilot can determine the percent of brake horsepower combinations and expected range in nautical miles for various temperatures and

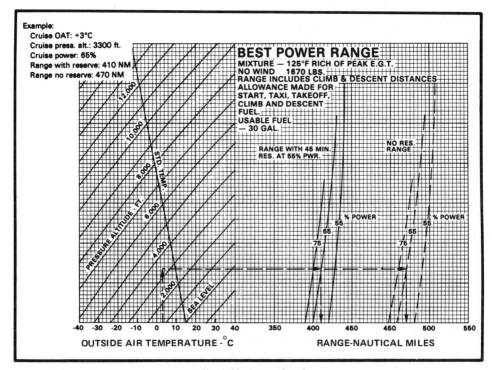

Fig. 1-69. Range Graph

pressure altitudes. For instance, at a temperature of 3° Celsius and a pressure altitude of 3,300 feet, utilizing 65% power in an aircraft with 30 gallons of usable fuel, the pilot can expect a range of 410 nautical miles with reserve, or 470 miles without reserve.

To determine the percent of brake horsepower for various altitude/r.p.m. combinations, the pilot should consult the engine performance chart. The chart in figure 1-70 shows that, at an altitude of 3,000 feet, approximately 2,325 r.p.m. must be used to obtain 65% power.

LANDING PERFORMANCE

Performance information for the landing phase of flight is also published in pilot's operating handbooks. Landing techniques used by pilots are more variable than for most other maneuvers, making published landing performance information less accurate than other types of performance data.

APPROACH SPEED

The pilot's operating handbook recommends an approach airspeed for various flap settings. This recommended indicated airspeed should be used

Fig. 1-70. Engine Performance

regardless of temperature and altitude combinations. Although temperature and pressure changes will change air density and, therefore, lift, a given indicated airspeed will continue to insure the same amount of lift. With an increase in temperature and a decrease in pressure, however, the true airspeed and resultant ground speed will increase for a given indicated airspeed. In less dense air, the airplane must move through the atmosphere faster to obtain a desired indicated airspeed.

This fact is important for pilots who attempt landing approaches at airports of varying elevations. A pilot who has made most landing approaches at low elevation airports soon becomes accustomed to the speed over the ground yielded by the normal approach speed and, therefore, begins to monitor the airspeed indicator less and less. A pilot attempting to use ground speed as the approach speed determinant at high elevation airports will find that the indicated airspeed will be significantly lower than the normal approach speed and may even approach a stall. This is why maintaining the proper pitch attitude in order to stabilize the airspeed on landing approaches is so important.

WEIGHT AND CONFIGURATION

Landing weight is another factor that must be considered during approaches. The pilot's operating handbook recommends the final approach speed based on maximum landing weight. As weight decreases, a corresponding decrease in speed may be appropriate. When the manufacturer gives a final approach speed range, the higher speed should be used at the maximum landing weight to increase maneuverability and make a go-around from an aborted landing less critical.

The use of flaps on a landing approach will vary with field conditions and

length. Normally, a short or soft field calls for the use of full flaps and a lower indicated approach speed.

LANDING PERFORMANCE TABLES

The landing performance table shown in figure 1-71 is used to compute landing capability using 40° of flaps and an approach speed of 52 knots indicated airspeed at 50 feet. The table indicates that both the ground roll and the distance to clear a 50-foot obstacle increase with altitude because of the higher ground speed resulting from a given indicated airspeed at higher altitudes.

In addition, values are decreased 10% for each 9 knots of headwind. For example, at a pressure altitude of 6,000 feet with an outside air temperature of 30°C and a 9-knot headwind, 526 feet of actual ground roll and 1,156 feet total distance to clear a 50-foot obstacle are required for landing.

LANDING PERFORMANCE GRAPHS

Landing performance graphs are often used to give the pilot information on landing distances. (See Fig. 1-72.) In this graph, landing distances are computed at various pressure altitudes and temperatures for one weight condition.

Referring to the graph in figure 1-72, the pilot finds that 1,600 feet will be required to land over a 50-foot obstacle with a two-knot tailwind, at a pressure altitude of 800 feet and a temperature of 13° Celsius.

The landing surface determines braking effectiveness and, therefore, affects the

LANDING DISTANCE

CONDITIONS:
Flaps 40°
Power Off
Maximum Braking
Paved, Level, Dry Runway
Zero Wind

NOTES:
1. Maximum performance technique.
2. Decrease distances 10% for each 9 knots headwind. For operation with tailwinds up to 10 knots, increase distances by 10% for each 2 knots.
3. For operation on a dry, grass runway, increase distances by 45% of the "ground roll" figure.

WEIGHT LBS	SPEED AT 50 FT KIAS	PRESS ALT FT	0°C		10°C		20°C		30°C		40°C	
			GRND ROLL	TOTAL TO CLEAR 50 FT OBS	GRND ROLL	TOTAL TO CLEAR 50 FT OBS	GRND ROLL	TOTAL TO CLEAR 50 FT OBS	GRND ROLL	TOTAL TO CLEAR 50 FT OBS	GRND ROLL	TOTAL TO CLEAR 50 FT OBS
1600	52	S.L.	425	1045	440	1065	455	1090	470	1110	485	1135
		1000	440	1065	455	1090	470	1110	485	1135	505	1165
		2000	455	1090	470	1115	490	1140	505	1165	520	1185
		3000	470	1115	490	1140	505	1165	525	1195	540	1215
		4000	490	1140	505	1165	525	1195	545	1225	560	1245
		5000	510	1170	525	1195	545	1225	565	1255	585	1285
		6000	530	1200	545	1225	565	1255	585	1285	605	1315
		7000	550	1230	570	1260	590	1290	610	1320	630	1350
		8000	570	1260	590	1290	610	1320	630	1350	655	1385

Fig. 1-71. Landing Performance Table

length of the landing roll. Dry, hard-surfaced runways provide the best braking while icy, grassy, or wet runways can significantly increase stopping distance.

WIND COMPONENT CHART

Since the amount of headwind is a determining factor in computing the takeoff and landing distance, the thorough pilot should never assume that the wind velocity is a direct headwind. The magnitude of crosswind and headwind components can be determined by using the wind component chart shown in figure 1-73. For example, assume the wind is reported from 350° at 20 knots for a takeoff on runway 32. The pilot notes that the angle between the wind and the runway direction is 30°.

By entering the chart at the 30° angle off the runway line (Point A) and proceeding downward until intersecting the 20-knot speed arc (Point B), the headwind component of 17 knots can be read directly left of the speed arc intersection (Point C), and a crosswind component of 10 knots can be read directly below the speed arc intersection (Point D). Therefore, the pilot would base takeoff performance computations on a 17-knot headwind component rather than a headwind of 20 knots.

The understanding and application of weight and balance data and performance tables, graphs, and charts benefit the pilot with safer operation of

Fig. 1-72. Landing Performance Graph

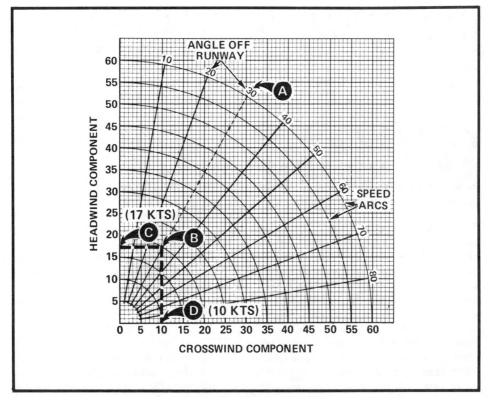

Fig. 1-73. Wind Component Chart

the aircraft. In addition, they result in maximum utility and performance from the aircraft.

WAKE TURBULENCE

One additional factor that can severely limit aircraft performance is wake turbulence. Of special concern to pilots of light aircraft is the turbulence created by large aircraft operating in the vicinity of the airport.

The greatest danger from heavy aircraft turbulence is the effect of *wingtip vortices*. These vortices are the result of high pressure air under the wings spilling around and over the wingtips to equalize the low pressure area above the upper wing surface. If one could actually see the vortices generated by the wings, they would appear as twin horizontal tornadoes originating at the wingtips. This aerodynamic phenomenon was discussed briefly in the aerodynamics section. (See Fig. 1-74.)

Fig. 1-74. Wingtip Vortices

These rotating cones of air are created as a result of the generation of lift by the wings of the aircraft. The wing transmits energy (proportional to the weight of the aircraft) to the air through which it flies. The intensity of this turbulence is directly related to the wing span, weight, forward speed of the aircraft, and density of the air. In general, the slower the speed of the aircraft, the shorter the wing span, and the greater the weight, the greater will be the velocity of the air in the vortex cores generated by the

aircraft. Therefore, the greatest turbulence is generated by a large aircraft when it is flying slowly at a high angle of attack. This condition primarily exists during takeoff, climbout, and landing.

Actual tests have demonstrated that vortex core velocities may exceed 90 knots immediately behind a heavy jet which is flying very slowly. In addition, experience has shown that the vortex cores tend to descend at 400 to 500 feet per minute to a level-off point 800 to 900 feet below the flight altitude of the jet.

At cruise, the airspeed is greatest; therefore, the aircraft weight is spread over the greatest amount of air. The turbulence thus created is at a minimum for that aircraft. Conversely, when the aircraft is on the ground, the wings are not supporting the weight of the aircraft and vortex cores are not generated. Prior to liftoff or after touchdown, wingtip vortices are almost non-existent.

PROCEDURES FOR OPERATING NEAR WAKE TURBULENCE

Some basic rules for takeoff behind a large aircraft include: (See Fig. 1-75.)

1. Start the takeoff roll from the same point as the large aircraft to insure liftoff prior to the large aircraft's point of takeoff. Climb out above or to one side of the large aircraft's flight path to avoid the turbulence.

2. When taking off after the landing of a large aircraft, be sure to plan the liftoff point beyond the touchdown area of the large aircraft.

3. Climb out parallel to the runway but on the upwind side since wind tends to blow the vortices to the downwind side of the runway.

4. In a no-wind condition, the wingtip vortices have a tendency to move outward (laterally) from the center of the flight path, thereby remaining over the runway. In this case, the situation

Fig. 1-75. Takeoff After a Large Aircraft

may dictate a delayed takeoff to allow the turbulence to dissipate.

In flight, if it is necessary to cross behind a large aircraft, pass slightly above its flight path to avoid the vortex.

Here are some good rules for landing behind a large aircraft: (See Fig. 1-76.)

1. If cleared to land close behind a large aircraft, it is the pilot's prerogative to refuse the landing clearance if the distance between aircraft is too short.

2. Avoid crossing the path of a large aircraft if possible. This can be accomplished by keeping the traffic pattern inside or above that of the aircraft ahead.

3. On approach, maintain the descent path at or above the descent path of the large aircraft and touch down beyond the place where the large aircraft is landing. It is well to maintain greater airspeed than normal to facilitate control if turbulence is encountered.

4. If a large aircraft has just taken off as the pilot approaches, he should plan his touchdown to take place well in advance of the large aircraft's liftoff point.

JET BLAST

The number of ground accidents involving loss of life, serious injury, and aircraft damage due to jet blast indicates that some pilots are not aware of this serious hazard. No pilot would deliberately taxi an aircraft in a hurricane, yet some have taxied behind a jet generating winds of hurricane force. Here, for example, are excerpts from an NTSB special study on jet blast: "aircraft flipped over from jet blast of DC-9"; "707 cleared for takeoff flipped aircraft on back."

The reasons for these accidents are clearly illustrated in figure 1-77. At idle thrust, a four-engine, wide-bodied jet generates winds of 50 m.p.h. at 50 feet behind it. However, at breakaway and takeoff thrust, hurricane-like winds are generated.

Fig. 1-76. Landing Behind a Large Aircraft

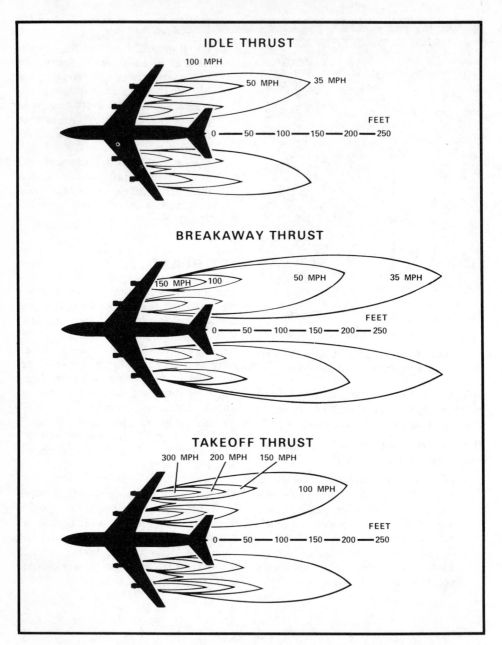

Fig. 1-77. Jet Blast Profiles

chapter 2

INTRODUCTION

In order for a pilot to be fully competent in an airplane, it is necessary that he understand the aircraft systems. Obtaining the maximum performance from an aircraft depends upon the pilot being familiar with the operation of the systems which provide fuel, electricity, power, and control of the aircraft on the ground and in flight. An understanding of the airplane systems provides a background which enables the pilot to perform normal duties and handle unexpected situations smoothly and safely.

SECTION A - FLIGHT CONTROL SYSTEMS

Aircraft control systems are classified as primary and secondary. The primary control systems consist of those which are necessary for the safe flight of an aircraft, such as ailerons, elevator (or stabilator), and rudder. Secondary control systems improve the performance characteristics of the aircraft, or relieve the pilot of excessive control forces. Examples of secondary control systems are wing flaps and trim systems.

AILERONS

The ailerons are located on the outboard trailing edges of both wings and are used to rotate the aircraft around the *longitudinal* or *roll axis*. These surfaces move in opposite directions from each other and are controlled by rotation of the pilot's control wheel. A series of chains, cables, bellcranks, and pulleys connect the ailerons to each other and to the control wheel in the cockpit. (See Fig. 2-1.)

Fig. 2-1. Aileron Control System

When the control wheel is rotated to the left, the right aileron moves down and the left aileron moves up. The downward deflected right aileron provides the outer panel of the right wing with increased camber on the upper surface. This creates a higher velocity airflow over this section of the wing, resulting in an area of lower pressure which causes the right wing to move up. Conversely, the left aileron, being deflected up, forces the left wing down by decreasing the lift produced by the left outer wing panel. The upward movement of the right wing and downward movement of the left wing causes the airplane to roll to the left.

When the control wheel is turned to the right, an opposite aileron movement results and the airplane rolls to the right. The airplane will continue to roll in the direction that the control wheel is turned until the controls are neutralized to establish the desired angle of bank.

ELEVATORS AND STABILATORS

The pitch motion around the *lateral* or *pitch axis* is controlled by a movable horizontal tail surface actuated by fore and aft movement of the control wheel. Two types of movable horizontal tail surfaces are used in today's aircraft to control the motion about the lateral axis: *elevators* and *stabilators*. (See Fig. 2-2.)

Elevators are movable control surfaces that are hinged to the horizontal stabilizer. Like ailerons, the elevators are connected to the control wheel by a system of control cables, pulleys, and bellcranks, while the horizontal stabilizer is fixed

Fig. 2-2. Elevator and Stabilator Control System

and provides horizontal stability for the airplane. A change in position of the elevators modifies the *camber* of the airfoil which increases or decreases lift.

The stabilator is a one-piece, horizontal tail surface that pivots up and down. A change in position of the stabilator changes the angle of attack resulting in an increase or decrease in lift on this surface. When the pilot wants to raise the aircraft nose, he applies back pressure on the control wheel. This moves the trailing edge of the stabilator tail surface up resulting in a negative angle of attack. This causes the tail to move down and the nose of the aircraft to move up.

An *anti-servo* tab, mounted on the trailing edge of the stabilator, moves in the same direction as the trailing edge of the stabilator (see Fig. 2-2) to provide the pilot with a control feel similar to that experienced with conventional elevators. Without this anti-servo tab, control forces from a stabilator would be so light that the pilot would have a tendency to over-control.

The function of the elevators or stabilator is to control the angle of attack of the wings. Climbs and descents are established by a change in the throttle setting with the elevators or stabilator adjusting the angle of attack of the wings.

RUDDERS

The *rudder* moves the aircraft about the *vertical* or *yaw axis* resulting in a motion known as *yaw*. The movement of the rudder is to the left or to the right and is controlled by movement of the rudder pedals connected to the rudder through a series of cables, pulleys, and bellcranks. These pedals are mounted under the instrument panel near the floor of the pilot's compartment. A *vertical stabilizer*, often called the *fin*, provides directional stability and a streamlined structure for mounting the rudder. (See Fig. 2-3.)

Pressure applied to the right rudder pedal displaces the rudder to the right. This increases the camber on the left side of the vertical tail surface, creating a low pressure area on the left side and a high pres-

Fig. 2-3. Rudder Control System

Fig. 2-4. Elevator Trim Controls

sure area on the right side. The resulting pressures cause the tail of the aircraft to move left and the nose to move right. Applying pressure to the left rudder pedal provides an opposite reaction. The rudder is used in conjunction with the ailerons to coordinate turns.

TRIM SYSTEMS

Several types of trim systems are provided to minimize elevator or stabilator control pressures. These systems are:

1. Trim tab.
2. Adjustable stabilizer.
3. Movable tail.

TRIM TAB

The trim tab system incorporates an adjustable trim tab which is mounted on the trailing edge of the elevator or stabilator. In the case of the stabilator, the anti-servo tab also serves as a trim tab. When serving as a trim tab, the anti-servo tab reacts to trim control movement the same as an ordinary tab.

The trim tab is controlled by a trim wheel or crank in the cabin. (See Fig. 2-4.) By adjusting the tab control, the pilot can reduce control wheel pressure for various elevator or stabilator settings. A tab-position indicator is incorporated in the tab-control mechanism to show the nose-up or nose-down position of the tab setting.

Placing the tab control to its full nose-down position moves the tab to its full-up position. (See left side of Fig. 2-5.) The tab, being up into the airflow over the tail, forces the trailing edge of the elevator or stabilator down. This brings the tail up and results in a nose-down movement of the aircraft.

Setting the tab control in the full nose-up position moves the tab to its full-down position. (See right side of Fig. 2-5.) With the tab in the down position, the air flowing under the horizontal tail surface hits the tab and forces the trailing edge of the elevator or stabilator up, giving the aircraft a nose-up movement. Trim tabs can be adjusted to provide various elevator or stabilator settings. Some aircraft have trim tabs on all movable primary control surfaces (aileron, elevator, and rudder).

ADJUSTABLE STABILIZER

The adjustable stabilizer trim system enables the entire stabilizer to be rotated by a control wheel or crank in the cabin. Hinges are provided at the aft end of the stabilizer so that the surface rotates when the screw jacks are turned. A tab-position indicator is incorporated in the stabilizer control mechanism to show the nose-up or nose-down position of the stabilizer setting.

Moving the trim control to the nose-down setting rotates the leading edge of

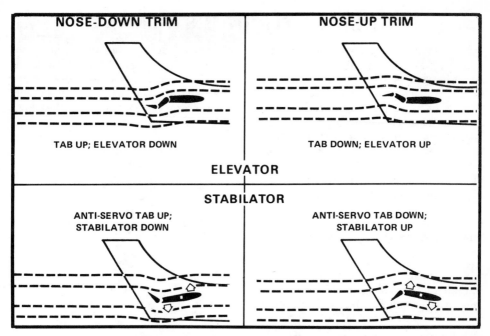

Fig. 2-5. Elevator and Stabilator Trim Action

the stabilizer up. In this position, the stabilizer has a higher angle of attack. This causes the tail to lift and results in a nose-down movement of the aircraft. Setting the trim control in the nose-up position reduces the angle of attack of the stabilizer. This results in an upward movement of the aircraft nose. The stabilizer can be set at any position between full-up and full-down to provide the amount of trim desired.

MOVABLE TAIL

The movable tail trim system permits the pilot to adjust the position of the tail to minimize elevator control pressures. There are no elevator trim tabs in this system. The complete empennage, or tail section, pivots to provide elevator trim.

Movement of the tail trim system is controlled by a control wheel in the cabin. A tab-position indicator shows the nose-up or nose-down setting of the tail.

When the trim control wheel is turned full forward, the complete tail rotates aft. This places the stabilizer in a higher angle of attack position, resulting in a nose-down movement of the aircraft.

Placing the trim control wheel in the nose-up position rotates the complete tail forward and reduces the angle of attack of the stabilizer. This results in the aircraft nose moving upward. The tail can be set in any position between full-up and full-down to provide the amount of trim desired.

SECTION B - FLIGHT INSTRUMENTS

One of the most important areas of aeronautical knowledge is flight instruments and their respective systems. Acquiring such a knowledge enables pilots to visualize what takes place behind an instrument panel and what makes each of the instruments function. In addition, with this knowledge, pilots are much more capable of interpreting the different types of information displayed on the instruments during the various conditions of flight.

THE MAGNETIC COMPASS

The magnetic compass was one of the first instruments to be installed in an aircraft and is still the *only direction-seeking instrument* found in most general aviation aircraft. (See Fig. 2-6.) The compass is a very reliable, self-contained unit and is independent of external vacuum or electrical power. To use it satisfactorily, however, the pilot must understand principles of magnetism and the various errors common to compass operation.

MAGNETIC PRINCIPLES

A magnet is a piece of metal that has the property of attracting another metal. The force of attraction is greatest at the poles or points near each end of the mag-

Fig. 2-6. The Magnetic Compass

net and least in the area halfway between the two poles. Lines of force flow from each of these poles in all directions, bending around and flowing toward the other pole to form a *magnetic field.* (See Fig. 2-7.)

Fig. 2-7. Lines of Force Around a Bar Magnet

A magnetic field surrounds the earth with lines of force oriented approximately to the North and South Magnetic Poles. Because the aircraft compass is oriented to the magnetic pole, in-flight allowance must be made for the *difference in location* of the geographic and magnetic poles if the heading reference is to be the geographic north pole.

Lines of equal magnetic declination or variation are called *isogonic lines* and are measured in degrees east or west of the earth's geographic North Pole. (See Fig. 2-8.) These lines are plotted in degrees of east or west variation on aeronautical charts. A line connecting the points of zero degrees variation is called the *agonic line.*

COMPASS CONSTRUCTION

The magnetic compass is located away from radios and electrical equipment to limit the effect of any magnetic disturbance in the aircraft. It contains a small internal light bulb for night illumination

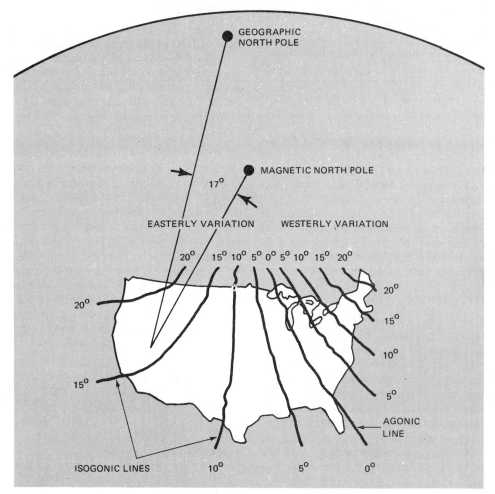

Fig. 2-8. Lines of Variation

which is mounted in the front of the instrument case.

The compass card is graduated in five-degree increments, and the magnetic headings (without the last zero) are printed every 30°. In addition, the compass card is equipped with a float to keep it in a horizontal position in the compass fluid. (See Fig. 2-9.) The pivot underneath the card rests on a jeweled bearing which permits the card to rotate freely, while two long magnets mounted underneath give the compass its directional quality. These magnets always attempt to align themselves with the magnetic field of the earth.

The float assembly is sealed in a chamber filled with acid-free, white kerosene. This liquid serves several purposes. First, due to buoyancy, part of the weight of the card is taken off the pivot which supports

Fig. 2-9. Magnetic Compass Card Assembly

the card. Second, the fluid decreases the erratic swing of the compass, known as oscillation, which may be the result of turbulence or rough pilot technique. In addition, the fluid lubricates the pivot point on the pedestal which serves as the mount for the float assembly and the compass card.

The float assembly is balanced on the pivot allowing free rotation of the card and a tilt of up to 18 degrees. At the rear of the compass bowl, a diaphragm is installed to allow for any expansion or contraction of the liquid, thus preventing the formation of bubbles or possible bursting of the case. Mounted behind the glass window is a *lubber* or reference line to designate the compass indication.

DEVIATION

Two small compensating magnets, adjustable by screws, are located in the top or bottom of the compass case to minimize *deviation*. Deviation is the deflection of the compass needle from a position of magnetic north as a result of local magnetic disturbance in the aircraft. Adjusting the compensating screws to minimize deviation is known as *swinging the compass*, a procedure which should be performed periodically by maintenance personnel.

The deviation noted should be recorded on a compass correction card. (See Fig. 2-10.) When flying compass headings, the pilot must refer to this card and make the appropriate adjustment for the particular heading he wishes to fly. It is important for the pilot to avoid placing metallic objects near the compass during flight, since this practice may induce large errors into the indications.

MAGNETIC DIP

A number of compass errors are caused by a deflection of the aircraft compass as it seeks alignment with the earth's lines of magnetic force. Lines of force in the earth's magnetic field are parallel to the earth's surface at the equator and curve increasingly downward closer to the magnetic poles.

The magnetic bars on the compass card tend to assume the same direction and position as the lines of force, thus, the bars are parallel to the surface of the earth at the magnetic equator. The magnetic bars point increasingly downward as the aircraft is moved closer to the magnetic pole. (See Fig. 2-11.) This characteristic is known as *magnetic dip* and is responsible for northerly turning error and acceleration/deceleration error.

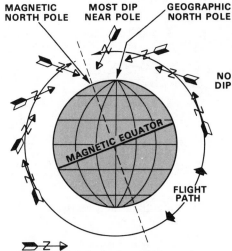

Represents Magnetic Bars Of Compass

Fig. 2-11. Magnetic Dip

TURNING ERRORS

Northerly turning error is the most pronounced of the in-flight errors and is

FOR (MH)	0°	30°	60°	90°	120°	150°	180°	210°	240°	270°	300°	330°
STEER (CH)	359°	30°	60°	88°	120°	152°	183°	212°	240°	268°	300°	329°
RADIO ON [X]						RADIO OFF [ ]						

Fig. 2-10. Compass Correction Card

most apparent when turning to or from headings of north and south. When the airplane is banked, the compass card also banks because of the centrifugal force acting upon it. While the compass card is in this banked attitude, the vertical components of the earth's magnetic field cause the earth-seeking ends of the compass to dip to the low side of the turn, giving the pilot an erroneous turn indication. (See Fig. 2-12.)

When making a turn *from a heading of north* in the Northern Hemisphere, the compass briefly gives an indication of a turn in the *opposite* direction. If this turn is continued east or west, the compass card will begin to indicate a turn in the correct direction, but it will *lag* behind the actual turn at a diminishing rate until within a few degrees of east or west. If the pilot makes a very gradual and shallow banked turn (less than five degrees) from a compass indication of north, it is possible to change the actual heading of the aircraft by 20° or more while still maintaining an indication of north on the compass.

When making a turn *from a heading of south,* the same set of forces will be in effect but the indications appear quite differently. The compass gives an indication of a turn in the *correct* direction, but at a much *faster* rate than is actually being experienced. As the turn is continued toward east or west, the compass indications will continue to *precede* the actual turn, but at a diminishing rate until within a few degrees of west or east.

ACCELERATION/DECELERATION ERRORS

Acceleration error can occur during airspeed changes and is most apparent on headings of east and west. Acceleration error is caused by a combination of inertia and the vertical component of the earth's magnetic field. Because of its pendulum-type mounting, the compass card tilts during speed changes. The momentary tilting of the card from the horizontal results in an error which is most apparent on headings of east and west. When *accelerating* on either of these headings, the error is in the form of an indication of a turn to the *north*, and when *decelerating*, the error is in the form of an indication of a turn to the *south*. A memory aid that helps pilots remember this relationship between airspeed change and the direction of error is the acronym "ANDS" — *Accelerate - North; Decelerate - South.*

NORTHERN HEMISPHERE TURNING ERROR

NORTHERN HEMISPHERE TURNING ERROR

Fig. 2-12. Northerly Turning Error

TURNS USING THE MAGNETIC COMPASS

A maximum of 15° of bank should be used when turning to headings utilizing the magnetic compass. When a 15° bank is used in turning north or south, the amount of roll-out lead is proportional to the latitude. For example, in turning *from south to north* in the area of 30° north latitude, a pilot would start a roll-out 30° *prior* to reaching north, plus a 5° lead to allow time for roll-out from the banking attitude. For example, to roll the airplane to a wings-level attitude on a heading of north, the roll-out should be initiated at either 035° or 325° depending on the direction of the turn.

To roll out on a heading of south, it is necessary to fly past 180°, the number of degrees of latitude minus the 5° lead. For example, in making a right turn from north to south at 30° north latitude with 15° bank, a roll-out should begin on a heading of 205°.

If its errors and characteristics are thoroughly understood, the magnetic compass offers the pilot a most reliable means of determining the heading of his airplane. To accurately read the compass, however, the pilot must be certain the airplane is flown level and at a constant airspeed.

OUTSIDE AIR TEMPERATURE GAUGE

The outside air temperature gauge is an important instrument used in the calculation of true airspeed in flight. (See Fig. 2-13.) It is mounted in the aircraft in a position where the temperature sensing element can be exposed to the outside air. Normally, a bright metal shield is used to protect the sensitive element of the gauge from direct sunlight and from damage.

The dial on most gauges is calibrated in both degrees Celsius and degrees Fahrenheit. When making airspeed calculations

Fig. 2-13. Outside Air Temperature Gauge

in flight, it is important for the pilot to read the correct scale — normally Celsius.

PITOT-STATIC PRESSURE INSTRUMENTS

PITOT-STATIC SYSTEM

Instruments connected to the pitot-static system (see Fig. 2-14) include the airspeed indicator, altimeter, and vertical speed indicator. This system includes a *pitot tube* for measuring *impact* (ram) air pressure and one or more *static ports* for measuring barometric *static* pressure (air pressure at flight altitude).

The pitot tube is usually located on the leading edge of the wing where there is a minimum of airflow disturbance from the various parts of the aircraft. (See Fig. 2-14.) Its opening faces the line of flight of the airplane and supplies ram air pressure to the airspeed indicator. It should be remembered that the pitot tube is not involved with the operation of any instrument other than the airspeed indicator.

The altimeter, airspeed, and vertical speed indicator cases are all vented to allow air pressure inside the cases to equalize with the outside air as the aircraft gains or loses altitude. This venting is accomplished by connecting these instrument cases to static ports, normally located on the side of the fuselage, as shown in figure 2-14, in such a position that they will not pick up ram or turbulent air pressures.

Fig. 2-14. Pitot-Static System

On some aircraft, the static vent holes are located in the pitot head, which also houses the pitot tube. In either location, the static vent is positioned to measure undisturbed atmospheric pressure only. Any change in pressures will be shown on the appropriate instrument after a lag of anywhere from one to nine seconds, depending on the design and construction of the instrument involved.

The pilot should check the pitot tube opening and the static vent openings during the preflight inspection to see that they are not clogged. Due to their location, the pitot tube and static vents are susceptible to outside elements such as dirt, water, and ice. Clogged or partially clogged openings may cause inaccurate instrument readings. The pilot should not blow into these openings since excess pressure can damage any of the three instruments.

AIRSPEED INDICATOR

The airspeed indicator measures the *difference* between impact and static pressure. When the airplane is parked on the ground, these two pressures are equal.

When the aircraft moves through the air, however, the pressure in the pitot line becomes greater than the pressure in the static line. (See Fig. 2-15.) This difference in pressure expands a small diaphragm into the area of lower pressure and this registers indicated airspeed on the instrument face in miles per hour, knots, or both. (See Fig. 2-16.) *The airspeed indicator displays the speed at which the airplane is moving through the air regardless of wind, and not the speed at which it is moving over the ground.*

Fig. 2-15. Airspeed System

Airspeed Definitions

There are three airspeed definitions of particular importance to the aviator: indicated airspeed, calibrated airspeed, and true airspeed.

Indicated airspeed (IAS). Indicated airspeed is the direct instrument reading the pilot obtains from the airspeed indicator. This value is uncorrected for variations in atmospheric density or position and instrument errors.

Calibrated airspeed (CAS). Calibrated airspeed is indicated airspeed corrected for position and instrument errors. Although aircraft and instrument manufacturers attempt to keep these to a minimum, it is not possible to eliminate them entirely throughout the airspeed operating range. For this reason, an airspeed calibration table in the pilot's operating handbook presents calibrated airspeed versus indicated airspeed for the normal airspeed range and for specific flap settings. Generally, the error is greatest at slow airspeeds, becomes less when the flaps are lowered, and reduces to a few knots in the cruising and high airspeed range. Variation between indicated and calibrated airspeed may be significant when calculating true airspeed for cross-country planning.

True airspeed (TAS). True airspeed is the actual speed of the aircraft through the airmass. The airspeed indicator registers true airspeed only under standard sea level conditions; that is, when the barometric pressure is 29.92 inches of mercury and the temperature is 15° Celsius.

Because air density decreases with an increase in altitude, the aircraft must fly faster at higher altitudes to cause the same pressure difference between pitot impact pressure and static pressure. Thus, true airspeed increases with a gain in altitude, even though the indicated airspeed remains the same.

Normally, the flight computer is used for true airspeed computations involving temperature and pressure altitude. Some aircraft, however, have an airspeed indicator which incorporates that portion

Fig. 2-16. Airspeed Markings

of the computer which is necessary for determining true airspeed. This instrument is sometimes called a *true airspeed indicator.*

Airspeed Limitations

The airspeed indicator incorporates color-coded markings to indicate important airspeed limits for the pilot. (See Fig. 2-16.) The following color codes are used:

1. A *red line* indicates the *never-exceed speed.* This speed should not be exceeded in any operation.

2. A *yellow arc* depicts the *caution speed range.* The aircraft should be operated with caution in this range and only in smooth air.

3. A *green arc* defines the *normal operating speed range.* The low-speed end of the green arc denotes the power-off stalling speed with the landing gear and the wing flaps retracted or in the

configuration designated by the manufacturer. The upper airspeed limit of the green arc denotes the maximum structural cruising speed which should not be exceeded except in smooth air and then only with caution.

4. A *white arc* specifies the speed range for operating with *fully extended wing flaps*. The low-speed end of the white arc represents the power-off stalling speed with landing gear and wing flaps extended. The upper limit is the maximum airspeed permissible with flaps extended.

NOTE: The colored markings on some older airspeed indicators are based on calibrated airspeed, while those in newer aircraft are based on indicated airspeed.

Maneuvering Speed

An important airspeed limit which is not marked on the face of the airspeed indicator is the *maneuvering speed*, the maximum speed at which application of full abrupt control movement will not overstress the aircraft. This speed generally is found on a placard or in the pilot's operating handbook. If severe turbulence is anticipated, the airspeed should be reduced to maneuvering speed or below and the aircraft held in as constant an *attitude* as possible.

ALTIMETER

The altimeter, as shown in figure 2-17, is a very important instrument in either VFR or IFR conditions. It is connected to the static system through an outlet in the back of the instrument case. The outlet serves as a vent to allow atmospheric pressure to move into and out of the instrument case as the aircraft climbs and descends.

The altimeter utilizes a stack of aneroid wafers as its pressure sensing element. All air has been evacuated from these

Fig. 2-17. Altimeter

disc-shaped metallic wafers so that changes in atmospheric pressure cause them to expand or contract. The pointers of the altimeter are connected by mechanical linkages to the wafers and present the atmospheric pressure, calibrated in feet, on the face of the altimeter.

As the aircraft climbs, the air moves out of the case due to the decrease in outside atmospheric pressure. This causes the sealed wafers to expand, resulting in a pointer movement showing increased altitude. (See Fig. 2-18.) As the aircraft descends, air moves into the case due to the increase of outside atmospheric pressure. This causes the wafers to contract, resulting in a pointer movement in the opposite direction to show decreased altitude.

Fig. 2-18. Aneroid Wafers Expand

Setting the Altimeter

A barometric scale is incorporated in the altimeter face. This scale is used when adjusting the altimeter to compensate for changes in atmospheric pressure. A knob is located at the bottom of the instrument, as shown in figure 2-17, for this adjustment.

FAA regulations specify the following concerning the altimeter: The cruising altitude of an aircraft below 18,000 feet MSL shall be maintained by reference to an altimeter that is set to the current reported altimeter setting of a station along the route of flight within 100 nautical miles. If there is no such station, the current reported altimeter setting of an appropriate available station shall be used. In an aircraft having no radio, the altimeter shall be set to the elevation of the departure airport or an appropriate altimeter setting available before departure. At or above 18,000 feet above sea level, the altimeter is set to 29.92 in. Hg, regardless of station pressure.

Types of Altitude

In aviation, height measurements are expressed as altitudes. The five most common types are indicated, pressure, density, true, and absolute. These heights are measured in distances either above ground level (AGL) or above mean sea level (MSL).

Indicated altitude is the altitude displayed on the aircraft altimeter when the altimeter is adjusted to the current altimeter setting. When the altimeter is set to the local altimeter setting on the ground, it should read field elevation or the height of the airport above mean sea level (MSL). In flight, temperature and pressure variations cause errors in indicated altitude as explained in the next section.

Pressure altitude is an altitude measured from the standard sea level pressure of 29.92 in. Hg. It is the actual reading of the altimeter when the barometric scale has been set to 29.92. Pressure altitude is used by all aircraft flying above 18,000 feet, by manufacturers when constructing performance charts, and by pilots for computer solutions of true airspeed, density altitude, and true altitude.

Density altitude is pressure altitude corrected for non-standard temperatures. It is used to determine aircraft performance, and many older aircraft performance charts are based on density altitude.

True altitude is the actual height above mean sea level (MSL). The altitude of all fixed, non-changeable objects is given in true altitude. Field elevations and obstructions such as mountains, radio antennas, and towers are given as true altitude on the navigational charts. These figures do not change with variable atmospheric conditions.

Absolute altitude is the height of an aircraft above the surface over which it is flying. This altitude is abbreviated AGL, above ground level.

Altimeter Indications

Altimeters are calibrated on the basis of the international standard atmosphere in which pressure, temperature, and lapse rate are assumed to have a fixed relationship (29.92 in. Hg, 15° Celsius, and a reduction of 2° Celsius per 1,000-foot increase in altitude, respectively). The only time the altimeter will indicate true altitude in flight is when the actual temperature and pressure conform to the assumed values in the standard atmosphere. Since this seldom is the case, the altimeter indications are subject to error. The amount of error depends upon how much the temperature and/or pressure deviates from standard. Even though the proper altimeter setting is used, in-flight temperature variations will cause errors in indicated altitude. Therefore, if terrain or obstacle clearance is a factor in the selection of a cruising altitude, pilots must remember to anticipate that *colder* than standard temperatures will place the aircraft *lower* than the indicated altitude.

The same situation exists when a pilot flies from a high-pressure area to a lower pressure area without changing the altimeter setting. A pilot maintaining the same indicated altitude will descend, leading him to believe that he is flying higher than he actually is. A good rule of thumb is *from high to low, hot to cold, look out below.*

Figure 2-19 illustrates this principle. To find the difference between true and indicated altitude over New Orleans, subtract the smaller barometric setting from the larger. Since one inch of mercury equals 1,000 feet of altitude, convert the difference into feet by moving the decimal point three spaces to the right.

Miami altimeter setting	30.07
New Orleans altimeter setting	29.77
	.30

.30 in. Hg = 300 feet

This is the error, in feet, between true and indicated altitude. When flying into a *low* pressure area, true altitude is *lower* than indicated altitude. When flying into a *high* pressure area, true altitude is *higher* than indicated altitude. Since the aircraft is being flown into low pressure, true altitude is 300 feet low, or 200 feet

Fig. 2-20. Altimeter with Three Pointers

MSL (500 feet indicated — 300-foot error = 200 feet true altitude).

The altimeter usually has three pointers to indicate altitude. (See Fig. 2-20.) The longest pointer indicates hundreds of feet, the middle-sized pointer indicates thousands of feet, and the shortest pointer indicates tens of thousands of feet.

When the 100-foot pointer makes one complete revolution, the 1,000-foot pointer moves to one, or 1,000 feet. When the 1,000-foot pointer makes one revolution, the short pointer will move to one, indicating 10,000 feet. This is why it is necessary to read the shortest pointer first, the middle pointer second, and the long pointer third. The middle-sized pointer and the short pointer are disregarded in reading the altimeter until they reach "one" on the altimeter dial.

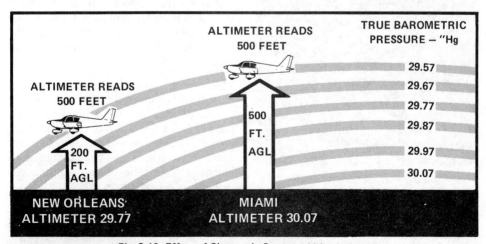

Fig. 2-19. Effect of Changes in Pressure Altitude Levels

In reading the altimeter in figure 2-20, the smallest pointer has not yet reached one, so the aircraft is less than 10,000 feet and the needle indication can be disregarded. The medium-sized pointer is between one and two which means the aircraft is above 1,000 feet but below 2,000 feet; therefore, the pointer indication is read as 1,000 feet plus whatever the long pointer indicates. In this case, the long pointer is on nine which signifies 900 feet. Putting together the information from the three pointers, the aircraft altitude is read as 1,900 feet.

VERTICAL SPEED INDICATOR

The vertical speed indicator (VSI) shows the rate of climb and rate of descent. (See Fig. 2-21.) This instrument is contained in a sealed case and also is connected to the static system. Inside the case, there is a diaphragm which is connected to the static pressure system. (See Fig. 2-22.) As the altitude changes, the static pressure changes to give pilots an indication of a *vertical* change. Just as the altimeter shows the amount of altitude change, the vertical speed indicator shows the *rate* of altitude change.

Fig. 2-21. Vertical Speed Indicator

This instrument actually measures the rate of change in the atmospheric pressure through the use of a *calibrated leak* built into the back of the instrument case. The rate of change is shown in feet per minute.

The VSI can be efficiently used as a trend instrument since it will *immediately* indicate any deviation from level flight. In turbulent air, the aircraft may be continually moving up and down, both because vertical gusts may change the pitch attitude and because the air itself is moving vertically. In turbulence, the VSI will make such rapid changes that it will be almost useless as a precision pitch instrument.

Fig. 2-22. Internal Components of Vertical Speed Indicator

The VSI will be very quick to show a climbing or descending *trend;* however, it has a characteristic lag of six to nine seconds before actually indicating the correct climb or descent rate. This lag is the result of the time necessary for pressure changes to take place inside the instrument. If pitch changes are small and are made slowly, the indication on the instrument will be a very close representation of the correct rate at any given instant. When a rapid or large pitch change or a combination of the two is made, the instrument may lag far behind the correct indication.

The vertical speed indicators used on most turbine-powered aircraft do not have the needle lag. The more precise and expensive VSI's give a correct instantaneous indication of the rate of climb or descent. These instruments use the principles of inertia and are known as instantaneous vertical speed indicators (IVSI).

GYRO INSTRUMENTS

Gyro flight instruments have played a major part in making instrument flight a practical part of modern-day flight. It is important for the pilot to understand their operation so the gyro instruments may be used correctly and effectively.

GYROSCOPIC PRINCIPLES

The primary trait of a rotating gyro rotor is its *rigidity in space* or gyroscopic inertia. Newton's First Law states in part: *A body in motion tends to move in a constant speed and direction unless disturbed by some external force.*

The rotor inside a gyro instrument maintains a constant attitude in space as long as no outside forces change its motion. This quality of stability is greater if the rotor has great mass and speed. Thus the gyros in aircraft instruments are of heavy construction and are designed to spin quite rapidly.

The three gyro instruments found in most general aviation aircraft are the attitude indicator, heading indicator, and turn-and-slip indicator or turn coordinator. (See Figs. 2-23, 2-24, and 2-25.)

The heading indicator and attitude indicator use gyros as an unchanging reference in space. Once the gyros are spinning, they stay in constant positions with respect to the actual horizon or direction. The aircraft heading and attitude can then be compared to these stable references. For example, the rotor of a universally-mounted gyro will re-

Fig. 2-23. Attitude Indicator

Fig. 2-24. Heading Indicator

main in the same position while the surrounding *gimbals*, or circular frames, are moved.

Fig. 2-25. Turn Indicators

PRECESSION

Another characteristic of gyros is *precession* which is a tilting or turning of the gyro axis in reaction to applied forces. When a deflective force is applied to the rim of a gyro rotor that *is not turning*, the rotor naturally moves in the direction of the force. However, when the gyro rotor *is rotating*, the same applied force would cause the rotor to move in a direction as though the force had been applied at a point 90° around the rim in the direction of rotation. This turning movement, or precession, places the rotor in a new plane of rotation. Unavoidable precession is caused by maneuvers and internal friction in the attitude and directional gyros. This causes slow drifting and minor erroneous indications in these instruments.

SOURCES OF POWER FOR GYRO OPERATIONS

A gyroscopic instrument can be operated by either the vacuum system or the electrical system. Most training aircraft are equipped with a turn coordinator that is driven electrically, and attitude and heading indicators that are vacuum powered. The advantage of using two different sources of power is that if one power source fails, the other source still is available to provide attitude reference.

VACUUM SYSTEM

The gyro instruments operated by the vacuum system are driven by air pressure differential. A vacuum pump creates a partial vacuum in the system. A central filtered air inlet to the system is located upstream from the gyros. As the result of the partial vacuum, air rushes into the system through the central filter and is routed to the gyro cases, causing the gyro wheels to spin. This air is exhausted into the atmosphere through the pump.

An engine-driven vacuum pump is the most common source of vacuum power for gyros installed in light aircraft. (See Fig. 2-26.) Pump capacity and size vary in different aircraft depending on the number of gyros to be operated. The system usually will have a relief valve to relieve excess vacuum.

A vacuum gauge is mounted on the instrument panel to inform the pilot of the operating suction of the system. This gauge indicates the difference, in inches of mercury, between the pressure at the central filter and at the pressure relief valve.

Fig. 2-26. Vacuum System

Older vacuum gyros require a setting between 2.75 and 4.25 inches of mercury; however, the new gyro systems require *higher* vacuum settings. Recommended settings for the new gyros may range from a low of 4.5 to a high of 5.8 inches of mercury, as indicated in the appropriate pilot's operating handbook. A reading below the recommended value indicates that the air flow is not spinning the gyros fast enough for reliable operation. On some aircraft, warning lights are used to indicate low or high vacuum pressure.

VENTURI

A venturi can be used in place of a vacuum pump and has the advantage of relatively low cost due to its simplicity of installation and operation. One or more ventures are usually mounted on the side of the aircraft where the airflow from the propeller will pass through them. (See Fig. 2-27.) The venturi is shaped like a pair of airfoils so that the air velocity is increased as it flows through. The increase in air velocity inside the venturi causes a low pressure area in the venturi, resulting in a partial vacuum in the line leading from the ventures to the gyro cases.

LOW-PRESSURE AREA

TO GYROS

Fig. 2-27. Ventures

ELECTRICALLY-DRIVEN GYROS

Aircraft that normally fly at high altitudes do not have a vacuum system since its operation would be limited in the thin, cold air of high altitudes. Alternating current (AC) is used to drive the gyros in the directional and attitude instruments. The AC power is provided by inverters which convert direct current to alternating current or by engine-driven AC generators or alternators.

GYRO ROTORS

Gyro rotors are mounted two ways, depending upon how the gyroscopic properties are to be used in the operation of the instrument. A freely or universally-mounted gyro is set on three gimbals with the gyro free to rotate in any plane. (See Fig. 2-28.) Regardless of the position of the gyro base, the gyro tends to remain rigid in space. In the attitude indicator, the horizon bar is gyro-controlled to remain parallel to the natural horizon. Changes in the position of the aircraft are shown pictorially.

Fig. 2-28. Universally-Mounted Gyro

The semi-rigid or restricted mounting employs two gimbals limiting the rotor to two planes of rotation. In the turn indicator, the semi-rigid mounting is used to provide controlled precession of the rotor. The precession force exerted upon the gyro by the turning aircraft causes the instrument to indicate a turn.

ATTITUDE INDICATOR

With its miniature aircraft and horizon bar, the attitude indicator is the one instrument that portrays the actual attitude of the real aircraft. Since it is connected to a gyroscope, the horizon bar remains *parallel* to the natural horizon. The relationship of the miniature aircraft to the horizon bar is the same as the relationship of the real aircraft to the actual horizon. (See Fig. 2-

29.) The horizon bar remains parallel to the actual horizon and the aircraft and instrument case revolve around it.

An adjustment knob is provided to move the miniature aircraft upward or downward inside the case. Normally the miniature aircraft is adjusted so that the wings overlap the horizon bar when the actual aircraft is in straight-and-level flight. The attitude indicator gives an instantaneous indication of even the smallest changes in attitude and has no lead or lag. It is very reliable if properly maintained. (See Fig. 2-29.)

When the aircraft's nose is raised above level attitude, the pictorial representation on the attitude indicator shows the same attitude in miniature. Besides showing pitch motion around the lateral axis, the attitude indicator also shows movement around the longitudinal or roll axis. (See Fig. 2-30.)

The instrument has an index at the top of the case which indicates the degree of bank by pointing to bank marks on either side of the instrument centerline.

Each large mark is equivalent to 30° of bank, and the small marks between the centerline and the first 30° index are each equal to 10° of bank.

When the aircraft is banked to the left, the horizon bar in the instrument maintains its position level to the actual horizon so that the left wing of the miniature aircraft on the instrument face moves below the horizon bar and the right wing moves above. (See Fig. 2-30, bottom right.) This is the same relationship that the full-sized aircraft has with the earth's horizon.

THE HEADING INDICATOR

The heading indicator is designed to operate without the magnetic dip errors inherent in the magnetic compass. Since it has *no* direction-seeking properties, the heading indicator must be set to a heading shown on the magnetic compass. The heading indicator also operates on the gyroscopic principle of rigidity in space with a plane of rotation that is vertical. The compass rose on the face of the instrument is geared to the gyro

Fig. 2-29. Internal Components of the Attitude Indicator

CLIMB

GLIDE

CLIMB AND LEFT BANK

15° BANK

GLIDE AND LEFT BANK

LEVEL FLIGHT

LEVEL FLIGHT;
LEFT BANK

Fig. 2-30. Relationship of Attitude Indicator to Natural Horizon

gimbal causing the card to turn as the aircraft turns. (See Fig. 2-31.) To use the heading indicator properly, the pilot must first turn an adjustment knob which rotates the card to the correct magnetic heading.

The heading indicator is subject to precession errors which cause the instrument to gradually move off the correct magnetic heading indication. While airborne, the heading indicator should be set to the magnetic compass, but only during straight-and-level, unaccelerated flight. Due to precession errors, the heading indicator should be checked at least every 15 minutes and reset when necessary. Even a heading indicator in perfect condition can drift from its original setting.

TURN-AND-SLIP INDICATOR

The *turn-and-slip indicator* is both a rate and quality of turn instrument. This instrument is shown in figure 2-32.

Fig. 2-31. Internal Components of the Heading Indicator

The sensitive element of the turn-and-slip indicator is a spinning gyro that is mounted in a frame (more commonly called a gimbal ring). This frame pivots and permits the gyro to rotate left and right. This freedom of movement gives the gyro the ability to indicate when the aircraft is turning.

A needle is located at the top to indicate the rate of turn. An inclinometer at the bottom is used to indicate the quality of the turn.

When the needle of the instrument is aligned with either the mark on the left or the mark on the right of the centerline, the aircraft will turn 180° in one minute, or 360° in two minutes. This is called a standard-rate turn. (See Fig. 2-33.) The reference marks to the left and right of the instrument centerline may be called *doghouses* because of their shape.

The inclinometer consists of a curved glass tube with a small black ball resting in the center. By observing this ball, the pilot can obtain the following information:

1. During a turn where the aircraft's controls are properly coordinated, the ball will remain in the center position, indicating to the pilot that the proper forces are reacting on the aircraft.
2. Whenever the ball moves to the outside of the turn, it indicates that the aircraft is in a skid and that the aircraft controls are not properly coordinated.

Fig. 2-32. Turn-and-Slip Indicator

Fig. 2-33. Standard-Rate Turn

3. When the ball moves to the inside of the turn, it indicates that the aircraft is in a slip and that the proper controls are not being applied to the aircraft.

TURN COORDINATOR

On many of the newer aircraft, the turn-and-slip indicator has been replaced with a *turn coordinator*. (See Fig. 2-34.) In this instrument, a small aircraft silhouette rotates to show that the aircraft is

Fig. 2-34. Turn Coordinator

turning. It utilizes an electric gyro that is canted approximately 35°. Due to the canted gyro, the small aircraft will bank whenever the actual aircraft is rotating about either the yaw or roll axis. (See Fig. 2-35.)

When the aircraft is turning left or right, the small aircraft silhouette will bank in the direction of the turn. When the wing of the aircraft silhouette is aligned with one of the lower index marks, the actual aircraft is in a standard-rate turn.

Roll rate also is sensed by this instrument because the gyro is tilted on its fore and aft axis, thus providing the pilot with an immediate indication of conditions that lead to a turn. After the bank angle for a turn has been established and the roll rate is zero, the aircraft symbol indicates only the rate of turn of the aircraft.

The use of the turn-and-slip indicator or the turn coordinator for turns would be virtually impossible without the use of the aircraft clock. Instrument turns are made by noting the position of the turn indicator and the elapsed time that the aircraft remains in the turn. For example, by holding a standard-rate turn for one minute, the aircraft would turn through 180°.

The inclinometer in the turn coordinator gives the same indications as the inclinometer in the turn-and-slip indicator. (See Fig. 2-36.)

USING THE FLIGHT INSTRUMENTS IN COMBINATION

The flight instrument group can be divided into two sets of instruments: one for controlling the altitude, and the other for direction. The altitude intruments, associated with the elevator and power controls, are the altimeter, the airspeed indicator, and the vertical speed in-

Fig. 2-35. Internal Components of Turn Coordinator

COORDINATED FLIGHT	SKID	SLIP
BALL IS CENTERED	BALL IS TO OUTSIDE OF TURN, TO COORDINATE: MORE BANK OR LESS LEFT RUDDER	BALL IS TO INSIDE OF TURN, TO COORDINATE: LESS BANK OR MORE LEFT RUDDER

Fig. 2-36. Turn Coordinator Interpretations

dicator. Aircraft direction, which is associated with aileron or bank control, is determined by checking the heading indicator and the turn coordinator or turn-and-slip indicator.

Each set of instruments is used in conjunction with the attitude indicator and/or outside visual reference. The techniques used for scanning the flight instruments and maneuvering the aircraft are the same when flying by outside visual references as when flying by instrument references alone. The difference is that the attitude indicator, to the instrument pilot, replaces what the VFR pilot sees outside the aircraft. (See Fig. 2-37.)

Fig. 2-37. Attitude Indicator Simulates Outside Visual References

SECTION C — THE RECIPROCATING ENGINE AND RELATED SYSTEMS

THE RECIPROCATING ENGINE

A reciprocating engine is the most widely used powerplant on general aviation aircraft today. (See Figs. 2-38 and 2-39.) The combination of the reciprocating engine and propeller is one of the most efficient means of converting the chemical energy of fuel into thrust for sustained flight.

In order to determine the power output of a reciprocating engine, a brake measuring device is attached to the drive shaft. Hence, the term *brake horsepower* (BHP) is used to denote the actual power developed by an engine. The output of any reciprocating engine is a direct function of the combination of engine torque, or twisting force, and rotation speed.

When a reciprocating engine is operated at high altitudes, efficiency of the engine diminishes as a result of lower air density and smaller volume of airflow into the engine. Therefore, a turbocharger may be added to the engine to compress air before it is injected into the engine cylinders. The turbine on a turbocharged engine is powered by exhaust gases from the engine. This compression increases air density so that an aircraft engine can operate at high altitudes and still produce the same amount of power as it would at sea level.

Engines designed for aircraft are similar in many ways to automotive engines; however, they are much lighter and a great deal more reliable. Aircraft engines are built of relatively expensive materials and, because of their construction and the wide variety of environmental conditions in which they operate, must be operated more carefully than the engine in a car. One noticeable difference between an aircraft engine and an automotive engine is that practically all aircraft engines are air cooled rather than liquid cooled.

COOLING THE ENGINE

The burning of fuel within the cylinder produces intense heat. Much of this heat is expelled with the escaping gases or exhaust but, to keep aircraft engines safely cooled, outside air must circulate around the cylinders.

The aircraft engine is built with thin metal fins projecting from the cylinder

Fig. 2-38. Top View of Four-Cylinder Aircraft Reciprocating Engine

Fig. 2-39. Side View of Four-Cylinder Reciprocating Engine and Propeller Combination

wall allowing heat to be carried away as the air flows past. (See Fig. 2-40.) The cooling air enters the engine compartment through openings in the front of the cowling and is routed over the engine cylinders by tight fitting baffles and expelled through one or more openings in the bottom of the cowling.

Most lower-powered aircraft have a fixed opening in the bottom of the cowling. The size of this opening is determined by the amount of airflow needed to cool the engine during climb conditions when the forward speed is low and the engine power is high. However, during cruise, the aircraft speed is higher than during a climb, and the engine power is at a reduced setting. Thus, more cooling air flows through the cowling with a fixed opening than is needed to adequately cool the engine.

The cooling air flowing over the cylinders causes drag, and the greater the amount of air flowing through the cowling, the greater the drag. Thus, if the volume of air can be reduced during cruise, the drag can be reduced. The cruising speeds of lower-powered aircraft are in the performance range where the increased cooling drag during cruise is not excessive. Therefore, the additional cost of devices to restrict the cooling air is not warranted.

Fig. 2-40. Engine Cooling

Care should be exercised to prevent running the engine at a higher than designed maximum operating temperature, as this will cause loss of power, excessive oil consumption, and detonation. It will also lead to serious permanent damage such as scored cylinder walls, burned and scored pistons and rings, and burned and warped valves. Excessively high oil temperatures can be avoided in aircraft not equipped with cowl flaps by richening the mixture, increasing the airspeed and/or reducing power.

COWL FLAPS

In higher performance aircraft, the cooling drag becomes more critical, and *cowl flaps* (small doors that open out of the cowling) are usually installed to control the flow of cooling air. (See Fig. 2-41.)

Fig. 2-41. Cowl Flaps

The control is provided in the cabin, so the pilot can adjust the cowl flaps to any position desired from fully open to fully closed.

The cowl flaps are adjusted to keep the engine operation within the temperature limitations indicated by the green arc on the cylinder head temperature and oil temperature gauges. The cowl flaps are usually fully open for taxi, takeoff, and climb. When an engine is operating on the ground, very little air flows past the cylinders (particularly if the engine is closely cowled), and overheating is likely to occur, especially on days with high air temperatures. Overheating may also oc-

cur during prolonged climbs because the engine is usually developing high power at a relatively low airspeed.

For cruising flight, the cowl flaps are normally closed to reduce drag and to maintain normal engine operating temperatures. The cylinder head temperature will dictate the amount of opening for the proper operating temperature.

CYLINDER HEAD TEMPERATURE GAUGE

The cylinder head temperature gauge is installed in aircraft equipped with cowl flaps and is located in the engine instrument group. (See Fig. 2-42.) This instrument gives the pilot an accurate indication of engine cooling by measuring the temperature of one of the aft cylinder heads. This instrument can always be checked against the oil temperature gauge to make sure that *neither* of the two instruments is giving erroneous readings.

The pilot should monitor the cylinder head temperature gauge frequently during steep climbs and when the outside air temperature is high. High cylinder head temperatures decrease the life of an

Fig. 2-42. Cylinder Head Temperature Gauge

engine and should be avoided by richening the mixture and opening the cowl flaps as needed.

CYLINDER BLOCK ARRANGEMENTS

The name for a type of internal combustion engine is derived from the arrangement of the cylinders around a central crankshaft. If the cylinders are arranged directly opposite to each other on the crankshaft, the engine is classified as an *opposed* type. (See Fig. 2-43.) If the

Fig. 2-44. Radial Engine

Fig. 2-43. Horizontally-Opposed Engine

cylinders, however, are mounted in a circle around the crankshaft, the engine is called a *radial* type. (See Fig. 2-44.) Most light aircraft engines are of the air-cooled, horizontally-opposed type, with four, six, or eight cylinders.

ENGINE POWER CYCLE

The reciprocating engine, like any other air-breathing engine, can be considered as a pump for air and fuel — the more air and fuel that is pumped through it per minute, the more energy is produced to turn the propeller to produce thrust. This pumping is carried on throughout the engine power cycle. The components of the engine necessary to complete a power cycle are shown in figure 2-45.

The engine power cycle consists of four strokes: *intake, compression, power,* and *exhaust.* (See Fig. 2-46.) The intake stroke occurs when the piston moves away from the cylinder head. During this stroke, the intake valve opens and the fuel/air mixture is drawn into the cylinder by the suction created by the movement of the piston.

Fig. 2-45. Engine Components

Fig. 2-46. Engine Power Cycle

The compression stroke takes place when the piston moves back toward the cylinder head. The intake valve closes, sealing off the top of the cylinder, and the fuel/air mixture is compressed into a small space to prepare for the next stroke.

The power stroke begins as the piston approaches the closed end of the cylinder and the spark plugs fire. The spark from the spark plug ignites the compressed fuel/air mixture, and a rapid, even burning of the mixture takes place in the combustion chamber, pushing the piston and revolving the crankshaft. The direction of the crankshaft's revolution on most air-

craft is clockwise (when viewed from the pilot's seat).

The last stroke of the power cycle is called the exhaust stroke and consists of the piston moving toward the cylinder head for the second time in this cycle. The exhaust and burned gases are forced out as the piston returns to the top of the cylinder.

The power cycle just described takes place in each of the engine cylinders at different times thereby creating an *overlap* of power cycles during any single revolution of the propeller. (See Fig. 2-47) The manner in which the pistons are connected to the crankshaft in order to provide *smooth continuous* power to the propeller is also shown.

DETONATION

Detonation is defined as abnormally rapid combustion. (See Fig. 2-48.) If the burning rate of the fuel is too fast, the pressure in the cylinder will build up very rapidly and the remaining mixture will detonate (explode suddenly). Continued operation when detonation is present can result in engine damage.

Some of the principal causes of detonation are low grade fuel, fuel/air mixture too lean, overheated mixture temperature, high cylinder head temperatures, and opening the throttle abruptly when the engine is running at slow speeds. Proper engine servicing and correct engine operating procedures prevent detonation.

PRE-IGNITION

Pre-ignition is the uncontrolled firing of the fuel/air charge in advance of normal spark ignition. Pre-ignition usually is caused by carbon deposits on piston heads, spark plugs, and valves. Pre-ignition may start detonation, and paradoxically, detonation may start pre-ignition. Moreover, pre-ignition can be as destructive as detonation. Proper maintenance and correct operation procedures are necessary for the prevention of pre-ignition.

Fig. 2-47. Crankshaft and Propeller

IGNITION SYSTEM

The function of the ignition system is to supply a spark to ignite the fuel/air mixture in the cylinders. To do this, the engine is equipped with an ignition system consisting of *two* magnetos, *two* spark plugs for *each* cylinder, ignition leads, and a magneto switch.

The basic source of current in an aircraft ignition system is a magneto wherein a permanent magnet is connected to a shaft rotated by the crankshaft of the engine. The current generated by the magnet is then strengthened by going through a set of breaker points and a secondary coiled circuit. At this point the voltage is approximately 20,000 volts, which is sufficient to jump a normal spark plug gap and ignite the fuel/air mixture in the

Fig. 2-48. Normal Burning and Detonation

cylinders. The high voltage produced in the secondary winding is then directed by the distributor to the proper ignition lead where it is conducted to the spark plug in the cylinder in sequence with the firing order of the engine.

The magneto has proved to be a very dependable type of ignition source since it operates completely independent of all other power sources. For aircraft engine applications, however, two magnetos are used, providing a dual ignition system that results in more efficient combustion for increased power and better engine performance. (See Fig. 2-49.) An aircraft engine will run on a single magneto, although a slight loss of engine r.p.m. and power will result. After the engine starts, the master switch can be turned off and the engine will continue to run using the magnetos for ignition.

Each cylinder has two spark plugs — one on top of the cylinder and the other on the bottom of the cylinder. Two plugs are provided for two reasons:

1. SAFETY FACTOR — one magneto fires one plug in each cylinder and the other magneto fires the other set of plugs making it possible for

Fig. 2-49. Dual Ignition

the engine to run on either set. Thus, if one magneto or a spark plug fails, the engine will continue to run safely. This is called dual ignition.

2. MORE EFFICIENCY — two spark plugs cause the fuel/air mixture in the combustion chambers to burn more evenly and produce more power.

The magneto switch is located on the instrument panel and provides the pilot with a means of switching from one of the ignition systems to the other, and back to both systems. (See Fig. 2-50.) It has four positions: OFF, RIGHT, LEFT, and BOTH. The RIGHT position checks the right magneto and its set of plugs; the LEFT position checks the left magneto and its set of plugs. With the switch in the BOTH position, the engine operates on dual ignition.

A malfunction in the ignition system can be determined by watching the tachometer and noticing the r.p.m. decrease when the system is switched from BOTH to RIGHT, and then from BOTH to LEFT. The permissible decrease in engine r.p.m. for operation on one set of plugs varies for different engines and the pilot's operating handbook should be consulted for this value.

If the engine quits completely when switched to one magneto or if it loses more than the specified amount of power, the aircraft must not be flown until the problem is corrected. Some of the spark plugs could be fouled by combustion deposits, wiring may have broken or come loose, or the magnetos may not be timed to fire the spark plugs at the proper time.

It is imperative that the pilot remember to turn the ignition switch to BOTH for

Fig. 2-50. Magnetos and Magneto Switch

flight and to turn it completely OFF after shutting down the engine. Even with the master electrical switch turned off, the engine of a parked aircraft can fire if the ignition switch is left on and someone moves the propeller.

Ignition system wiring is shielded to prevent interference with the operation of the aircraft radio equipment. Broken shielding or a loose contact in the ignition system often sounds like static on the radio receivers.

ENGINE LUBRICATION SYSTEM

Oil, used primarily to lubricate the moving parts of the engine, also helps reduce engine temperature by reducing friction and removing some of the heat from the cylinders. The oil is supplied from a sump, or tank, by an oil pump and by splashing caused by the rotating crankshaft. (See Fig. 2-51.) The oil filler cap is readily accessible through an access door in the cowling.

There is also a dipstick for measuring oil quantity. (See Fig. 2-51.) It is important that pilots check oil quantity during the preflight inspection.

Many different types of aviation oil are available. The recommended type and weight normally are placarded on the cowling access door or listed in the pilot's operating handbook.

OIL PRESSURE GAUGE

The oil pressure gauge is one of the primary engine instruments and usually is found in a grouping with the oil temperature and fuel gauges. (See Fig. 2-52.) It indicates the pressure in pounds per square inch under which the oil of the engine lubricating system is being supplied to the moving parts of the engine. The oil pressure gauge also incorporates color markings to indicate when oil pressure is in the proper range for safe engine operation. The red line at the lower end of the scale indicates minimum

Fig. 2-51. Engine Oil System

idling pressure and the red line at the upper end of the scale indicates the maximum allowable oil pressure. The green arc designates the normal operating range.

The oil pressure gauge is one of the first instruments that the pilot should observe after the engine is started. Most aircraft manufacturers recommend that if the oil pressure does not start to rise within 30 seconds in the summer and within one minute in the winter, the engine should be shut down and checked. In cold weather, the oil in the lines congeals and may become very heavy; therefore, a longer period of time is allowed during winter to permit the thick, cold oil to move up into the instrument.

Fig. 2-53. Oil Temperature Gauge

oil leaves the oil cooler and enters the engine to be routed to the bearings. The temperature of the oil is measured as it enters the engine, not as it leaves the engine.

The pilot should monitor the oil temperature gauge closely during maneuvers that may cause high engine temperatures. High oil temperatures are usually noted along with high cylinder head temperatures, and any discrepancy in their indications probably indicates that one or the other of the instruments is malfunctioning.

The oil temperature gauge is also color-coded. The upper red line shows maximum allowable temperature for continuous operation. A green arc defines the normal operating range.

THROTTLE

The amount of fuel/air mixture that moves into the engine cylinders is regulated by the throttle valve. (See Fig. 2-54.) A throttle control in the pilot's compartment is connected to this valve to regulate the power output of the engine. Forward movement of the throttle opens the throttle valve and increases the engine speed, while aft movement slows the engine down. (A complete discussion of the carburetor is included in Section D of this chapter.)

Fig. 2-52. Oil Pressure Gauge

OIL TEMPERATURE GAUGE

The oil temperature gauge is normally located adjacent to the oil pressure gauge on the instrument panel so that they can be observed at the same time. (See Fig. 2-53.) It should be remembered that the oil temperature will not react as quickly as the oil pressure gauge. In cold weather, the oil temperature on some aircraft need not be within the green arc until the takeoff roll is started.

The bulb for measuring the temperature is located in the oil circulation system of the engine on the pressure side of the oil pump, usually at the place where the

Fig. 2-54. Throttle and Throttle Valve

After the fuel and air become mixed in the carburetor, the mixture travels past the throttle valve and through the intake manifold to the engine cylinders where it enters the combustion chambers (engine cylinders) through the intake valves. After the combustion takes place, the exhaust gases leave the combustion chamber on the exhaust stroke. These gases pass through the exhaust valve into the exhaust manifold to the engine muffler and then into the atmosphere through the exhaust pipe.

TACHOMETER

The tachometer measures the rate at which the engine crankshaft is revolving in revolutions per minute (r.p.m.) and is very important in making power adjustments for takeoffs, climbouts, descents, and cruise control. (See Fig. 2-55.) It is calibrated in hundreds of r.p.m.'s and usually incorporates a recording mechan-

Fig. 2-55. Tachometer

ism to keep an accurate record of the engine hours. This recording mechanism is very similar to the mileage indicator on the automobile speedometer.

On an aircraft using a fixed-pitch propeller, the tachometer is the *only* instrument available to the pilot for making power settings. The readings on this instrument are controlled by the throttle when a fixed-pitch propeller is used, or by the propeller control in the case of a constant-speed propeller.

The tachometer is also used when making magneto checks before takeoff or for maintenance checks on the engine. In addition, it will indicate the formation of carburetor ice for an aircraft equipped with a fixed-pitch propeller since the restriction of air flow to the engine cylinders due to carburetor ice causes a drop in engine r.p.m.

The tachometer is color-coded for easy interpretation. The green arc indicates the normal range, the yellow arc shows the caution range, and the red line is the maximum allowable r.p.m. Pilots should operate the aircraft engine at a continuous setting within the green arc.

MECHANICAL TYPE TACHOMETER

The mechanical type tachometer found on most single-engine aircraft uses a flexible driveshaft to transmit the crankshaft rotation to the instrument. The driveshaft is connected directly from the engine to the tachometer and is supported along its routings to prevent it from whipping as the shaft rotates.

MANIFOLD PRESSURE GAUGE

An engine with a fixed-pitch propeller turns at a speed determined by the throttle setting and atmospheric air pressure. With this kind of engine, the pilot has no way to control propeller pitch so the tachometer indications of engine speed are direct indications of power output. When a constant-speed propeller is used, however, the r.p.m. of the engine in cruising flight will remain constant, since the propeller automatically changes pitch to maintain the desired engine speed. In this case, a manifold pressure gauge is a required instrument in order to determine proper throttle settings. (See Fig. 2-56.)

The manifold pressure gauge indicates the engine's power and is controlled by the throttle. The tachometer shows the engine r.p.m. set with the propeller control by the pilot. The two instruments are located in close proximity so that reference can be made to both gauges when making power settings.

Fig. 2-57. Manifold Pressure Gauge Hook-Up

gauge. When carburetor ice forms, a decrease in manifold pressure results due to the fact that the air flow to the engine is restricted by the formation of ice. (The formation of carburetor ice is discussed in Section D.)

To help the pilot make power settings commensurate with the various flight conditions, the manifold pressure gauge has a colored range marking on its dial to indicate the proper range of operation.

AIRCRAFT PROPELLERS

The propeller consists of a control hub with two or more blades attached. The propeller assembly is rotated by the aircraft engine; the rotary action of the blades converts engine power into thrust.

Fig. 2-56. Manifold Pressure Gauge

The manifold pressure gauge indicates, in inches of mercury, the pressure inside the engine intake manifold that carries the fuel/air mixture to the cylinders. (See Fig. 2-57.) When the engine is not running, the manifold pressure gauge will indicate the existing atmospheric pressure. When the engine is running, the pistons create a partial vacuum, causing the manifold pressure to indicate below atmospheric pressure. A supercharger-equipped engine is capable of producing manifold pressure higher than atmospheric pressure.

Carburetor ice can be detected by a drop in the indication of the manifold pressure

The action of the propeller can be visualized by assuming that the rotating propeller is a rotating airfoil. Figure 2-58 shows various cross sections of a typical propeller. It can be noted that the propeller cross sections have a well-defined airfoil shape. As the propeller blade rotates through the air, a low-pressure area is created on the front, or curved, side. Thus, thrust is produced as the aircraft is actually pulled into this low-pressure area in front of the propeller.

Each small section of the propeller blade is set at a different angle to the plane of rotation, resulting in an infinite number of angles. The sections near the tip

SIDE VIEW   FRONT VIEW   CROSS SECTION

Fig. 2-58. Typical Propeller Blade

rotate in a larger arc and travel at a greater speed. This gradual decrease in blade angle gives the propeller blade its twisted appearance and maintains a uniform thrust throughout most of the diameter of the propeller.

A propeller with low blade angles, known as a *climb propeller*, provides the best performance for takeoff and climb, while one with high blade angles, known as a *cruise propeller*, is more adapted to high speed cruise and high altitude flight. Aircraft manufacturers choose propellers that are best for the primary function of the aircraft; therefore, when using a fixed-pitch propeller, some compromises must be made.

The propeller installed in light aircraft may be of either the fixed-pitch variety or the constant-speed type. (See Figs. 2-59 and 2-60.) The term *pitch*, when applied to propellers, should not be confused with pitch as it relates to an aircraft's attitude. A propeller's pitch is the number of inches that it would move

Fig. 2-59. Fixed-Pitch Propeller

Fig. 2-60. Constant-Speed Propeller

ficiency as it does in air. Pitch is proportional to blade angle (the angle between the chord line of the blade and the propeller's plane of rotation).

FIXED-PITCH PROPELLERS

The fixed-pitch propeller used on most training type aircraft has a blade angle that cannot be changed by the pilot. (See Fig. 2-59.) The blade angles normally are designed to obtain the best performance while the aircraft is *cruising*. However, low propeller blade angles are desirable on aircraft operating at high altitude airports and on those equipped with floats where takeoff and climb performance is more critical. If the propeller

forward in one revolution if it were moving through a solid medium and did not undergo any slippage or loss of ef-

Fig. 2-61. Engine Oil System Schematic with Propeller Governor

is mounted directly to the crankshaft, it will turn at the same speed as the engine, so the throttle is the only power control and the tachometer is the only power indicator required in the cockpit.

CONSTANT-SPEED PROPELLERS

An airplane equipped with a constant-speed propeller has two power controls, a throttle and a propeller control. The throttle controls the power output of the engine, which is registered on the mani-fold pressure gauge. The propeller control regulates the r.p.m. of the propeller (and also the r.p.m. of the engine, which is registered on the tachometer). The desired r.p.m. is set by the pilot and a propeller governor automatically changes the blade angle to counteract any tendency of the engine to vary from the setting. As mani-fold pressure is increased as a result of applying more throttle, the propeller governor automatically increases the pitch of the blades to maintain the same r.p.m. The same is true conversely when the throttle setting is decreased.

The propeller control permits a low blade angle for takeoff and climb, and a higher blade angle for cruise. Therefore, a con-stant-speed propeller is more efficient than a fixed-pitch propeller in the various realms of flight.

Oil is supplied to the propeller governor from the engine under pressure supplied by the engine oil pump. (See Fig. 2-61.) The governor senses engine speed varia-tions and directs oil into and out of the propeller dome as needed to move the propeller blades to maintain the desired engine speed.

Oil enters the dome and moves the pis-ton aft, which rotates the blades to in-crease pitch whenever the engine tends to rotate at an r.p.m. higher than that set by the propeller control. (See Fig. 2-62.) This causes the engine to slow down since the propeller is taking a bigger "bite." When the engine slows down, the oil flows out of the dome and the piston moves forward. This action rotates the blades to a lower pitch and the engine speeds up.

PROPELLER BLADE

ENGINE CRANKSHAFT

PROPELLER DOME

OIL FROM ENGINE

LINK

SPRING

PISTON

OIL ENTERS TO MOVE PISTON AFT TO INCREASE PITCH

OIL LEAVES AND SPRING MOVES PISTON FORWARD TO DECREASE PITCH

Fig. 2-62. Schematic of Typical Constant-Speed Propeller Components

SECTION D — AIRPLANE FUEL SYSTEMS

The primary function of the fuel system is to supply fuel to the engine. The two general types of fuel systems used in light aircraft are the gravity and fuel-pump types. (See Figs. 2-63 and 2-64.) Most low-horsepower, high-wing aircraft utilize the gravity-feed type fuel system, while most low-wing aircraft and most high-horsepower, high-wing aircraft utilize the fuel-pump system.

TYPES OF FUEL SYSTEMS
GRAVITY-TYPE FUEL SYSTEM

In the gravity-type fuel system illustrated in figure 2-63, the fuel tanks are usually mounted in the wings of high-wing aircraft, which places them *higher* than the engine carburetor. The resultant gravitational pressure from the height of the fuel above the engine is sufficient to supply all of the fuel needs of the engine. Fuel flows by means of gravity from the fuel tanks through a fuel selector valve and fuel strainer into the engine. (See Fig. 2-63, items 13, 11.)

In the carburetor (see Fig. 2-63, item 9), the fuel is mixed with air and the resultant fuel/air mixture is ducted to the engine cylinders through an intake manifold. Fuel quantity gauges, cali-

1. Fuel Tank Vent	7. Mixture Control	12. Fuel Strainer Drain Valve
2. Fuel Tank Filler Cap	8. Fuel Primer Nozzle	13. Fuel Selector Valve
3. Fuel Tank Interconnect Vent	(At Engine Cylinder)	14. Fuel Line Strainer
4. Fuel Quantity Transmitter	9. Carburetor	15. Fuel Tank Drain Plug
5. Fuel Primer Pump	10. Fuel Quantity Gauges	
6. Throttle	11. Strainer (With Sediment Bowl)	

Fig. 2-63. Typical Gravity-Type Fuel System

brated in gallons or pounds, show the amount of fuel in each tank.

FUEL-PUMP TYPE FUEL SYSTEM

The fuel-pump system, shown in figure 2-64, incorporates an engine-driven pump (item 7) instead of gravity to supply fuel pressure. Since the fuel pressure derived from a fuel pump is not dependent upon the height of the fuel tanks above the engine, this system is especially beneficial to low-wing aircraft where the fuel tanks are located in the wings below the engine.

To provide a back-up system for the engine-driven pump and to start fuel flowing under pressure before the engine is running, an electrical fuel-boost pump is installed in the system with other components or submerged in the tanks themselves. The electrical boost pump is operated with a switch in the cockpit and is normally not required except for starting. As is true of components of any aircraft system, however, the guidelines in the pilot's operating handbook for the fuel boost pumps should be followed.

FUEL SUPPLY SYSTEM

This system incorporates all of the components which are used to store and transport fuel to the engine. Included are the fuel tank lines, valves, and strainers.

1. Fuel Filler Cap	7. Engine-Driven Fuel Pump	13. Fuel Quantity Transmitter
2. Fuel Tank	8. Primer Nozzle (At Cylinder)	14. Fuel Tank Vent
3. Fuel Primer	9. Carburetor	15. Fuel Line Strainer
4. Throttle	10. Fuel Quantity Gauges	16. Fuel Tank Drain
5. Mixture Control	11. Fuel Strainer	17. Fuel Selector Valve
6. Electric Fuel Boost Pump	12. Fuel Strainer Drain Valve	

Fig. 2-64. Fuel Pump-Type Fuel System

FUEL TANKS

The fuel tanks are usually mounted in the wings and are serviced through filler caps located on top of the wings. The tanks should be filled each evening before storing the aircraft to prevent condensation of moisture in the tanks. Water and sediment are heavier than fuel and will settle in the lowest areas of the fuel system; therefore, drain plugs or valves are located on the bottom of the fuel tanks and are used to drain water or sediment at 100-hour intervals or when water is found in the fuel strainer.

FUEL TANK VENT AND OVERFLOW DRAINS

In order for fuel to flow from the tanks to the engine, the tanks must be vented to the outside atmosphere. Fuel tank vents may be found in the filler caps, or a tube extending from the wings may function as a vent. (See Fig. 2-63, item 1.) If only one opening to the outside is available for two tanks, then a cross-over vent between the two fuel tanks is supplied.

When the aircraft is parked and exposed to direct heating from the sun, fuel expands in the tanks. An overflow drain must be present to release fuel and prevent the tanks from bursting. This drain may be through the fuel tank vent or a separate opening. Many times, especially after refueling and on hot days when fuel expansion takes place, fuel may be seen dripping from these drains. This is quite normal.

FUEL QUANTITY GAUGE

Another important instrument is the fuel quantity gauge. (See Fig. 2-65.) It should be checked before every flight. In fact, prior to long flights, the pilot should not take for granted that this instrument is correct. A visual check of the fuel should be made.

A fuel-quantity transmitter is mounted in the fuel tank and senses fuel level. In most training aircraft, it is an electrical

Fig. 2-65. Fuel Quantity Gauge

unit and consists of a float, a mechanical linkage, and a transmitter, which contains an electrical resistance strip. The float moves up and down with the fuel level and rotates an arm in the transmitter. This causes the electrical resistance of the circuit to change. Electric wires transmit this electrical value to the fuel gauge which deflects the pointer to indicate the fuel quantity remaining in the tanks. (See Fig. 2-66.)

FUEL SELECTOR VALVES

A fuel selector valve is installed in a fuel system to provide a means for the pilot to select fuel from various tanks for efficient fuel management. There are many kinds of fuel valves, from the simple on-off valves to the complex multiple tank selector valves. A common type of valve used in general aviation aircraft has four positions: left tank, right tank, both tanks, and off. (See Fig. 2-67.) This valve is placed in the cabin of the airplane within easy reach of the pilot.

FUEL STRAINER

After passing from the fuel tank through the fuel selector valve, fuel flows through

Fig. 2-66. Fuel Gauge System

Fig. 2-67. Fuel Selector Valve

a fuel strainer before it reaches the carburetor. The *fuel strainer* is located at the lowest point in the fuel system and is used to trap any foreign particles or moisture that might accumulate in the system.

Since water is *heavier* than gasoline, it will settle out at the lowest point in the system. The location of the strainer at this point, plus the restrictive effect of the filter element, permits the water to be separated from the fuel and collected in a sump bowl at the base of the strainer assembly.

Before flight, the fuel strainer should be drained and checked for the presence of water. In cold weather, the water that accumulates could freeze and stop the flow of fuel. In warm weather, an excessive accumulation of water, if not drained, could flow into the carburetor and stop the engine. If water is found in the fuel strainer, there is probably water in one or more of the wing fuel tank sumps. Although the strainer has the capacity of collecting any water from the tanks before it reaches the engine, it is a good practice to drain enough fuel from the tanks to remove any water that may be present. The pilot should use a *clean*, transparent container to verify the content of drained matter. If an excessive amount of water or solid

matter is found, further checking is called for.

PRIMER

A small hand pump, called the primer, is located on the instrument panel. (See Fig. 2-68.) This device is used to pump fuel *directly* into the engine cylinders prior to starting and is especially useful for cold weather starts. Its sole purpose is to prime the engine so it will be more easily started.

Fig. 2-68. Fuel Primer

FUEL PRESSURE GAUGE

For those fuel systems which use a fuel pump, a fuel pressure gauge is installed to permit the pilot to monitor the fuel pressure. (See Fig. 2-69.) Should the fuel pressure drop, indicating that the engine-driven pump is malfunctioning, the pilot

Fig. 2-69. Fuel Pressure Gauge

would switch to the electric fuel boost pump to keep the engine supplied with fuel.

The location of the fuel pressure gauge is shown in figure 2-70. Fuel flows from the fuel tanks to the pump where it is routed under pressure to the carburetor. The fuel pressure gauge is usually connected to the system at the carburetor. From here, a line carries fuel directly to the gauge, where its pressure is displayed on the instrument dial.

Fig. 2-70. Fuel Pressure Gauge Installation

ENGINE FUEL SYSTEM

This system serves the function of distributing fuel to the engine at the correct time and in the correct amounts. It is made up principally of the carburetor and associated parts, or the fuel injector and associated components.

CARBURETOR SYSTEM

It can be seen in figures 2-63 and 2-64 that the carburetor is one of the final steps in the flow of fuel from the tanks to the combustion chamber. The aircraft carburetor is designed to measure the correct quantity of fuel, mix it with air in the proper proportion, and atomize the mixture before it enters the combustion chamber.

Fuel enters the carburetor at the float valve and flows into the carburetor float chamber until it reaches a certain level. (See Fig. 2-71.) When the float rises to a

predetermined height, it shuts off the float valve, and no additional fuel is allowed to enter the carburetor until fuel is used by the engine. The float chamber is vented so that pressure will not build up in the chamber as the aircraft climbs to altitude.

The outside air, on its way to the engine, first passes through an air filter, which is located at the carburetor air intake in the front of the engine cowling. (See Fig. 2-72.) This filter should be periodically checked for cleanliness since operations on gravel and dirt runways and taxiways eventually cause filter clogging.

After the air is filtered, it passes through a venturi in the carburetor. (See Fig. 2-71.) This venturi creates a low-pressure area in the throat of a carburetor in a manner similar to a vacuum venturi. With the float chamber vented to the atmosphere and a low pressure in the venturi, the fuel is forced to flow by atmospheric pressure from the float chamber to the carburetor throat. The fuel makes its exit in the carburetor throat through the main jet and becomes mixed with the air flowing in from the outside.

MIXTURE CONTROL

A mixture control knob, located on the instrument panel, meters the amount of fuel that passes through the main jet in the carburetor and also regulates fuel

Fig. 2-71. Carburetor Components

Fig. 2-72. Air Intake System

consumption. (See Fig. 2-73.) The mixture control knob, usually found near the engine throttle on the aircraft panel, will normally be colored red (an indication to use caution). This control enables the pilot to adjust the *ratio* of the fuel/air mixture that goes into the cylinders.

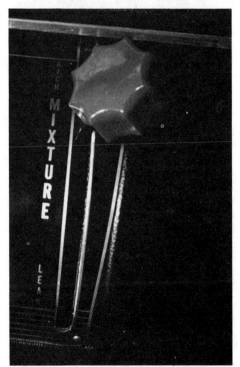

Fig. 2-73. Mixture Control Knob

If the fuel/air mixture is too lean (too little fuel for the amount of air in terms of weight), rough engine operation, sudden cutting out, backfiring, detonation, overheating, and appreciable loss of engine power may occur. Lean mixtures must be especially avoided when an engine is operating near its maximum output such as during takeoff, climbs, and go-arounds. At altitudes of less than 5,000 feet, an excessively lean mixture may cause serious overheating and loss of power.

If the fuel/air mixture is too rich (too much fuel for the amount of air in terms of weight), rough engine operation and an appreciable loss of engine power may also occur. Excessive fuel will cause below normal temperatures in the combustion chamber. Since spark plugs need sufficient heat to burn any excess carbon and lead, the plugs may become fouled if the mixture is too rich.

The most common mixture control system is the needle type, as illustrated in figure 2-71. By moving the mixture control knob forward, the mixture needle retracts and allows fuel to flow freely to the discharge nozzle in the carburetor throat (richer mixture). By pulling the mixture control knob aft, the mixture needle moves into the fuel line to restrict the amount of fuel. With the same amount of air passing through the carburetor throat, the restricted fuel flow causes a leaner fuel/air mixture.

Carburetors are normally calibrated for sea level operation, which means that the correct mixture of fuel and air will be obtained at sea level with the mixture control in the *full rich* position. As altitude increases, the air density decreases, which means that a cubic foot of air will not weigh as much as at lower altitudes. This means that as the flight altitude increases, the weight of air entering the carburetor decreases, although the volume remains the same.

The amount of fuel entering the carburetor depends on the volume and *not* the weight of air. Therefore, as altitude increases, the amount of fuel entering the carburetor remains approximately the same for any given throttle setting if the position of the mixture control remains unchanged. Since the same amount (weight) of fuel is entering the carburetor, but a lesser amount of air, the fuel/air mixture becomes richer with increased altitude.

To maintain the correct fuel/air ratio, the pilot must be able to adjust the amount of fuel mixed with the incoming air as altitude increases. This is accomplished by leaning the mixture. Reference should be made to the pilot's operating handbook for proper fuel leaning technique.

CARBURETOR HEAT SYSTEM

Carburetor icing can cause loss of power or even engine stoppage in flight. The vaporization of fuel combined with the expansion of air as it passes through the carburetor causes a sudden cooling of the fuel/air mixture. The temperature of the air passing through the carburetor may drop as much as 40° Celsius (70° Fahrenheit). Water vapor in the air is condensed by this cooling and, if the

temperature in the carburetor reaches freezing or below, the moisture is deposited as frost or ice inside the carburetor passages. (See Fig. 2-74.) Even a slight accumulation of this deposit will reduce power and may lead to complete engine failure, particularly if the throttle is partly or fully closed.

Fig. 2-74. Carburetor Ice

Carburetor icing is possible with temperatures as high as 40° Celsius (104° Fahrenheit) and humidity as low as 50 percent. However, it is most likely with temperatures below 20° Celsius (68° Fahrenheit) and relative humidity above 80 percent. As the temperature decreases to 0° Celsius (32° Fahrenheit), or as the humidity increases, the likelihood of carburetor icing increases. It should be remembered that during low or closed throttle settings, an engine is particularly susceptible to carburetor icing because the ice can more easily form on the throttle valve.

The pilot first becomes aware that carburetor ice may be forming by one of two indications. On aircraft equipped with

CODE
- ◊ COLD AIR
- ◆ HOT AIR

CARBURETOR HEAT VALVE

CARBURETOR HEAT ON

CARBURETOR

OUTSIDE AIR ◊

ENGINE EXHAUST

exhaust muffler

OUTSIDE AIR ◊ ◊

CARBURETOR AIR FILTER

HEATER MUFF

EXHAUST PIPE

CARBURETOR HEAT CONTROL

CARBURETOR HEAT VALVE

CARBURETOR HEAT OFF

Fig. 2-75. Typical Carburetor Heat System

a fixed-pitch propeller, a loss of engine r.p.m. appears on the tachometer. On aircraft equipped with a constant-speed propeller, a loss of manifold pressure is noted. There is no reduction in r.p.m. in an engine with a constant-speed propeller since propeller pitch is automatically adjusted to compensate for the loss of power, thus maintaining constant r.p.m. In either of the two cases, a roughness in engine operation may develop later.

To eliminate this ice, a carburetor heat system is installed in the airplane. Outside air is ducted through a heater muff where the air is heated to a temperature that melts ice. After the air has been heated, it is routed to a valve that is controlled by a carburetor heat control knob located on the instrument panel. Pulling out the carburetor heat knob opens the carburetor heat valve, allowing hot air to pass through the carburetor where it mixes with the fuel, melts the ice, and continues on to the engine cylinders. (See Fig. 2-75.)

REFUELING

Static electricity formed by the flow of fuel through the hose and nozzle during refueling creates a fire hazard. To prevent a spark from igniting the fuel fumes, a *ground wire* should be attached to the aircraft before the cap is removed from the tank. The refueling nozzle should be grounded to the aircraft before refueling is begun and throughout the refueling process. The fuel truck should also be grounded to the aircraft and the ground. If the pilot must refuel from cans or drums, the fuel should be strained through a chamois skin to prevent contamination from entering the tanks.

USING THE PROPER FUEL

There are several kinds of aviation gasoline, and it can be dangerous to use the wrong kind. Although personnel who service airplanes are usually very careful about this, the *pilot* is the individual responsible for obtaining the proper grade of fuel. The flight manual always specifies the grade of fuel required for the aircraft engine, and this information is marked on placards next to the filler cap.

Each grade of gasoline is manufactured according to certain specifications so that engine designers can tailor their engines to the characteristics of a particular fuel grade. Each grade has an octane rating, or performance number, and is dyed a standard color so pilots and servicing personnel can recognize each of the grades of fuel. A reciprocating engine will not run on turbine fuel which is colorless and smells like kerosene. The various fuels and associated colors are listed below; however, it is important to note that if two grades of fuel are mixed, the fuel will become clear.

```
80 . . . . . . . . . . . . . . . . . . . . . . . . . red
100LL . . . . . . . . . . . . . . . . . . . . blue
100 . . . . . . . . . . . . . . . . . . . . . green
Turbine fuel . . . . . . . . . . . . colorless
```

Using aviation fuel rated higher than specified does not improve engine operation, but is not considered harmful if used only for a short period of time. If the grade of fuel required for an aircraft is not available, the next higher grade should be used — *never a lower grade.* Using a lower grade of fuel is definitely harmful under any circumstances because it may cause loss of power, excessive heat, burned spark plugs, burned and stuck valves, high oil consumption, and detonation.

SECTION E — ELECTRICAL SYSTEMS

Electrical energy usually is supplied by a 14-volt or 28-volt direct-current system which is powered by an engine-driven generator or alternator. An electrical sys-tem schematic, like the one illustrated in figure 2-76, shows the various circuits and sources of electrical power and can be found in most pilot's operating

Fig. 2-76. Typical Electrical System

handbooks. An electrical storage battery serves as a standby power source, supplying current to the system when the generator or alternator is inoperative. The battery is used for actuating the starter and for operation of equipment when the engine is not running.

ALTERNATORS/ GENERATORS

Alternators, as opposed to generators, have the advantages of lighter weight, no danger of overload, relatively constant power output (even at engine speeds approaching idle) and lower maintenance. Alternators produce alternating current (AC), which is changed into direct current (DC) for use in the electrical system. This energy is then transferred to a bus bar, which breaks down and distributes the current to the various electrical components of the aircraft. Control of the charging current and voltage is accomplished by a voltage regulator.

AMMETER

Probably the most important of the electrical instruments, when it is utilized in the aircraft, is the ammeter. (See Fig. 2-77.) It indicates when the generator or alternator is charging the storage battery. When the pointer is deflected to the

right side of the instrument, electrical energy is flowing into the battery from the generator or alternator. When the pointer is deflected to the left side, more electrical energy is being used than is being replaced by the generating system.

Normally, the generator starts charging at 1,000 or 1,200 r.p.m. Alternator systems, however, produce electrical power at a lower engine r.p.m.

On many single-engine aircraft, a warning light is used in lieu of an ammeter. This light remains off at all times when the electrical-power generating system is functioning properly. It illuminates when the battery or external power is turned on prior to starting the engine and when there is insufficient engine r.p.m. to produce current. It also illuminates if the generator or alternator becomes defective.

MASTER SWITCH

A master switch controls the entire aircraft electrical system except the ignition system which obtains its electrical energy from the magnetos. Newer aircraft have a split-type battery/alternator switch so each electrical supply unit can be checked separately. (See Fig. 2-78.) Turning the master switch or battery/alternator switch to "on" supplies electricity to all electrical equipment circuits in the aircraft. Some equipment which may use the electrical

Fig. 2-77. Ammeter

Fig. 2-78. Split Type Battery/Alternator Switch

system as their source of power are landing lights, taxi lights, navigation lights, flashing beacon, instrument lights, dome lights, starter, pitot heater, stall warning indicator, cigarette lighter, radios, turn coordinator, fuel gauges, and fuel boost pumps.

FUSES/CIRCUIT BREAKERS

Electrical fuses or circuit breakers are provided in the various electrical circuits to protect them from electrical overloads. (See Fig. 2-79.) Spare fuses are carried in the pilot's compartment in the event

a fuse must be replaced in flight. In the case of circuit breakers, resetting the breaker *usually* will reactivate the circuit unless an overload or short exists. If an overload or short occurs, the circuit breaker will continue to pop, indicating an electrical problem.

A pilot is expected to know the location of the circuit protection device for each electrical component. Normally, the name and amperage for the circuit are written near the appropriate circuit breaker or fuse.

Fig. 2-79. Circuit Breaker Panel

chapter 3

AIRPORTS, COMMUNICATIONS, AND AIR TRAFFIC CONTROL

INTRODUCTION

In most cases, the airplane, unlike many other vehicles, has a highly predictable base of operations — the airport. Generally, flights originate and terminate at the airport and a portion of the fledgling pilot's new environment is the physical setting and characteristics of the particular airport at which he is taking his flight training. The knowledge gained from a study of airports will enable the pilot to quickly feel at home while operating in this new environment.

Furthermore, in order for the pilot to gain the greatest utility from his aircraft, it is important for him to understand radio communications. Today, the major portion of air traffic control is based on voice communications, making the mastery of this subject an important endeavor for the pilot.

SECTION A - AIRPORTS

There are more than 10,000 airports within the borders of the United States that serve all types of aviation activities. These range from large metropolitan airfields with several runways serving a variety of aircraft operations, to small grass strips suitable only for light aircraft. (See Fig. 3-1.) Learning about airports is an important aspect of flight training.

RUNWAY NUMBER

Each runway is assigned a number which is determined from the magnetic direction of the runway. The runway's magnetic direction is rounded off to the nearest ten degrees and the last zero is omitted. For instance, the approximate magnetic direction of runway 21 is 210°, while runway 3 has a magnetic direction of approximately 030°. The actual magnetic direction for runway 3 could be any number from 025° to 034°, all of which, when rounded off to the nearest ten degree heading, would be 030°.

The runway number is usually displayed on the approach end of each runway in large numerals that are easily read from the air. The runway number, of course, is different at each end of a runway strip because the magnetic directions are 180° apart, or reciprocals of each other. For example, a runway aligned with magnetic north and south is called runway 36 on the end where landings are to the north, and runway 18 on the end where landings are made to the south.

The one or two number system is used for two reasons. Using one or two numbers instead of three makes the runway name shorter and easier to say. Also, this practice permits larger numerals on the end of the runway, which makes it easier to identify the runway from the air. (See Fig. 3-2.)

Fig. 3-1. Simple and Complex Airports

Fig. 3-2. Airport Runway Markings

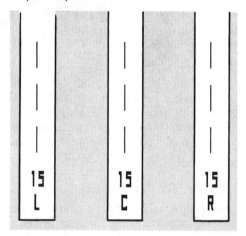

Fig. 3-3. Parallel Runways

If parallel runways exist, they must still have the *same* number since their directions are the same. For this reason, a suffix letter is added to differentiate between runways. For two parallel runways, the letter "L" designates left, and the letter "R" indicates right. In the case where three parallel runways exist, the letters "L," "C," and "R" are used, with the letter "C" standing for center. Reading from left to right, the runways shown in figure 3-3 are called "one five left," "one five center," and "one five right."

It is important to remember that runways are numbered in relation to the *magnetic* North Pole and not true north. Thus, the magnetic compass in the aircraft should agree with the runway designation (within ±5°) when the aircraft is aligned with the runway. Also, navigation aids such as VOR stations, radio beacons, and instrument landing systems are laid out according to magnetic direction. This permits the various courses, emanating from these facilities, to be shown on charts in alignment with the runway used for an instrument approach. In addition, wind directions reported by control towers are given with reference to magnetic north so that a comparison between wind and the runway direction can be made.

ACTIVE RUNWAYS

The term *active runway* refers to the runway in use at a particular time. This is normally determined by wind direction. At some locations, however, a calm wind runway is designated when the wind is below a specific velocity, such as five knots. In this case, the calm wind runway is used for all takeoffs and landings regardless of wind direction. Winds of higher velocity, however, may dictate the use of a different runway.

RUNWAY MARKINGS
BASIC RUNWAY MARKINGS

The *basic markings* on runways used for VFR (visual flight rules) operations consist of runway direction numbers and centerline marking. In addition to runway numbers located on the approach ends, centerlines are added to help the pilot align his aircraft with the runway during landings and takeoffs. (See Fig. 3-4.) At airports utilizing sod runways, the ends may be marked with L-shaped corner threshold markers to indicate when the aircraft is over the end of the

Fig. 3-4. Basic Runway Markings

runway. (See Fig. 3-5.) Runway numbers may be absent from the ends of grass, dirt, or sod runways, or they may be indicated by inlaid white stones, concrete, or other material that will contrast with the surface.

Fig. 3-5. Sod Runway Markings

NON-PRECISION INSTRUMENT RUNWAY MARKINGS

Specific markings are added to the basic runway markings to designate additional information. For example, a *threshold marker*, consisting of two sets of four parallel marks, indicates the runway is served by a non-precision approach facility (such as a VOR station) and is intended for landings in instrument conditions, as well as for VFR landings. (See Fig. 3-6.)

Fig. 3-6. Non-Precision Instrument Runway Markings

PRECISION INSTRUMENT RUNWAY MARKINGS

Touchdown zone, fixed distance markings, and side stripes usually are added

FIXED DISTANCE MARKERS
(1,000 feet)

TOUCHDOWN ZONE STRIPES
(500 feet)

ADDITIONAL STRIPES AT
500 FOOT INTERVALS

Fig. 3-7. Precision Runway Marking

to the runway markings to designate *precision instrument runways* which are served by a precision approach facility, such as an instrument landing system (ILS). (See Fig. 3-7.) The 500-foot spacing of these stripes can be used by the pilot to determine how much runway has been used on landing or takeoff. For example: touchdown zone stripes mean 500 feet have passed; fixed-distance markers—1,000 feet; first set of two stripes—1,500 feet; second set of two stripes—2,000 feet; first set of single stripes—2,500 feet; and the last set of stripes—3,000 feet.

DISPLACED THRESHOLDS

The *threshold* of a runway is sometimes displaced from what would appear to be the beginning of the runway. The threshold line is used to mark the start of the usable portion of the runway, and a pilot should not land until he has crossed this mark. The purpose of a displaced threshold is to insure that the initial landing touchdown is made farther down the runway.

The obvious question that comes to mind is, "If it is not to be used, why was the runway extended that far?" It must be remembered, however, that runways are used in both directions. As an overrun or a landing rollout area from the op-

posite direction, displaced thresholds are perfectly satisfactory.

Most thresholds are displaced because of obstacles at the end of the runway that necessitate additional clearances when approaching to land. The obstacle may be a road, trees, or towers. An obstacle may have been added, or a hazard may have developed after the runway was built. In most cases, however, the obstacle was there when the runway was built, and the runway was extended up to the obstacle so that the additional length could be used in a landing rollout from the other direction.

Displaced thresholds for basic VFR and instrument runways are marked as shown in figure 3-8. Note that the no-landing portion of each runway has arrows painted on the centerline to point to the threshold line. The top illustration in figure 3-8 shows two examples of displaced thresholds on VFR runways. The centerline arrows direct the pilot's attention to the displaced threshold. In addition, arrowheads are painted adjacent to the threshold lines to emphasize the beginning of the usable portion of the runway. These arrowheads are used only on VFR runways.

An example of a displaced threshold on an instrument runway is shown in the

Fig. 3-8. Displaced Threshold Marking

lization to prevent erosion. This stabilization may have the appearance of full strength pavement, but is not intended to support aircraft. Usually, the taxiway edge marking will define this area, but confusion may exist as to which side of the side stripe the full strength pavement is located. Where such a condition exists, the stabilized area is marked as shown in figure 3-9.

Fig. 3-9. Stabilized Area

lower picture in figure 3-8. Centerline arrows are also utilized on the no-landing portion to help the pilot locate the runway threshold. However, arrowheads are not used adjacent to the threshold, because the parallel marks designating an instrument runway provide adequate visual emphasis.

STABILIZED OR DECEPTIVE AREAS

Holding bays, aprons, and taxiways are sometimes provided with shoulder stabi-

OVERRUN, STOPWAY, AND BLASTPAD AREAS

Overrun, stopway, and blastpad areas of runways are marked with a chevron pattern as shown in figure 3-10. These areas are not structurally capable of withstanding loads created by landing, taking off, or taxiing aircraft. The shoulders or edges of some runways are also marked with chevrons. This means they are strictly stabilized shoulders or understrength areas of the runway, and are not meant to withstand landing loads.

Fig. 3-10. Overrun and Stopway Areas

CLOSED RUNWAYS

A runway or taxiway that is *closed* to all operations is marked with a large "X" at each end. If the entire airport is closed, each runway could be "Xed" out, or the operator could place a large "X" near the tetrahedron, or in the center of the segmented circle. (See Fig. 3-11.)

Fig. 3-11. Closed Runway Markings

TAXIWAYS

Taxiways are very important to airport operations, enabling traffic to move to and from runways without interfering with aircraft taking off or landing. These taxiways lead from the runways to aircraft storage, tiedown, maintenance, and fueling areas on the airport. The *open white* portion of figure 3-12 shows typical taxi routes.

Taxiway centerlines are marked with a continuous yellow line, while the edges are marked with two continuous lines six inches apart. Holding lines consist of two continuous lines and two dashed lines, perpendicular to the taxiway centerline. Standard holding lines appear 100 to 200 feet from the runway edge. However, at runways equipped for Category

Fig. 3-12. Taxiways (White Areas)

II operations, the CAT II holding lines are two solid lines perpendicular to the taxiway centerline. These are connected by solid lines parallel with the taxiway, as shown in figure 3-13.

The placement of Category II holding lines is determined by the localizer, glide slope, and obstacle critical areas. The objective of these lines is to keep taxiing aircraft far enough away from the navigation facilities and the runways to eliminate any interference with the landing aircraft. When Category II operations are being conducted, taxiing aircraft will be advised by ground control.

PARKING AREAS

Parking areas are provided on airports and are used by transient and local unhangared aircraft. Servicing of aircraft for fuel and oil is also performed in this area. Ropes or chains attached to tiedown rings embedded in concrete are used to tie the airplane down and to keep it from overturning in high wind conditions. An alternate method of providing tiedowns is to string a long cable and attach ropes or chains to it. This method accommodates a large variety of aircraft sizes. A secure tiedown should be accomplished whenever an aircraft is parked outside and left unattended.

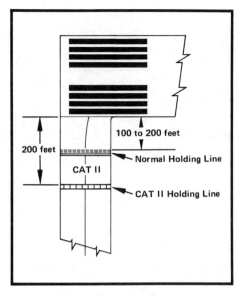

Fig. 3-13. Taxiway Markings

FIELD ELEVATION

Airport elevation information is very important to the pilot. Airport (field) elevation is measured at the highest usable landing surface on the airport and is specified on the various navigation charts in feet above mean sea level (MSL). Before takeoff, the pilot should set the current altimeter setting in the Kollsman window. By doing this, the altimeter should read very close to field elevation. (See Fig. 3-14.) In addition, pilots should also check the field elevation prior to landing to determine the altitude used in the airport traffic pattern.

WIND DIRECTION INDICATORS

Since the wind direction determines the runway to be used for landings and takeoffs, there must be a means for the pilot to determine the direction from which the wind is blowing. Various devices are used for this purpose. During takeoffs and landings, airplanes fly as directly into the wind as possible.

WIND SOCK

The oldest and most common wind indicating device is the wind sock. The wind sock is nothing more than a cone-shaped

Fig. 3-14. Altimeter Setting Prior to Takeoff

Fig. 3-15. Wind Sock

Fig. 3-16. Wind Tee

device built of durable, flexible material. When the wind blows through the large end of the cone, it causes the *small end* to stand out and point *downwind*. The amount of extension can also give an indication of the velocity of the wind. In addition, a fluttering wind sock indicates gusty conditions. Lights are often placed above the wind sock for night illumination. (See Fig. 3-15.)

Fig. 3-17. Tetrahedron

WIND TEE

Some locations use a wind tee, as illustrated in figure 3-16, to indicate wind direction. The tail of the airplane-shaped tee acts as a weathervane to position the wing-like structures into the wind. In other words, the "airplane" points into the wind in the direction of takeoff or landing.

LANDING DIRECTION INDICATOR

A *tetrahedron* is used to indicate the direction of landings and takeoffs, as shown in figure 3-17. It is placed near the center of the field and may be set manually to indicate the preferred direction for runway use. The small end of the tetrahedron points in the direction of landing. Flood lights or other types of lights may be used to illuminate the tetrahedron at night.

AIRPORT LIGHTING

Airport *runway lights* are *white* and will illuminate the runway sufficiently for runway alignment. *Green* lights are placed on the *threshold* of the runway to show a pilot the beginning of the usable landing surface at night. (See Fig. 3-18.) *Taxiway lights*, on the other hand, are *blue*, which distinguishes them from runway lights.

With all the other lights on the ground, it would be difficult to find an airport at night without the *rotating beacon* used to designate the airport. The airport beacon rotates in a clockwise direction at a constant speed, thus producing the visual effect of light flashes at regular intervals. The rotation speed provides 12 to 15 flashes per minute.

Airport beacons incorporate color combinations to indicate various types of airports. For example, white and green alternating flashes denote a lighted land

RUNWAY LIGHTS (WHITE)

THRESHOLD LIGHTS (GREEN)

TAXIWAY LIGHTS
(BLUE)

Fig. 3-18. Airport Runway Lights

ground visibility in the airport control zone is less than three miles and/or the ceiling is less than 1,000 feet. (This concept is explained in Chapter 5.) This means an ATC (air traffic control) clearance is required for landings and takeoffs at airports that are surrounded by controlled airspace. During the hours of darkness, instrument or IFR (instrument flight rules) conditions are indicated by flashing lights outlining the tetrahedron or wind tee.

A *flashing amber light*, near the center of the segmented circle or on top of the wind sock, control tower, or adjoining buildings, means that a right traffic pattern is in effect for the active runway.

Red beacons, with a flash rate of 12 to 40 flashes per minute, are used to mark flight hazards such as towers or tall buildings.

APPROACH LIGHTS

Various types of *approach lights* are installed on the extended centerline of run-

airport (see Fig. 3-19), while white and yellow flashes inform the pilot that the beacon serves a lighted water airport. Military airport beacons flash *alternating* white and green, but are differentiated from civilian airport beacons by two quick white flashes between the green flashes. (See Fig. 3-19.)

Operation of the airport rotating beacon during daylight hours indicates that the airport is below VFR (visual flight rules) landing minimums. Therefore, the

Fig. 3-19. Rotating Beacons

ways equipped with instrument landing systems to guide the pilot during IFR operations. These are especially helpful for runway alignment after the pilot descends through the clouds during an instrument approach. (See Fig. 3-20.)

Fig. 3-20. Approach Lights

VASI SYSTEM (Visual Approach Slope Indicator)

A *visual approach slope indicator* system (VASI) is located on some runways to help the pilot maintain a normal glide path to a safe touchdown point on the runway. This system is *only* usable in VFR conditions or after a pilot executing an instrument approach is clear of clouds.

The VASI system consists of a set of upwind and downwind lights that indicate to the pilot when he is on the proper glide path. When approaching the runway at the proper angle, the downwind set of lights (those closest to the pilot) on both sides of the runway will appear white and the upwind lights (those farthest from the

pilot) will be red. (See Fig. 3-21.) By maintaining a rate of descent to the runway corresponding to the VASI glide slope (normally $2\frac{1}{2}^{O}$ to 4°), the airplane will touch down midway between the two sets of lights.

If the aircraft strays above the glide slope, the upwind lights will change to pink and then to white. When *well above* the approach path, both sets of lights will be illuminated white.

If the aircraft descends below the glide path, the downwind lights will change to pink and then to red. When operating *well below* the glide path, the upwind and downwind lights will appear red. In this situation, the pilot can expect to land short of the normal touchdown point. (See Fig. 3-21.)

AIRPORT TRAFFIC

The airport traffic pattern is very important as a means of separating aircraft using the same airport. A flight pattern is set up around each runway for use by approaching and departing traffic. An airport would be a disorganized, chaotic snarl if there were no means for approaching the field and flying a standard pattern. Traffic patterns are normally left; i.e., turns are made to the left. (See Fig. 3-22.) Nonstandard patterns require turns to the right. (See Fig. 3-23.)

TAKEOFF LEG

The airport traffic pattern can be broken down into various segments. After take-

Fig. 3-21. The VASI System

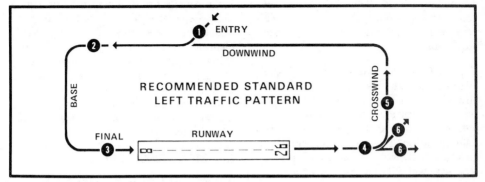

Fig. 3-22. Left Traffic Pattern at Uncontrolled Airport

1. Enter pattern in level flight, abeam the midpoint of the runway, at pattern altitude.

2. Maintain pattern altitude until abeam approach end of the landing runway, on downwind leg.

3. Complete turn to final at least 1/4 mile from runway.

4. Continue straight ahead until beyond departure end of runway.

5. If remaining in the traffic pattern, commence turn to crosswind leg beyond the departure end of the runway, within 300 feet of pattern altitude.

6. If departing the traffic pattern, continue straight out, or exit with a 45° turn in the direction of traffic beyond the departure end of the runway after reaching pattern altitude.

Fig. 3-23. Right Traffic Pattern at Uncontrolled Airport

off, it is recommended that the pilot climb straight ahead until within 300 feet of pattern altitude. This is called the *upwind or takeoff leg.*

CROSSWIND LEG

The *crosswind leg* is flown perpendicular to the takeoff leg and is flown after completing a 90° turn. When a pilot has established an appropriate interval behind any aircraft, he turns 90° and continues the climb to the traffic pattern altitude. The pilot should plan to be at pattern altitude before turning to the downwind leg.

DOWNWIND LEG

If the pilot desires to remain in the traffic pattern, he will turn another 90° to place the aircraft on the *downwind leg.* This leg is parallel to the runway, but flown in the opposite direction of the intended landing. Normally, the downwind leg is flown at 1,000 feet above the ground, but this height can vary to accommodate individual airport requirements.

The 1,000 foot AGL (above ground level) altitude is called the traffic pattern altitude. To determine the MSL (mean sea level) altitude, the 1,000 foot AGL pattern altitude should be added to the field elevation. This MSL altitude is the altitude that will be indicated on the altimeter while flying the downwind leg.

When the aircraft is opposite the touchdown point, the pilot reduces power, slows the aircraft to the speed used for the approach, and begins to descend for the landing.

BASE LEG

The 90° turn from downwind to a flight path *perpendicular* to the runway places the pilot on the *base leg*. The descent to the runway is continued on this leg and most final landing checks are performed.

FINAL APPROACH

After the pilot makes a descending turn from base leg, the flight path should be aligned with the runway centerline. This portion of the traffic pattern is known as the *final approach*.

TRAFFIC PATTERN ENTRY

Traffic pattern entry at airports with an operating control tower is specified by the tower operator. At uncontrolled airports, traffic pattern altitudes and entry procedures vary according to established local procedures. Pilots should familiarize themselves with these procedures and follow local flight instructor recommendations. At unfamiliar airports, airport advisory service or UNICOM, when available, should be utilized for receipt of traffic pattern and landing information.

TRAFFIC PATTERN DEPARTURE

When a control tower is in operation, the pilot can request and receive approval for a straight-out, downwind, or right-hand departure. This departure request should be made while asking for takeoff clearance. At airports without an operating control tower, the pilot should comply with the departure procedures established for that airport. These procedures may be posted by airport operators so pilots can become familiar with the local rules.

SEGMENTED CIRCLE

A segmented circle is normally located around the wind sock, tetrahedron, or wind tee at *uncontrolled* airports. The use of L-shaped markers on the periphery of the circle indicates the direction of traffic patterns for the various runways on the airport. Figure 3-24 shows the segmented circle corresponding to two airport runways, illustrating how L-shaped markers distinguish left and right-hand traffic patterns.

The leg of the "L" pointing inward toward the circle can be thought of as the final approach for the runway of corresponding direction. The leg perpendicular to the "final approach" leg of the "L" can be likened to the base leg of the appropriate runway. By noting whether the "L" marker indicates a left or right turn from "base" to "final," the pilot can determine the direction of traffic flow for a particular runway. For example, aircraft taking off to the east (runway 9) would use a left traffic pattern and aircraft landing to the north (runway 36) should fly a right pattern.

Fig. 3-24. Segmented Circle and L-Markers

SECTION B - RADIO COMMUNICATIONS

COMMUNICATIONS SYSTEMS

Through the use of diagrams, it is possible to study the flow of two-way communications. Figure 3-25 shows that voice signals travel from the microphone to the transmitter, where they are changed to radio signals. The radio signals are then carried by a wire to the antenna, where they are broadcast in all directions and received by radio receivers in control towers or other radio stations.

Fig. 3-25. Transmitting

Figure 3-26 shows that aircraft radio receivers are very similar to the radios utilized in a person's home and automobile. Radio signals are broadcast or transmitted from the transmitting station, such as a control tower, and received by the antenna on the airplane. From here, the signals are carried to the radio receiver where they are converted to voice signals which are heard by the pilot, either through earphones or through a speaker system.

Fig. 3-26. Receiving

VHF COMMUNICATIONS EQUIPMENT

Airborne radios are different from automobile and home radios in that **airborne** communication requires two-way conversation. Therefore, aircraft radios generally consist of a *transmitter, receiver, antenna, microphone,* and *speaker* or *headset;* home and auto radios only provide a receiver with associated components such as an antenna and speakers.

When the transmitter and receiver are housed in one unit and have only one or a common frequency selector as shown in figure 3-27, the radio is known as a transceiver.

Fig. 3-27. Combined Transmitter and Receiver Unit

There are two communication terms with which pilot should become familiar. Single channel simplex communications involve using the same frequency for both transmitting and receiving. Dual channel or double channel communication consists of using a different frequency for transmitting than for receiving. (See Fig. 3-28.)

TUNING

Most modern VHF radios incorporate crystal-controlled tuning. With this system, the pilot automatically receives the desired frequency once he selects the proper setting on the tuning dial. (See Fig. 3-29.)

Fig. 3-28. Communication Terms

Fig. 3-30. Microphone

Fig. 3-29. Crystal-Controlled Tuning

Fig. 3-31. Correct Microphone
Handling Techniques

Most training aircraft are equipped with a combination navigation/communications (nav/com) radio system. The communications side is a radio transceiver (combined transmitter and receiver) for two-way voice communications in the frequency range of 118.00 to 135.975 MHz. Radio navigation signals and one-way voice communications are received on the navigation side, which operates in the range of 108.00 to 117.95 MHz. (See Fig. 3-29.)

A nav/com radio permits two-way communications using either a simplex or multiplex system. *Simplex* communications use the same frequency for both transmitting and receiving. Only the com side of the radio is needed for simplex communications. *Multiplex* communications involve use of separate frequencies for transmitting and receiving. The nav and com sides of the radio are used simultaneously. This system is used frequently by flight service stations to reduce interference. They sometimes transmit to aircraft over a VHF omnidirectional range (VOR), which

operates on navigational frequencies, and receive on two-way communications frequencies.

USING THE MICROPHONE

The first and most basic factor in good communications between pilots and controllers is the proper use of the microphone. The hand microphone is the most common type found in training aircraft. (See Fig. 3-30.) In order to obtain clear, readable transmissions, most hand microphones should be held so that the lips are lightly touching the face of the mike as shown in figure 3-31. Using the mike in this position allows the pilot to use a normal conversational volume level, and also prevents the transmission of most background noise. Also, the person transmitting should speak *directly* into the mike. Even though the microphone is held close to the lips, the transmission will sound fuzzy and indistinct if the words are spoken across the face of the mike.

The radio microphone has a key or button that must be depressed during trans-

(ICAO) INTERNATIONAL PHONETIC ALPHABET

A	.—	Alfa	(Al-fah)	N	—.	November	(No-vem–ber)
B	—...	Bravo	(Brah-voh)	O	———	Oscar	(Oss-cah)
C	—.—.	Charlie	(Char-lee)	P	.——.	Papa	(Pah-pah)
D	—..	Delta	(Dell-tah)	Q	——.—	Quebec	(Keh-beck)
E	.	Echo	(Eck-oh)	R	.—.	Romeo	(Row-me-oh)
F	..—.	Foxtrot	(Foks-trot)	S	...	Sierra	(See-airrah)
G	——.	Golf	(Golf)	T	—	Tango	(Tang-go)
H	....	Hotel	(Hoh-tell)	U	..—	Uniform	(You-nee-form)
I	..	India	(In-dee-aH)	V	...—	Victor	(Vik-tah)
J	.———	Juliett	(Jew-lee-ett)	W	.——	Whiskey	(Wiss-key)
K	—.—	Kilo	(Key-loh)	X	—..—	X ray	(Ecks-ray)
L	.—..	Lima	(Lee-mah)	Y	—.——	Yankee	(Yang-key)
M	——	Mike	(Mike)	Z	——..	Zulu	(Zoo-loo)

Fig. 3-32. (ICAO) International Phonetic Alphabet

missions and released once the message is complete. This key triggers a switch in the radio transmitter which enables the radio to transmit voice signals on the selected frequency as long as the mike key is held in the depressed position. The pilot should be careful *never* to depress the transmitter key when another pilot or controller is transmitting on the same frequency. Doing this is known as *cutting out* another transmission. All that will be heard on the frequency when two stations are transmitting at the same time is a loud *squeal.*

RADIO PHRASEOLOGY

A pilot's world is a small one. Within a few hours, an airplane can travel hundreds of miles, and in certain parts of the world, international boundaries can be crossed many times in a single day. To overcome the language barriers, the various countries of the world organized the International Civil Aviation Organization (ICAO) and adopted English as the international aviation communications language. This international organization also adopted a phonetic alphabet to be used when making radio transmissions.

The phonetic alphabet is shown in figure 3-32 and consists of words in lieu of letters. This substitution is necessary because many letters of the English language sound alike. For example: B, C, D, E, T, V, and Z could be confused with one another during a radio transmission.

SPECIAL RADIO PHRASES

Due to the large number of radio-equipped aircraft, some radio frequencies have become very crowded, making it highly desirable to reduce the length of transmissions. For this reason, the following radio phraseology has been developed to aid in decreasing transmission time.

Radio Phrase	Meaning
ACKNOWLEDGE	Let me know that you have received and understood this message.
AFFIRMATIVE	Yes.
CORRECTION	An error has been made in this transmission. The correct version is ...
GO AHEAD	Proceed with your message.
HOW DO YOU HEAR ME	Self-explanatory.

3-15

I SAY AGAIN	Self-explanatory.
NEGATIVE	That is not correct.
OUT..........................	This conversation is ended and no response is expected. The word *out* is infrequently used since most often it is obvious when the conversation has terminated.
OVER	My transmission is ended and I expect a response from you. The word *over* is omitted if the message obviously needs a reply.
READ BACK	Repeat all of this message back to me.
ROGER	I have received all of your last transmission. (This word is used to acknowledge receipt and should not be used for other purposes.)
SAY AGAIN	Repeat what you have said.
SPEAK SLOWER................	Self-explanatory.
STAND-BY	If used by itself means "I must pause for a few seconds." If the pause lasts longer than a few seconds, or if the phrase is used to prevent another station from transmitting, it must be followed by the ending *OUT*.
THAT IS CORRECT	Self-explanatory.
VERIFY	Check with originator.
WORDS TWICE	a. As a request: "Communications are difficult. Please say every phrase twice." b. As information: "Since communication is difficult, every phrase in this message will be spoken twice."

NUMBERS

Sometimes numbers also are difficult to understand in radio transmissions; therefore, they always should be enunciated clearly. Single-digit numbers are pronounced in the same way as they sound except for the number "nine" which is spoken as *niner* in radio conversations.

The ICAO adopted this substitute pronunciation because the sound of "nine" in German means "no."

Two or more digit numbers are generally spoken as single-digit numbers in series. Such as:

37 — *three seven.*

485 — *four eight five.*
0956 — *zero niner five six.*

VHF and UHF radio frequencies are spoken as follows:

122.6 — *one two two point six.*
118.7 — *one one eight point seven.*

For a frequency in the low/medium band, the word kiloHertz is added after the numbers. For example:

337 — *three three seven kiloHertz.*
242 — *two four two kiloHertz.*

An exception to this practice is the identification of airways. For example: *Victor Twelve* or *Victor Thirteen East* are both VHF airways.

Since altimeter settings always consist of two digits followed by a decimal point and two more digits, the decimal point is dropped. For example:

29.95 would be stated as *two niner niner five* and 30.15 would be reported as *three zero one five.*

Round numbers up to 9,000, such as for ceiling heights, flight altitudes and upper wind levels are spoken in accordance with the following examples:

800   — *eight hundred*
1,300 — *one thousand three hundred*
4,500 — *four thousand five hundred*
9,000 — *niner thousand*

Numbers above 9,000 are spoken by separating the digits preceding the word thousand. Some examples are:

10,000 — *one zero thousand*
18,500 — *one eight thousand five hundred*

The pronunciation of numbers also is involved when expressing time. To simplify this type of communication when there is no danger of confusion, time is stated as minutes past the hour such as *one zero* meaning ten minutes past the hour; or *four three* meaning 43 minutes past the hour.

TWENTY-FOUR HOUR CLOCK SYSTEM

The 24-hour clock system is used to eliminate the confusion resulting from the 12-hour system duplicated in both the a.m. and p.m. An expression of time using the 24-hour system consists of a four-digit number. The first two digits indicate the hour and the last two figures represent minutes past the hour. The hours are numbered consecutively from midnight to midnight, or from zero to 24. Some examples of time involving the a.m. are as follows:

0000 — *zero zero zero zero* (midnight)
0715 — *zero seven one five* (7:15 a.m.)
1200 — *one two zero zero* (noon)

Time in the p.m. is expressed according to the following examples:

1409 — *one four zero niner* (2:09 p.m.)
2259 — *two two five niner* (10:59 p.m.)

Since a pilot in an aircraft is capable of passing through several time zones during the course of a flight, a universal method of time was adopted to simplify the problems resulting from time changes. The time used for flights, flight plans, communications, etc., is the time at Greenwich, England, a city located on the zero degree line of longitude. This time is referred to as *Greenwich Mean Time* (GMT) and *Zulu Time.*

Because the sun rises over Greenwich, England, when it is still night time in the United States, the time is always later when expressed in Zulu than when expressed in local time in any time zone in the United States. To convert from the local time, then, it is necessary to add the appropriate number of hours to the local time to determine GMT or Zulu time. The location of the time zones in the United States is illustrated in figure 3-33.

To convert from one time to another, a pilot may use the following tables:

Fig. 3-33. Time Zones

To Convert From	To GMT
Eastern Stand. Time....	add 5 hours
Central Stand. Time....	add 6 hours
Mountain Stand. Time..	add 7 hours
Pacific Stand. Time	add 8 hours

The 24-hour clock system is used for local and Greenwich times. When a pilot requests local and Greenwich time from an FAA facility, he will hear Greenwich time stated first and then the local time. For example: time 0532 CST (1132 GMT) would be spoken as: *time one one three two Greenwich; zero five three two Central.* Current time checks, when requested, are stated to the nearest quarter minute.

FREQUENCY UTILIZATION

Radio frequencies are identified by a numerical value, depending upon the number of cycles per second (Hertz) made by the specific frequency. Due to the very high number of cycles involved, it is convenient to use the term *kiloHertz (kHz)* and *MegaHertz (MHz)* when referring to frequencies. One thousand cycles per second equals one kiloHertz and 1,000,000 cycles per second denotes one MegaHertz.

Radio frequency ranges refer to a group of frequencies with an upper and lower cycle limit. There are four frequency ranges which are utilized in aircraft communications. They are: L/MF (low/medium frequency range); HF (high frequency range); VHF (very high frequency range); and UHF (ultra high frequency range).

L/MF BAND

Figure 3-34 shows the frequency allocation chart as determined by the Federal Communications Commission. Notice that the low frequency range is from 30 to 300 kHz, and the medium frequency range extends from 300 to 3,000 kHz. Lower frequencies allocated by the FCC for aircraft communications extend from 200 to 415 kHz, including portions of both the low and medium frequency

Fig. 3-34. Low/Medium Frequency Band

Fig. 3-35. Radio Frequency Bands in General Use in Aviation

range. This aircraft band is referred to as the L/MF band.

HF BAND

The high frequency (HF) band includes frequencies from 3,000 to 30,000 kHz. Although many frequencies in this range have been allocated to aviation, the use of high frequencies has gradually decreased to the point that the high frequency band is no longer considered an important system of communication for *domestic* operations.

VHF BAND

The very high frequency (VHF) band is the *most* important portion of the frequency spectrum to the *private pilot* and includes frequencies from 30 MHz to 300 MHz. For comparison, the relationship of the popular FM radio band and certain TV channels (two through six) to the aviation frequencies is shown. (See Fig. 3-35.)

The frequency range of 108.0 MHz through 117.95 MHz is used for air navigation aids, such as the instrument landing

system (ILS), VHF navigation stations (VOR), and provides simultaneous voice reception over these frequencies. The frequency range allotted for civilian aviation voice communication is from 118.0 MHz to 135.975 MHz. It should be emphasized that the VHF band is by far the most commonly used in general aviation.

UHF BAND

The ultra high frequency (UHF) band includes frequencies from 300 MHz to 3,000 MHz. This band of frequencies has been reserved for use by various government agencies including the military. In addition, distance measuring equipment (DME), and the glide slope (vertical guidance) portion of the ILS system operate with signals in the UHF band.

CHARACTERISTICS AND LIMITATIONS OF RADIO SIGNALS

Knowledge of the characteristics and limitations of the various frequency bands used by pilots is important in order to obtain the greatest efficiency from radio equipment. The low/medium and high frequencies can be bounced back from

Fig. 3-36. Signal Bounce from Ionosphere

Fig. 3-37. Line-of-Sight Limitation

the ionosphere (a shell of electrically charged particles surrounding the earth), and are not affected by intermediate obstruction or line-of-sight restrictions. (See Fig. 3-36.) This frequency band provides its best advantage to the pilot for low altitude, long range reception of navigational signals and weather information. The greatest disadvantage is static, especially in areas of precipitation.

The greatest disadvantage of the VHF and UHF frequencies is the line-of-sight limitation. Any obstruction, including the curvature of the earth, will interfere with VHF communications. The line-of-sight feature restricts the reception distance of VHF and UHF signals for low altitude

communications and navigation. (See Fig. 3-37.)

The normal reception distances for VHF frequencies, listed below, are based upon the radio line-of-sight signal and assumes there are no intervening obstructions between the transmitter and receiver. Examples of various reception distances are tabulated below:

Feet Above Ground Station	Reception Distance (Nautical Miles)
1,000	39
3,000	69
5,000	87
10,000	122
15,000	152
20,000	174

SECTION C - AIR TRAFFIC CONTROL

Knowing how to use the various facilities provided by the FAA for air traffic control makes flying easier and safer. The air traffic control (ATC) system is based on voice communications between controllers and pilots, necessitating an expansive network of communication facilities. These facilities can be divided into terminal and enroute services.

AIRPORT TERMINAL FACILITIES

AUTOMATIC TERMINAL INFORMATION SERVICE

Automatic terminal information service (ATIS) is provided at busy terminal airports. The information is broadcast continuously and includes such information as weather, altimeter setting, runways, and instrument approaches in use, tower frequencies, and surface winds. ATIS may be assigned a VHF frequency or may be broadcast over the voice feature of a navaid near the airport. The correct frequencies can be found on the sectional chart or in the *Airport/Facility Directory*, which is discussed in a later chapter. Figure 3-38 shows the directory entry for Stapleton International Airport at Denver, Colorado. Figure 3-39 shows the ATIS information on a sectional chart.

The following is a sample broadcast of an ATIS recording for arriving aircraft.

"Stapleton Airport, information Charlie, 800 scattered, ceiling measured 4,000 overcast, visibility 20, wind 180 at four, temperature 38, altimeter 30.32, ILS approach runway 26L in use, landing runway 26L and 26R, frequency 118.3. Notice to airmen, runway 35 closed until 1600 Zulu. Airman advisory, fog bank east of the airport, visibility three miles. Stapleton VFR arrivals contact approach control, north 120.5, south 120.8. VFR arrivals advise if transponder equipped on initial contact. Inform controller on initial contact that you have received information Charlie."

As indicated in the last sentence of the recording, the pilot should notify the controller on initial contact that ATIS information has been received. As an example, *"Denver Radar, Cessna 6721X, 20 north, squawking 1200, landing Denver, information Charlie."*

Fig. 3-39. ATIS Frequency—Sectional Chart

---

§ **STAPLETON INTL** (DEN) 4.3 E GMT-7(-6DT) 39°46'27"N 104°52'39"W   **DENVER**
   5333   B   S4   **FUEL** 100, JET A   OX 1, 3   CFR Index D   LRA   **H-1C, L-6E, 8G, A-2G**
   RWY 17L-35R: H12000X200 (CONC-GROOVED) S-200+, D-200+, DT-360+, HIRL, CL .3% up S   **IAP**
     B-747 and C5 acft restricted to maximum gross weight of 1.1 million pounds
     RWY 17L: VASI   **RWY 35R:** ALSF2, TDZ

      COMMUNICATIONS: ATIS 125.6-**ARR** 124.45-**DEP**   **UNICOM** 122.95
       DENVER FSS (DEN) on fld 122.6 122.35 122.2 122.1R (303) 321-0031
    ® **DENVER APP CON** 128.05 125.3 120.5 (North) 127.05 (South)
       DENVER TOWER 118.3 (East/West) 119.5 (North/South)   **GND CON** 121.9   **CLNC DEL** 127.6   **PRE-TAXI CLNC** 127.6
    ® **DENVER DEP CON** 128.05 (320°-100°), 123.85 (101°-319°)
       TCA Group II see VFR Terminal Area Chart

Fig. 3-38. ATIS Frequency – Airport/Facility Directory

Fig. 3-40. Tower Controller

CONTROL TOWER

The airport control tower is responsible for all airborne traffic, including aircraft landing, taking off, and operating within the airport traffic area (that is, within a five statute mile radius, including airspace less than 3,000 feet AGL). A clearance must be received before taxiing onto a taxiway, taking off, or landing. On initial contact with the tower, the aircraft call sign, location, and the pilot's intentions should be given. Tower frequencies are listed in the *Airport/Facility Directory* and printed near the airport symbol on aeronautical charts. (See Fig. 3-41.)

A typical clearance is ". . . *cleared for takeoff.*" The pilot's action should be to taxi onto the runway and take off as soon as practicable. If the controller says ". . . *cleared for immediate takeoff,*" there may be another aircraft on final approach or some other traffic factor that requires the pilot to expedite the takeoff.

Sometimes, a takeoff sequence may be given, such as *"Piper 1724G, number two for departure behind the twin Cessna."* This is not a clearance to take off. Takeoff clearance will be issued at the appropriate time.

Fig. 3-41. Control Tower Radio Frequency

The pilot may be cleared to ". . . *taxi into position and hold.*" Upon receipt of this instruction, the pilot should taxi onto the runway, line up, and stop until a takeoff clearance is received.

After takeoff, the pilot must remain on the tower frequency until out of the airport traffic area. In order to deviate from the standard departure pattern, tower permission is necessary.

When arriving at a tower controlled airport, initial contact should be made with the tower about 15 miles from the airport. Contact *must* be established before entering the airport traffic area. A clearance to land may be received immediately if there is no other traffic in the pattern. Normally, however, a landing sequence is given, such as *"1724G, number two, follow the Beechcraft turning base."*

Most control towers have light guns that can be used to issue a limited amount of instructions in the event of a radio communications failure. These guns emit an intense narrow beam of red, green, or white light, and have sighting devices for precise aiming. All pilots are required to

Fig. 3-42. Controller Operating Light Gun

know the light signals and their meanings, as shown in figure 3-43.

If it is necessary to land at a controlled airport with the radio inoperative, the pilot should remain outside or above the airport traffic area until the direction and flow of traffic have been determined. The pilot can then join the traffic pattern while keeping a careful watch for other aircraft and maintaining visual contact with the tower to receive light gun signals. The signals can be acknowledged by moving the ailerons or rudder during daylight, or by blinking the landing or navigation lights at night.

GROUND CONTROL

Not all tower-equipped airports have separate ground control frequencies, but most do. The correct frequency can be found in the *Airport/Facility Directory*. When contacting ground control, the pilot should state the aircraft identification, location on the airport, and his intentions. If ATIS information has been received, ground control should also be informed of that fact. For example, *"Arapahoe Ground, Grumman 2678U, with information Charlie, north ramp, taxi to active for southeast departure."*

A typical reply is, *"2678U, taxi to runway 28."* An instruction to taxi *to* the active runway is authorization to taxi *to* the assigned runway, crossing any runways (except the active runway) that intersect the taxi route. It does *not* constitute clearance to taxi *onto* the active runway. The correct procedure is to taxi to the runup area near the end of the active runway and contact the control tower when ready for takeoff clearance.

APPROACH AND DEPARTURE CONTROL

Some airports have approach and departure control located at the tower

Color and Type of Signal	On the Ground	In Flight
Steady Green	Cleared for takeoff	Cleared to land
Flashing Green	Cleared to taxi	Return for landing (to be followed by steady green at proper time)
Steady Red	Stop	Give way to other aircraft and continue circling
Flashing Red	Taxi clear of landing area (runway) in use	Airport unsafe - do not land
Flashing White	Return to starting point on airport	(No Assigned Meaning)
Alternating Red and Green	General warning signal	Exercise extreme caution

Fig. 3-43. Light Gun Signals

facility. (See Fig. 3-44.) At other airports, however, approach and departure control are located separately from the tower. These facilities provide traffic separation through the use of radar and are most commonly used for IFR operations.

Fig. 3-44. Approach and Departure Control

At some busy terminals where it is desirable to exercise control of traffic until they leave the airport traffic area, the control tower may request that departing VFR aircraft contact departure control and arriving aircraft contact approach control. The departure or approach control frequency will be given at the time the pilot is told to change frequencies.

Arriving and departing VFR aircraft may also *request* Stage I service (radar advisory service for VFR aircraft) and it will be provided if the IFR traffic load allows the controller to provide the service. Departure and approach control frequencies are listed in the *Airport/Facility Directory*.

ENROUTE VFR COMMUNICATIONS

FLIGHT SERVICE STATION

A major communications facility which the VFR pilot uses quite extensively is the *flight service station* (FSS). Flight service station attendants provide pilots with all types of flight information such as current altimeter settings, advisories on enroute weather conditions which

might be encountered, and any other information which would be of help during a cross-country flight. (See Fig. 3-45.) In addition, flight service stations can supply complete preflight weather briefings.

Fig. 3-45. FSS Communicating with Aircraft

Several radio navigation facilities may be *remotely controlled* by one flight service station. The controlling FSS and its communication and navigation frequencies at each location are shown on the sectional charts and may be found in the *Airport/Facility Directory*. The standard FSS communication frequencies and the codes used to indicate the available frequencies are listed in the "Radio Aids to Navigation" legend on the front panel of each sectional chart.

It should be noted that on the actual sectional chart, VHF radio frequencies and facilities are shown in blue, and information pertaining to low and medium frequency facilities is shown in magenta. Figure 3-46 provides an interpretation of FSS codes used on charts. The following numbered items correspond to the numbered callouts in that illustration.

1. An information box with a heavy border line indicates a flight service station. The standard FSS simplex communication frequency of 122.2 and the emergency frequency of 121.5 are available, unless otherwise noted.
2. Communication frequencies which are provided in addition to

Fig. 3-46. FSS Frequency Codes

the standard FSS frequencies are shown above the box. A frequency followed by the letter "R" means that the navigation facility receives this frequency only; likewise, the letter "T" indicates that the FSS facility can only transmit on this frequency. If no letter follows the frequency, it is a simplex frequency.

3. The navigation frequency (and TACAN channel if the station is a VORTAC) is shown inside the box, along with the station identification letters and Morse code. An underlined frequency indicates that there is no voice on the frequency; only the Morse code is audibly transmitted.

4. If the FSS has enroute flight advisory service, this is noted by filling in the top corners of the information box. When this service is indicated, the pilot may contact the weather briefing service directly on the frequency of 122.0.

5. A square indicates a transcribed weather broadcast (TWEB) is available at this navigation aid.

6. A flight service station without a navigation facility is shown in a heavy line box containing only the name of the FSS.

7. An information box with a thin line border denotes a navigation facility without a flight service station or a navigation facility controlled by a remote FSS. A box without frequency and remote FSS notations indicates that no FSS communication is available.

8. The FSS controlling a remote navigation facility is shown in a bracket under the thin line information box.

One common method used in contacting flight service stations is to transmit on frequency 122.1 MHz and receive the FSS on the VOR frequency. On the initial call to a flight service station, it is important to indicate the frequency being monitored.

A commonly used simplex frequency is 122.2 MHz. When using this frequency, it is possible to transmit and receive the flight service station on the same frequency. Another simplex frequency used by many flight service stations is 123.6 MHz.

When arriving at an uncontrolled airport where a flight service station is located, it is possible to receive airport advisory service on the frequency of 123.6 MHz. Flight service stations exercise no control over arriving or departing airport traffic; however, they can provide information on wind speed, direction, weather conditions, and any known traffic in the traffic pattern. When arriving at an airport with a flight service station, the pilot should contact the FSS and request an airport advisory.

AIR ROUTE TRAFFIC CONTROL CENTERS

The safety of IFR traffic is the *prime* responsibility of *air route traffic control*

Fig. 3-47. Air Route Traffic Control Center

Fig. 3-48 UNICOM Frequency

centers .(ARTCCs). (See Fig. 3-47.) The United States is divided into 21 of these centers that jointly coordinate the flow of IFR traffic between their assigned areas. The centers throughout the country each have direct communications with adjacent centers. Each center is geographically divided into sectors with individual controllers directing IFR traffic in those sectors. As a flight leaves one sector for another, the controller's responsibility is passed to a controller working in the adjacent sector.

Today, most aircraft that are flying at sufficiently high altitudes are controlled by ARTCCs through the use of radar. In some cases, VFR pilots may take advantage of radar service from air traffic control centers. Again, this is dependent upon the amount of IFR traffic a particular controller is handling.

UNICOM

UNICOM stations are privately operated advisory stations located at many airports. These stations can provide information as to wind direction and velocity, runway in use, and any known traffic in the traffic pattern. UNICOM also can be used to arrange aircraft services, to relay personal messages, and to request general information about the area. The *Airport/Facility Directory* and aeronautical charts indicate the availability of UNICOM and the frequency assigned to each station. Figure 3-48 shows how UNICOM frequencies are listed on charts. If a tower or an FSS is not available, it is wise for the pilot to use UNICOM to determine airport data and to announce his intentions during each segment of the takeoff or landing.

After establishing radio contact, the initial call when inbound to an airport might be *"Jasper County UNICOM, Cessna 2158U, five miles south for airport advisory."* Since the UNICOM frequency is not always being monitored, there may be no reply. However, a typical reply is *"58U, runway 35 is in use, left-hand traffic, wind is about 340° at five, no reported traffic."* Remember, this information is *advisory* in nature and can be supplied by anyone at the airport. It is not official data.

When broadcasting your position, the pilot should call *"Jasper County traffic"* to include any aircraft in the area; for example, *"Jasper County traffic, 58U entering left downwind for touch-and-go, runway 35."* Remember, not all aircraft may be monitoring UNICOM. Collision avoidance remains the pilot's responsibility.

MULTICOM

The MULTICOM, or multiple communications, frequency of 122.90 MHz is used for the coordination of air-to-air and air-to-ground operations involving private aircraft. For example, aircraft engaged in agricultural activities, forest fire fighting, and parachute jumping use this frequency. MULTICOM also is used by aircraft operating into and out of non-tower airports without FSS or UNICOM service. When operating in such an environment, the pilot should monitor the MULTICOM frequency and use it to announce his intentions prior to taking off or entering the traffic pattern.

When departing the airport, he should tune to 122.9 MHz and listen before taxiing. The pilot should then broadcast his position on the airport and his intentions. After completing his pre-takeoff checklist, he should make an announcement before taxiing onto the active runway for takeoff.

EMERGENCY PROCEDURES

One of the frequencies that all pilots should memorize is 121.5 MHz. This is the international frequency for emergency use. Flight service stations, control towers, and air route traffic control centers maintain a listening watch on this single-channel communications frequency. The pilot's initial call-up should be *"Mayday, Mayday, Mayday"* if he has an emergency or is in distress. If he is not in immediate distress but is uncertain or desires to alert ground personnel, then he should preface his message with *"Pan, Pan, Pan."*

For aircraft equipped with a radar beacon transponder, the emergency transponder code is 7700. (See Fig. 3-49.)

If an aircraft so equipped experiences an emergency, the pilot should select code 7700. Doing this will automatically activate an alarm at the appropriate radar facility. In addition, the radar blip of the aircraft selecting the code will light up to a higher intensity on the radar screen.

D/F, or direction finding equipment, can be an invaluable aid to a lost or disoriented pilot. The equipment consists of a directional antenna system and a VHF and UHF radio receiver. The D/F display indicates the magnetic direction of the aircraft from the station each time the aircraft transmits. Where D/F equipment is tied into radar, a strobe of light is flashed from the center of the radar scope in the direction of the transmitting aircraft. In order to utilize D/F equipment, the pilot should contact the nearest tower or flight service station.

If an emergency or alert situation develops, the pilot should remember the four C's. They are:

1. *Confess* your predicament to any ground radio station. Don't wait too long.

2. *Communicate* with your ground radio link and pass on as much of the distress or alert message on the first transmission as possible.

3. *Climb*, if possible, for better radar and D/F detection. If flying at low altitude, the pilot's chance for establishing radio contact is improved by climbing.

4. *Comply* — especially comply, with the advice and instructions received.

When a pilot is in doubt of his position or feels apprehensive for his safety, he should not hesitate to request assistance.

Fig. 3-49. Transponder Emergency Code

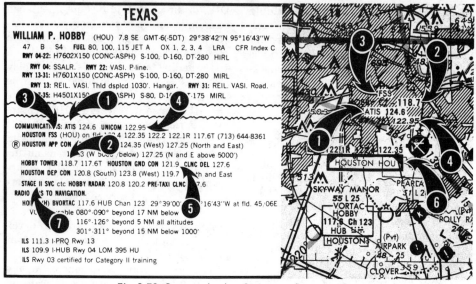

Fig. 3-50. Communication Codes and Frequencies

EMERGENCY LOCATOR TRANSMITTERS

Emergency locator transmitters are required by law for most light airplanes and are important equipment for pilots flying over mountainous or sparsely populated terrain. A certain "G" load normally is required to activate these beacons, or they may be activated from the cockpit. Once activated, they send out signals which, when picked up by search aircraft, will lead searchers directly to the downed aircraft.

REVIEW

A short review of radio frequencies as they are listed in the *Airport/Facility Directory* and on sectional charts is listed below. The following item numbers correspond to the numbered callouts in figure 3-50.

1. ATIS is received on 124.6 MHz at Houston.
2. The primary Hobby Tower frequency is 118.7 MHz.
3. The Houston Flight Service Station is located on the field.
4. The UNICOM frequency is 122.95 MHz.
5. The Houston Ground Control frequency is 121.9 MHz.
6. The heavy line box on the chart indicates a flight service station. The standard frequencies of 122.2 and 121.5 MHz are available, as well as the frequencies 122.4 MHz, 122.35 MHz, and 121.1 MHz (receive only). The triangles in the upper corner of the box indicate enroute flight advisory service is available on the frequency 122.0 MHz.
7. Stage II radar service (radar advisory and sequencing service for VFR aircraft) is available through Hobby Radar.

Careful review of these two important sources of communication information will enable the pilot to quickly locate radio frequencies and interpret the coding.

chapter 4

WEIGHT AND BALANCE

INTRODUCTION

Modern, light aircraft are designed so they can be kept within their balance limits with a minimum of pilot effort. However, as aircraft cabins become longer to provide greater payloads, better seating arrangements, and more comfort, weight and balance limits can be exceeded by improper loading.

This chapter points out the importance of weight and balance to aircraft performance, stability, and control, and describes the consequences if weight and balance limits are exceeded. The first section explains weight and balance theory and how an aircraft will react to various loading conditions. The following section explains the various methods for checking weight and balance.

SECTION A - WEIGHT AND BALANCE THEORY

THE IMPORTANCE OF WEIGHT

Almost every aspect of aircraft performance is influenced by the weight of the aircraft and its contents. For example, compared to a properly loaded airplane, an overweight airplane has a higher takeoff speed, longer takeoff run, reduced angle and rate of climb, shorter range, reduced cruising speed, higher stalling speed, and longer landing roll. Loading an aircraft too heavily can decrease its performance to a dangerous level, and can create the risk of structural damage caused by turbulence, maneuvering, or hard landings.

Several guidelines have been established to help insure proper aircraft loading.

Among these are maximum takeoff, landing, and ramp weights. These weights are provided by the manufacturer and approved by the Federal Aviation Administration. They are set as operating limitations after consideration of such factors as performance, structural strength, and type of operation.

Aircraft manufacturers use a large safety factor in establishing these limitations, and modern aircraft are actually capable of carrying loads that are well above those expected during normal operations. To exceed the aircraft structural limitations is usually quite difficult; however, maximum weight increases the chances that the structural limitations will be exceeded.

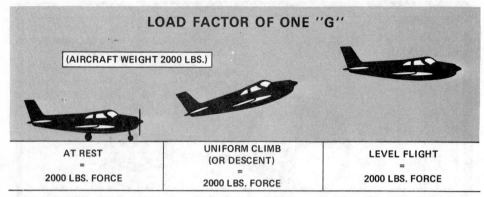

Fig. 4-1. Aircraft Experiencing One "G" Force

In order to understand how the weight of the aircraft determines the loads imposed on it during takeoff, flight, and landing, it is important that the student recall the term *load factor*. Load factor, as applied to aircraft stresses, is a ratio of actual load to aircraft weight. It is determined by dividing the actual load being applied to the structure of the aircraft by the total weight of the aircraft. Load factors are usually expressed in "G's."

A "G" is equal to the force of gravity or the actual weight of an object at rest. Therefore, if an aircraft was subject to a load factor of two "G's," the force would increase its effective weight to two times its normal weight.

For example, an aircraft has a load factor of one "G" when at rest on the ground, when in a uniform climb, or when flying straight and level in smooth air. (See Fig. 4-1.) In other words, the aircraft landing gear, or wings in flight, under these conditions, carries a load equal to one times the loaded weight of the aircraft.

When an aircraft in coordinated, level flight is turning in a 60° bank, it is subject to a load factor of two. (See Fig. 4-2.) This means the wings are lifting two times the weight experienced in straight-and-level flight. If the airplane weighed 2,000 pounds, the effective weight of the aircraft in a 60° bank is 4,000 pounds.

An airplane flying in gusty air is subject to sudden jolts that impose additional loads on the aircraft structure. The loads imposed by gusts are dependent upon the speed at which the aircraft penetrates them. It is somewhat like driving a car over a bumpy railroad track; if the person drives over it slowly, the car will bounce mildly; but if he drives over it fast, the car will bounce violently with the shock absorbers and springs hitting the frame. (See Fig. 4-3.)

Gusts are actually turbulent columns or layers of air that are rising, descending, or moving at different velocities. Flying through turbulent air at high speeds causes the wings to be subjected to severe bumps which result in high load factors. (See Fig. 4-4.)

It is for this reason that a pilot should slow his aircraft when he encounters severe gusty conditions. The pilot should adjust his airspeed when in turbulent con-

Fig. 4-2. Aircraft Experiencing Two "G's"

Fig. 4-3. Speed Affects Load Factor

ditions so the *maneuvering speed* specified in the pilot's operating handbook is not exceeded.

CHECKING AIRCRAFT WEIGHT

Information concerning proper aircraft loading is contained in the airplane weight and balance forms and the pilot's operating handbook. To insure that these operating limits are not exceeded, it is necessary to calculate the aircraft's loaded weight by adding the total load to the empty weight of the aircraft.

The aircraft empty weight is defined in two ways.

1. *Basic empty weight* means the weight of an aircraft including unusable fuel, full operating fluids, full engine oil, and optional equipment. Most recently manufactured aircraft use this term.

2. *Empty weight*, or *licensed empty weight*, has the same meaning as basic empty weight, except that drainable engine oil is not included. This definition applies to most older aircraft. Basic empty weight can be determined by adding the weight of the oil (7.5 pounds per *gallon*) to the licensed empty weight.

The pilot may encounter several other terms pertaining to aircraft weight. They are defined in the following list.

1. *Maximum ramp weight* is the maximum weight approved for ground maneuvers. It includes weight of fuel used for start, taxi, and runup.

2. *Maximum takeoff weight* is the maximum weight approved for the start of the takeoff run.

3. *Useful load* is the difference between takeoff weight (or ramp weight, if applicable) and basic empty weight.

4. *Payload* is the weight of occupants, cargo, and baggage.

5. *Usable fuel* is the fuel available for flight planning.

6. *Unusable fuel* is the fuel remaining after a runout test has been completed in accordance with government regulations.

DESCENDING COLUMNS OF AIR

RISING COLUMNS OF AIR

Fig. 4-4. Gusts

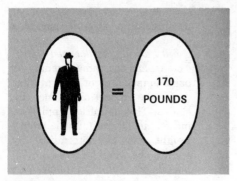

Fig. 4-5. Average Size Person

Fig. 4-6. Actual Weights of Baggage and Cargo

The pilot can easily check the loaded weight of the aircraft by adding together the following items.

1. Basic empty weight
2. Weight of fuel load
3. Weight of pilot and passengers
4. Weight of baggage and/or cargo

Basic empty weight can be determined by checking the aircraft weight and balance forms. These forms may be placed in the airplane separately, or they may be included in an approved flight manual.

Since fuel weighs six pounds per gallon, the total fuel weight is computed by multiplying the number of gallons of fuel onboard times six. If the pilot and passengers are of average stature, a weight of 170 pounds per person can be used. (See Fig. 4-5.) For children from 2 to 12 years old, an average weight of 80 pounds can be used. If extra large people are to be carried or if the aircraft is being loaded near its maximum weight, actual pilot and passenger weights should be used. Actual cargo and baggage weights should always be used. (See Fig. 4-6.)

An example of a weight check is:

Basic empty weight	1,729.5 lbs.
Pilot	170.0 lbs.
Passengers (3)	510.0 lbs.
Fuel (30 gallons)	180.0 lbs.
Baggage	50.0 lbs.
Total weight	2,639.5 lbs.

Assuming that the aircraft has a maximum takeoff weight of 2,650 pounds, its total weight of 2,639.5 pounds is under the maximum weight, and the aircraft is *not* overloaded.

THE IMPORTANCE OF BALANCE

In addition to checking weight, it is necessary to know that the aircraft is balanced within approved limits. The balance condition of an aircraft can be determined by locating its *center of gravity* (CG), which is the imaginary point where an aircraft would balance if suspended, as shown in figure 4-7. The *CG limits* are the forward and aft center of gravity locations within which the aircraft must be operated at a given weight, as shown in figure 4-8.

The center of gravity and CG limits are usually specified in inches from a *reference datum*, which is an imaginary

Fig. 4-7. CG = Center of Gravity

Fig. 4-8. Center of Gravity Range

Fig. 4-10. Safe Elevator Control

vertical plane from which all horizontal distances are measured for balance purposes. There is no fixed rule as to the location of the reference datum, as illustrated in figure 4-9. It often is located on the nose of the aircraft or at some point on the aircraft itself, such as the firewall. In some cases, it is located a certain distance forward of the nose of the aircraft. The manufacturer has the choice of reference datum location.

As long as the center of gravity is maintained within the CG range specified by the manufacturer, the elevator control surfaces are capable of controlling the aircraft through all flight speed ranges — from stall speeds to the highest approved speeds. (See Fig. 4-10.)

EFFECTS OF FORWARD LOADING

Longitudinal stability is the resistance of an aircraft to nose-up and nose-down

pitching motions. This stability increases as the CG moves forward. Since an airplane is dependent on the elevator to supply pitch control, the forward CG limit is established at a point where the increased stability will not exceed the ability of the elevator to provide this control. (See Fig. 4-11.)

If the CG is located forward of the forward CG limit, the following conditions exist, mildly at first, but becoming more severe as the CG moves farther and farther forward away from the CG range.

1. The aircraft becomes too stable. It has very little pitching tendency, but extra heavy elevator control forces are required to pull the nose up.
2. A CG that is forward of the forward CG limit is dangerous in that the aircraft will not have adequate elevator force to hold the tail down in the tail-low attitude during landing. (See Fig. 4-12.)
3. Also, a CG that is forward of the CG limit is dangerous for take-

Fig. 4-9. Datum Location

Fig. 4-11. Forward CG

Fig. 4-12. Unsafe for Landing

Fig. 4-13. Difficult Stall Recoveries

off. A nose-heavy aircraft will require longer ground runs and faster speeds before the nose can be raised for takeoff. If the runway is short, an extremely forward CG airplane could fail to become airborne in time to clear obstacles at the end of the runway.

4. Furthermore, if the weight distribution of the aircraft is located farther forward, additional down force on the tail must be developed through elevator back pressure in order to produce a critical angle of attack. If the elevators are already in the full-up position, the additional aerodynamic force must be generated by increased airflow over the horizontal tail surfaces. In order to do this, the airspeed must be greater; therefore, the *stall speed increases*.

This increase in stall speed could become a critical factor during takeoff, landing, or when performing a go-around from a missed approach to landing.

5. The nose-over tendency of conventional geared aircraft also increases as the CG moves farther forward of the approved limits.

AFT CENTER OF GRAVITY

If the aircraft should be loaded so that the CG is located behind the aft CG limits, the following conditions become noticeable, becoming more severe as the CG moves farther aft away from the CG range:

1. The aircraft becomes tail-heavy. This is a dangerous condition because it may be difficult to recover after maneuvering. (See Fig. 4-13.)

2. As the CG moves farther aft, the aircraft becomes more unstable and difficult to control.

3. Exceeding the aft CG limit seriously affects longitudinal stability and may reduce the chances of recovery from stalls and spins.

The aft CG limit is more apt to be exceeded with full gross weight conditions because loads in the back seats and baggage compartment have the greatest effect on moving the CG aft.

In order to keep the CG from moving too far back, a good rule of thumb to follow when loading the aircraft is *place the heaviest passengers and cargo forward and locate the lighter loads in the aft cabin or cargo area*.

WEIGHT AND BALANCE PRINCIPLES ILLUSTRATED

Children playing on a teeter-totter illustrate the basic principles involved in balance theory. The teeter-totter is in a balanced condition when the children adjust their distances from the *fulcrum*, or pivot point, so that their respective weights will balance.

For example, suppose that each child weighs 50 pounds. To balance the teeter-totter, they must each sit an equal distance from the fulcrum. (See Fig. 4-14.)

Fig. 4-14. Equal Weights and Distance

Fig. 4-16. Distance = Arm

However, if another child of 50 pounds sits at one end, the teeter-totter is unbalanced. In order to balance the teeter-totter, it is necessary that the fulcrum be moved toward the two children until the balanced condition is regained. (See Fig. 4-15.)

These examples show that, in addition to weight, the distance the weight is located from the fulcrum also affects the balance condition. This distance is usually called the *arm* in weight and balance calculations. (See Fig. 4-16.)

The tendency for an object to rotate is equal to its weight multiplied by its distance (or arm) from the fulcrum. This product is called *moment* and is usually stated in pound-inches.

For example, a 10-pound weight supported from a 24-inch arm would have a mo-

ment of 240 pound-inches (see Fig. 4-17). The teeter-totter is used to illustrate this. A 50-pound child located at an arm of 100 inches from the fulcrum has a moment of 5,000 pound-inches. (See Fig. 4-18.)

In order to balance this child, it is necessary to create a moment on the opposite side of the fulcrum of 5,000 pound-inches also. If a child weighing 100 pounds is to sit on the opposite side, where does he sit to balance the teeter-totter? (See Fig. 4-19.)

To determine the arm for the 100-pound child, the moment of 5,000 pound-inches is divided by the child's weight (5,000 ÷ 100 = 50 inches). Thus, the heavy child must sit at an arm of 50 inches from the fulcrum to balance the lighter child. This example illustrates how a weight can be located to balance an object when the fulcrum is fixed. (See Fig. 4-19.)

Fig. 4-15. Different Weights,
Move Fulcrum

Fig. 4-17. Weight x Arm = Moment

Fig. 4-18. Moment = 5,000 Pound-Inches

Fig. 4-20. Where is the Balance Point?

A different problem exists if the seats on the teeter-totter are fixed and only the fulcrum can be moved. For example, a 50-pound child is sitting on the left end and a 100-pound child is sitting on the right end. The distance between them is 200 inches and the teeter-totter itself weighs 40 pounds. When the children got on, the fulcrum was located 20 inches to the left of the center of the teeter-totter. Where is the new balance point? (See Fig. 4-20.)

In order to differentiate between the moments on one side of the teeter-totter from those on the opposite side, the arms (or distances) on the left side of the fulcrum will be labeled "minus" and those on the right side "plus." (See Fig. 4-21.)

The moment on the left side is equal to its arm, which is -80 inches (50 x [-80] = -4,000 pound-inches). Note that the moment is minus because it is located on the left side of the fulcrum.

The child's moment on the right side is 100 pounds x (+120 inches) = +12,000 pound-inches.

The weight of the teeter-totter board is 40 pounds and its center is located +20 inches from the fulcrum. Therefore, the board's moment is 40 pounds x (+20 inches) = +800 pound-inches.

Adding the moments of the child and the board, it is found that a total moment of +12,800 pound-inches exists on the right side of the fulcrum.

Now, the moments on both sides of the fulcrum can be compared. On the left side is -4,000 pound-inches versus +12,800 pound-inches on the right. The teeter-totter is certainly not balanced. Where should it balance? (See Fig. 4-22.)

The arm of the balance point can be located as follows:

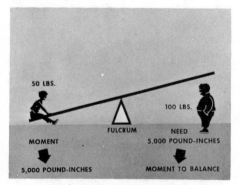

Fig. 4-19. Where Does He Sit?

Fig. 4-21. Plus and Minus Arms

Fig. 4-22. Unbalanced

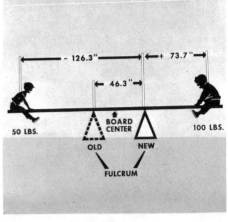

Fig. 4-23. Balanced

1. Add all the moments together, +12,800 - 4,000 = +8,800 pound-inches.

2. Next, add the weights of the children and board together. (50 + 100 + 40 = 190 pounds.)

3. Divide the total moment of +8,800 pound-inches by the total weight of 190 pounds. (+8,800 ÷ 190 = +46.3 inches.)

Since the arm is plus, it means that the balance point is 46.3 inches to the right of the old fulcrum. Relocating the fulcrum to this new position balances the teeter-totter. This results in the child on the left being located 126.3 inches from the fulcrum and the child on the right being 73.7 inches from the fulcrum. (See Fig. 4-23.)

A comparison can be made between the airplane and the teeter-totter.

1. The datum of the airplane can be likened to the fulcrum on the teeter-totter. Since the fulcrum is arbitrarily placed on the teeter-totter to provide a reference point for balance calculations, it could be located anywhere. In the case of the airplane, the manufacturer determines the datum location. (See Fig. 4-24.)

2. The center of gravity of the airplane is equivalent to the balance point of the teeter-totter. (See Fig. 4-25.)

3. The empty weight of the airplane can be compared to the weight of

Fig. 4-24. Datum and Fulcrum Compared

Fig. 4-25. Comparison: CG — Balance Point

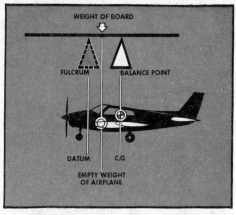

*Fig. 4-26. Comparison: Empty Weight —
Weight of Board*

the teeter-totter board. (See Fig. 4-26.)

4. The various loads the airplane carries, such as oil, pilot, passengers, cargo, baggage, and fuel can be compared to the children's weights.

5. All arms located to the left of the datum are labeled *minus* and all arms located to the right of the datum are labeled *plus*. (See Fig. 4-27.)

Fig. 4-27. Comparison: Plus and Minus Arms

SECTION B
WEIGHT AND BALANCE CALCULATION

Since weight and balance is so critical to the safe operation of an aircraft, it is important to know how to check this condition for each loading arrangement. There are three basic methods which can be used to check weight and balance. These are:

1. Computation method
2. Graph method
3. Table method

The computation method can be used to check the weight and balance condition of any aircraft, regardless of size. Since this method is rather time-consuming, manufacturers usually supply the pilot with graphs or tables to eliminate lengthy computations. The computation method, however, is the basis for all weight and balance control. This method provides the basic procedures for locating the aircraft center of gravity.

NOTE:

Aircraft manufactured in past years may specify a licensed empty weight rather than a basic empty weight. Licensed empty weight does not include engine oil. When operating such an aircraft, additional computations are required to account for the oil weight and moment.

COMPUTATION METHOD

Weight and balance theory provides a basis for understanding the computation method. The following steps are involved in weight and balance control using this method.

1. List the basic empty weight, fuel, pilot, passengers, baggage, and cargo, along with their respective weights and arms. (If licensed empty weight must be used, be sure to include the weight and arm of the engine oil.)

2. Multiply the weights and arms together to find the moment of each item.

3. Add the weights to get total loaded weight of the airplane.

4. Add the moments to find the total moment.

5. Divide the total moment by the total weight to obtain the CG location of the fully loaded aircraft.

6. Compare the total weight to the maximum certificated weight and the CG location with the forward and aft CG limits. Adjust the load as necessary to keep the aircraft loaded within approved limits.

SAMPLE PROBLEM USING COMPUTATION METHOD

The following information is obtained from the pilot's operating handbook and from the passengers.

1. The reference datum is located forward of the aircraft firewall.

2. Aircraft basic empty weight: 1,290 pounds; arm: 85.0 inches.

3. Pilot and front seat passenger are located at 85.5 inches. The weight of the pilot is 165 pounds, and the weight of the front seat passenger is 120 pounds.

4. Rear seat passengers are located at 117.0 inches. The combined weight of the rear passengers is 290 pounds.

CG Location Limits: 84.0 to 95.8 inches aft of datum Maximum Certificated Weight=2,150 lbs	Weight (Lbs)	Arm Aft Datum (Inches)	Moment (In-Lbs)
Basic Empty Weight	1,290	85.0	109,650.0
Pilot and Front Passenger	285	85.5	24,367.5
Passengers, Aft	290	117.0	33,930.0
Fuel (50 Gallon Maximum)	240	95.0	22,800.0
Baggage Area 1			
Baggage Area 2	45	133.3	5,998.5
Total Loaded Airplane	2150	91.5	196,746.0

Fig. 4-28. Weight and Balance Worksheet

5. Fuel load: 40 gallons; arm: 95.0 inches.

6. Baggage weight in Area 2: 45 pounds; arm: 133.3 inches.

7. CG limits: from 84.0 inches to 95.8 inches.

8. Maximum takeoff weight: 2,150 pounds.

Given these facts, determine whether or not the aircraft is loaded within weight and balance limits. The problem is worked according to the following steps:

1. Record the known facts on a work sheet which contains four columns: item, weight, arm, and moment, as shown in figure 4-28.

2. After the description, weight, and arm of each item are recorded, multiply the weights and arms together to obtain their moments. (See Fig. 4-28, item 1.)

3. Add all the values in the weight column. This yields a total weight of 2,150 pounds. Enter this at the bottom of the weight column (item 2).

4. Add the moments in the moment column. This value is 196,746.0 pound-inches (item 3).

5. Next, divide the total moment by the total weight (196,746.0 ÷ 2,150 = 91.5). This gives 91.5 inches, which is the distance that the airplane's loaded CG is located aft of the datum (item 4).

6. Compare the CG and total weight with the CG limits and maximum takeoff weight. The CG limits extend from 84.0 to 95.8 inches. Since the value of 91.5 inches falls within these limits, the aircraft is properly balanced. Also, since the aircraft weight of 2,150 pounds is not above the 2,150-pound maximum takeoff weight, the aircraft is not overloaded.

GRAPH METHOD

Now that weight and balance theory and the computation method are known, the student can proceed with the other methods of checking weight and balance.

The graph method is an easy way to perform weight and balance analysis. It eliminates the multiplication and division steps involved in the computation method because the moments can be read directly from a loading graph.

The loading graph contains a separate load line for each item. For example, the graph shown in figure 4-29 has the loading lines for pilot and front passenger, fuel, aft passengers, baggage area 1, and baggage area 2.

To find the moment of an item using the graph method, as shown in figure 4-29, proceed as follows:

(1) First, locate its load line on the graph, such as the pilot and front passenger load line.

(2) Then, find the weight of the item on the left side of the graph.

(3) Proceed horizontally along this weight line until the load line is reached.

(4) At this point, drop vertically down and read the moment on the scale at the bottom of the chart. The value is approximately 24. The moment is actually 24,000 pound-inches because the figures on this scale have been divided by 1,000 to make the numbers on the chart smaller and, therefore, more easily handled.

The *center of gravity limits* graph illustrated in figure 4-30, graphically depicts

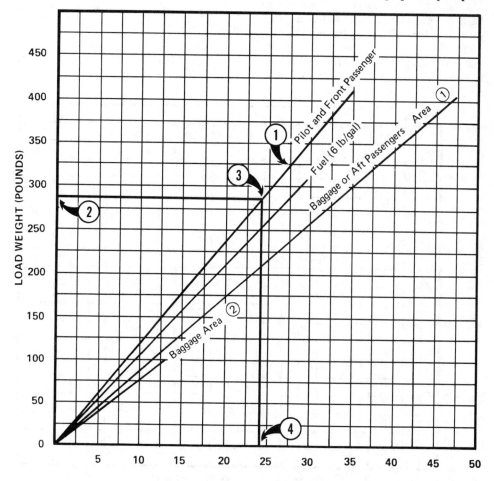

MOMENT/1000 (POUNDS-INCHES)

Fig. 4-29. Sample Loading Graph

the CG range. After the actual center of gravity location has been determined, proper loading can be assured by locating the point where the total weight and CG location intersect. The point of intersection should fall within the boundaries of the depicted limits.

SAMPLE PROBLEM USING GRAPH METHOD

A sample problem should be worked to become better acquainted with the graph method. In this problem, the aircraft is loaded with two persons in the front seat. The pilot weighs 180 pounds and the front passenger weighs 160 pounds. The aircraft will carry 25 pounds of baggage in area 1. In addition, 22.5 gallons of fuel will be on board.

Using the graph method, the problem is worked by entering the aircraft load items on a work sheet, similar to the one illustrated in figure 4-31.

1. The airplane basic empty weight and moment are 1,100 pounds and 35,900 pound-inches, respectively. This data is found in the aircraft weight and balance forms.
2. The fuel load is 22.5 gallons, 135 pounds.
3. Pilot and front passenger combined weights are 340 pounds.
4. Cargo in area 1 weighs 25 pounds.

The moment for the pilot and front passenger can be found by referring to figure 4-32.

① First, locate the appropriate load line.

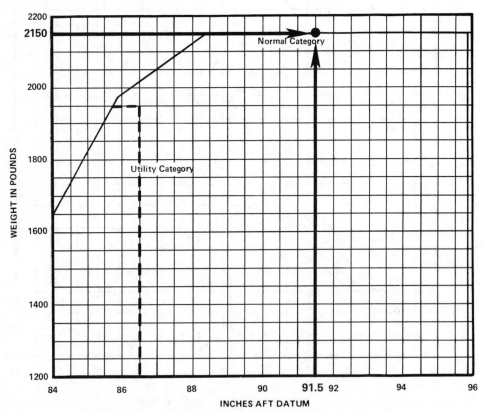

Fig. 4-30. Center of Gravity Limits

SAMPLE LOADING PROBLEM	SAMPLE AIRPLANE	
	Weight (lbs.)	Moment (lb.-ins. /1000)
1. Basic Empty Weight (Use the data pertaining to your airplane as it is presently equipped. Includes unusable fuel and full oil)	1100	35.9
2. Usable Fuel (At 6 Lbs./Gal.) Standard Tanks (22.5 Gal. Maximum)	135	5.7
Long Range Tanks (35 Gal. Maximum)		
Reduced Fuel (As limited by maximum weight)		
3. Pilot and Passenger (Station 33 to 41)	340	13.3
4. Baggage - Area 1 (Or passenger on child's seat) (Station 50 to 76, 120 Lbs. Max.) ·	25	1.6
5. Baggage - Area 2 (Station 76 to 94, 40 Lbs. Max.)		
6. TOTAL WEIGHT AND MOMENT	1600	56.5
7. Locate this point (1600 at 56.5) on the Center of Gravity Moment Envelope, and since this point falls within the envelope, the loading is acceptable.		

Fig. 4-31. Weight and Balance Worksheet

Fig. 4-32. Moment of Pilot and Front Passenger

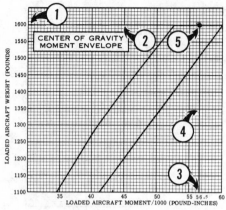

Fig. 4-33. Center of Gravity Location

① First, locate the total weight of 1,600 pounds on the scale located on the left side of the graph.

② Draw a horizontal line through this value across the graph.

③ Next, locate the total moment on the scale at the bottom of the graph.

④ Draw a line vertically upward from this point.

⑤ The CG position is at the point where the vertical and the horizontal lines intersect.

② On the left side of the graph, locate 340 pounds, which is the total weight of the pilot and front passenger.

③ Proceed horizontally along this line to the "pilot and front passenger" load line.

④ From the intersection point on the load line, proceed vertically downward to the horizontal scale at the bottom of the graph. At this point, the value is 13.3, which is actually 13,300 pound-inches. Record 13.3 in the moment column of the work sheet.

Proceed in a like manner to obtain the moments for the remaining load items and record them on the work sheet. When all of the weights and moments are determined, add each column to get the total weight and total moment. This step is the same as that performed in the computation method. The total weight is 1,600 pounds, and the total moment/1,000 is 56.5 lb.-in.

To check whether the CG is within the approved limits, locate the total weight and total moment on the *center of gravity moment envelope* shown in figure 4-33. No division is necessary, but the following steps are required:

The aircraft is correctly loaded because the CG location does not fall outside of the center of gravity envelope.

If a similar loading problem is encountered with the total weight below the maximum takeoff weight, but the center of gravity aft of the maximum limit, the pilot should attempt to reload the aircraft so the heavy objects are located more toward the front of the cabin or baggage area and the lighter objects toward the rear.

Final aircraft loading can be checked by determining the new weight and moments, entering the values on the work sheet, and rechecking the CG location relative to the center of gravity envelope.

TABLE METHOD

Another method of checking weight and balance is the table method. This method also eliminates both the multiplication and division operation involved in the computation method. Instead of graphs, the table method provides tables which list the useful load weights and moments. (See Fig. 4-34.)

For example, item 1 on figure 4-34 shows a table for the baggage compartment.

Fig. 4-34. Useful Load Weights and Moments Table

Note that weights are provided in 10-pound increments along with their respective moments. In order to simplify computations, the moments listed on this chart are divided by 100. This keeps the numbers small and easy to handle.

Assume that the aircraft is going to carry 120 pounds of baggage. What is its moment? Locate the weight of 120 pounds (see Fig. 4-34, item 2) and read the moment in the column to the right of the weight (item 3). It is found that the moment value for 120 pounds of baggage is 200. Since this value has been divided by 100, the moment is actually 20,000 pound-inches.

The table method also provides a moment limits vs. weight table for insuring that the total aircraft weight and moment are within approved limits. (See Fig. 4-35.) This table provides forward and aft moment limits for each weight. If the aircraft total moment falls within the forward and aft moment limits for the weight involved, the aircraft is safely loaded.

For example, assume that the aircraft has a loaded weight of 2,950 pounds and a total moment of 324,600 pound-inches. The pilot can check whether or not the aircraft is loaded within approved limits by referring to the moment limits vs. weight table and proceeding as follows:

1. First, locate the loaded weight of 2,950 pounds (item 1).
2. Observe that the forward limit is 314,500 pound-inches (item 2) and the aft limit is 346,600 pound-inches (item 3). Note that the values in the table have to be multiplied by 100 to get the moments.
3. Since the aircraft total moment of 324,600 pound-inches is within these limits, the aircraft is safely loaded.

MOMENT LIMITS vs WEIGHT

WEIGHT POUNDS	MOMENT/100 FWD LIMIT	MOMENT/100 AFT LIMIT	WEIGHT POUNDS	MOMENT/100 FWD LIMIT	MOMENT/100 AFT LIMIT
2300	2452	2703	3125	3331	3672
2325	2479	2732	3150	3358	3701
2350	2505	2761	3175	3385	3731
2375	2532	2791	3200	3411	3760
2400	2558	2820			
2425	2585	2849	3225	3438	3789
2450	2612	2879	3250	3465	3819
2475	2638	2908	3275	3496	3848
2500	2665	2938	3300	3528	3878
2525	2692	2967	3325	3560	3907
2550	2718	2996	3350	3592	3936
2575	2745	3026	3375	3624	3966
2600	2772	3055	3400	3656	3995
2625	2798	3084	3425	3688	4024
2650	2825	3114	3450	3720	4054
2675	2852	3143	3475	3753	4083
2700	2878	3173	3500	3785	4113
2725	2905	3202	3525	3817	4142
2750	2932	3231	3550	3850	4171
2775	2958	3261	3575	3882	4201
2800	2985	3290	3600	3915	4230
2825	3012	3319	3625	3948	4259
2850	3038	3349	3650	3981	4289
2875	3065	3378	3675	4014	4318
2900	3091	3408	3700	4047	4348
2925	3118	3437	3725	4080	4377
2950	3145	3466	3750	4113	4406
2975	3171	3496	3775	4146	4436
3000	3198	3525	3800	4179	4465
3025	3225	3554	3825	4213	4494
3050	3251	3584	3850	4246	4524
3075	3278	3613	3875	4280	4553
3100	3305	3643	3900	4313	4583

Fig. 4-35. Moment Limits vs Weight

SAMPLE PROBLEM USING TABLE METHOD

The table method for solving weight and balance problems involves the use of a loading form as shown in figure 4-36 and the following procedure. (The numbers below match the item numbers on the loading form.)

NOTE: *All moments are divided by 100 to simplify computations.*

---

1. Record the basic empty weight and moment obtained from the weight and balance data form in the pilot's operating handbook.

2. Use the standard weight of 170 pounds for each of the two front seat occupants. As shown in figure 4-34, item 4, the moment/100 for one 170-pound front seat occupant in the aft position is 190. Double this value to get the total moment/100 of 380.

3. For the two 170-pound occupants of the optional third and fourth

seats, use the same procedure. Total moment/100 in this case is 245 × 2, or 490. (See Fig. 4-34, item 5.)

4. As shown in figure 4-34, item 6, the moment/100 for 90 pounds of baggage is 150.

5. Fuel weight is obtained by multiplying the fuel load of 100 gallons by 6, then the fuel moment is determined. (See Fig. 4-34, item 7.)

6. The maximum ramp weight or the maximum weight approved for ground maneuvers is 3,916 pounds. This aircraft is loaded to that maximum weight.

7. The fuel used during start, taxi, and takeoff for this aircraft is estimated to be 16 pounds at an average moment/100 of 19. These values must be subtracted from the ramp weight and moment to obtain the takeoff weight and moment.

8. Since the maximum takeoff weight of this aircraft is 3,900 pounds, it is loaded to the maximum.

ITEM	WEIGHT	MOM/100
1. BASIC EMPTY CONDITION	2546	2775
2. FRONT SEAT OCCUPANTS	340	380
3. 3rd & 4th SEAT OCCUPANTS OR BENCH SEAT OCCUPANTS	340	490
4. AFT BAGGAGE	90	150
5. FUEL LOADING (100 gal.)	600	702
6. SUB TOTAL RAMP CONDITION (3916 LBS. MAX.)	3916	4497
7. *LESS FUEL FOR START, TAXI, AND TAKEOFF	−16	−19
8. TOTAL TAKE-OFF CONDITION	3900	4478

*Fuel for start, taxi, and takeoff is normally 16 lbs. at an average mom/100 of 19.

Fig. 4-36. Weight and Balance Loading Form

To insure that the center of gravity is within approved limits, use a moment limits vs. weight table, as shown in figure 4-37. At a weight of 3,900 pounds, the total moment/100 of 4,478 falls within the forward and aft limits of 4,313 and 4,583. If the total moment/100 had been less than 4,313, items loaded forward would have to be reduced or shifted aft. If the total moment/100 had been greater than 4,583, items loaded aft would have to be reduced or shifted forward.

MOMENT LIMITS VS WEIGHT				
MOMENT/100		WEIGHT POUNDS	MOMENT/100	
FWD LIMIT	AFT LIMIT		FWD LIMIT	AFT LIMIT
3012	3319	3625	3948	4259
3038	3349	3650	3981	4289
3065	3378	3675	4014	4318
3091	3408	3700	4047	4348
3118	3437	3725	4080	4377
3145	3466	3750	4113	4406
3171	3496	3775	4146	4436
3198	3525	3800	4179	4465
3225	355	3825	4213	4494
3251		3850	4246	4524
3278		3875	4280	4553
3305	3643	3900	4313	4583

Fig. 4-37. Moment Limits for
Maximum Takeoff Weight

Any time an aircraft is loaded up to or near maximum takeoff weight, as the aircraft was in this problem, there are other questions to consider even though the weight and balance are within limits. For example, were the weights used estimates or actual? A 200-pound passenger would have caused the aircraft to be over the maximum takeoff weight. Is a safe takeoff possible at maximum weight considering runway length, field elevation, and atmospheric conditions? For the answer to this question, aircraft performance should be carefully checked according to the procedures described in Chapter 1, Section C.

chapter 5

INTRODUCTION

An understanding of *meteorology* is one of the most important areas of knowledge for the aviator. Throughout the history of aviation, adverse weather has hampered flight operations, resulted in schedule delays for airlines, and has been the cause of accidents for "un-weather-conscious" pilots. Much research has been devoted to the development of sophisticated instruments and radio gear in an attempt to conquer the limitations to flight imposed by weather. Today, modern aircraft are capable of flying in most kinds of meteorological conditions and can perform instrument landings in extremely marginal conditions of ceiling and visibility.

In spite of man's technological achievements, certain *severe weather conditions* occasionally occur, making flight impossible. The violence of thunderstorms, the blindness caused by fog, and the turbulence resulting from high velocity winds can outmatch the capabilities of even the most sophisticated aircraft.

The study of the earth's atmosphere, weather, and basic meteorology is not only an exciting and challenging endeavor, but a prerequisite for even the novice pilot.

SECTION A - WEATHER THEORY

BASIC ATMOSPHERIC CIRCULATION

The weather on this planet is mainly produced by two factors: the *sun* and the *ro-*

Fig. 5-1. Solar Reradiation

tation of the earth. The majority of atmospheric heating is the result of reradiation of the sun's rays from the surface of the earth. Approximately 85% of the heat absorbed by the atmosphere is caused by heating from the ground below, while about 15% is produced by the direct rays of the sun as they pass through the atmosphere on their path to the earth. (See Fig. 5-1.)

HEATING OF THE EARTH

Heating of the air surrounding the earth is not equal over the entire surface. Various types of surfaces over the face of the earth such as foliage, sand, mountains, and shadows tend to vary the amount of reradiation of the sun's heat energy. But the major reason for uneven heating is the difference in the *angle of incidence* of the sun's rays as they strike various parts of the globe. The angle of incidence is the angle between the sun's rays and the surface they are striking. During the beginning of spring and fall, the sun is centered directly over the equator, and the angle of incidence between the sun's rays and the surface of the earth at the equator is 90°. In other words, the rays are striking the surface directly at the equator. At this point, a square foot of sunrays centers its heat over one square foot of the earth's surface. The greatest concentration of heat and the largest possible amount of reradiation result from this 90° angle of incidence. (See Fig. 5-2.)

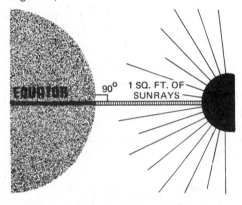

Fig. 5-2. Angle of Incidence at Equator

Due to the curvature of the earth, the angle of incidence of the sun's rays decreases toward both the North and South Poles. North and south of the equator, a square foot of sunrays is not concentrated over one square foot of the surface, but over a *larger area*. This lower concentration produces less reradiation of heat over a given surface area and less atmospheric heating results. At the North and South Poles, the angle of incidence is so small that very little heating of the atmosphere occurs, resulting in extremely cold air temperatures. Basically, then, overall air temperatures decrease moving south or north from the equator. (See Fig. 5-3.)

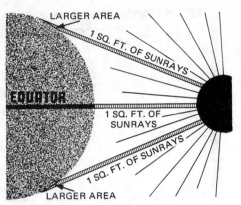

Fig. 5-3. Concentration Change of Solar Radiation

The unequal heating of the earth's atmosphere causes a *large air-cell circulation pattern*. The density of air determines whether the air will rise or descend. If air is more dense than the surrounding atmosphere, it will sink, while air that is less dense than its surroundings will begin to rise. Heated air at the equator becomes less dense and begins to rise. Conversely, cold air at the poles is very dense and sinks toward the surface of the earth as shown in figure 5-4.

The large cell circulation pattern around the earth can be likened to a pan of water over a burning flame. As the water directly over the flame at the bottom center of the pan is heated, it becomes less dense compared to the cooler water around the rim of the pan. The water over the flame rises to the top of the pan where it cools and flows outward toward the edge. As the water moves toward the edge, it cools further, becomes more dense, and begins to sink to the bottom. Because of the circulation pattern that is generated, this water works its way back toward the center to be heated again to continue the circulation. (See Fig. 5-4.)

THE ROTATING EARTH

If it were not for the rotation of the earth and other complicating factors, the same simple circulation pattern would take place over the globe. Air would move directly from the high density area (high pressure area) over the poles toward the

Fig. 5-4. Large Cell Circulation Pattern

low density area (low pressure area) at the equator to be reheated and circulated back toward the poles. In reality, however, a *three-cell circulation pattern* over each hemisphere develops.

As air rises over the equator, it begins to move northward and southward toward the poles. Due to the rotation of the earth, the air moving from the equator northward is deflected to the east in the Northern Hemisphere. At approximately 30° N. latitude, much of the air is moving east causing a pile-up of air which sinks and forms a relatively constant high pressure area at this latitude. The remainder of the air continues northward to the North Pole. The sinking air at 30° N. latitude reaches the surface and spreads outward, both north and south. The air that moves south at 30° N. latitude completes one cell of the circulation pattern (see Fig. 5-5, item 1). The air that moves north becomes part of another cell between 30° N. latitude and 60° N. latitude (see Fig. 5-5, item 2).

To complete the three-cell circulation pattern, the air descending from the North Pole southward collides with the air moving north from the 30° N. latitude high pressure area. As these two air masses meet and rise, a *semi-permanent low pressure area* is produced near 60° N. latitude. Therefore, a third circulation pattern between 60° N. latitude and the North Pole develops. (See Fig. 5-5, item 3.)

Due to the uneven heating of the earth's surface and the resultant three-cell circulation pattern of the air, four relatively permanent pressure systems exist — a low pressure area over the equator, a high pressure system at 30° N. latitude, a low at 60° N. latitude, and a high pressure area at the North Pole. If it were not for the rotation of the earth, air would constantly move directly from high pressure areas to low pressure areas. However, due to *Coriolis effect*, a circular flow around pressure centers develops.

CORIOLIS EFFECT

The natural rotation of the earth causes an apparent force to be exerted on the atmosphere which deflects the air toward the right in the Northern Hemisphere, and toward the left in the Southern Hemisphere. In fact, any free-moving body has an apparent deflection as it moves above the rotating earth. When viewed from some point out in space, a free-moving body would appear to follow a straight line. However, to a viewer on the earth, the path of a free body would appear to curve. Therefore, this "force" is only apparent, but the deflection certainly is in effect when using the earth as a reference point.

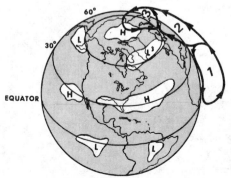

Fig. 5-5. Three-Cell Circulation Pattern

Due to Coriolis effect, the air moving around the high pressure system at the North Pole circulates clockwise, and due to pressure differential moves outward from the center of the high. This produces the prevailing wind system known as the *polar easterlies*. (It is important to remember that wind directions are labeled according to the direction *from* which they are blowing.) At 60° N. latitude, the circulation about the semi-permanent low is counterclockwise and inward toward the center of the low. This produces the *northeast tradewinds*. At 30° N. latitude, air circulates clockwise around the high and produces the *prevailing westerlies*. (See Fig. 5-6.)

Fig. 5-6. Prevailing Wind Systems

AIR MASSES

An air mass is an extensive body of air whose temperature and moisture characteristics are approximately the same at a given altitude throughout the body of air. Air masses are formed over large areas of water or land. An air mass may range in size from hundreds to thousands of square miles in area, with a depth of approximately three to eight miles. (See Fig. 5-7.)

If a body of air having uniform properties of temperature and moisture comes to rest or moves very slowly over a large area, it begins to take on the corresponding characteristics of the surface. In general, the weather conditions prevailing at a certain location at a particular time are dependent upon the characteristics of the prevailing air mass, or the *interaction* between two air masses. The interaction of two air masses is known as a *front* and will be discussed later in this chapter.

Except where fronts exist, the weather conditions on the surface covered by an air mass will be similar throughout the entire area. There will be, however, variations produced by local geographic features such as large bodies of water, mountains, or valleys.

AIR MASS SOURCE REGIONS

A source region is the locale where an air mass acquires its identifying properties of temperature and moisture. The most common air mass source regions are large snow or ice covered polar regions, tropical oceans, and large desert areas. (See Fig. 5-8.) The mid latitudes, which have

Fig. 5-7. Air Mass

irregular surface features, are less common source regions since air has little opportunity to stagnate in the mid latitudes because weather systems are constantly on the move in these areas.

Air masses formed in the area of 60° north latitude and northward will be cold and are called *polar* air masses. Also, air masses originating over land will be relatively dry and are termed *continental*. For example, one source of *continental polar* air masses is the area between the Hudson Bay and the Rocky Mountains. (See Fig. 5-8.)

If an air mass is formed over water it will acquire moisture and be known as *maritime*. As illustrated in figure 5-8, one source region for *maritime polar* air masses is over the waters south of the Aleutian Islands. *Tropical* air masses are formed over land and water in the region from about 20° to 50° north latitude and naturally these air masses

are quite warm. (See Fig. 5-8.) Air masses may be further designated by source, such as Atlantic, Pacific, or Gulf.

AIR MASS MODIFICATION

Air masses that form over a given source region vary in their properties of temperature and moisture from season to season, as the characteristics of the source region vary.

The extent of air mass modification is dependent upon the length of time a mass remains over a source region and the difference between the original temperature of the air and that of the underlying surface.

Once an air mass has formed in a source region it may move out from this source region on a trajectory of course across the country and carry with it the temperature and moisture characteristics of its *origin*. Much of this movement is due to the basic atmospheric circulation pattern

Fig. 5-8. Air Mass, Trajectory, and Source Regions

Fig. 5-9. Cumulus Clouds

Fig. 5-10. Stratus Clouds

discussed previously. The air mass is then further modified by the *surface over which it moves*, although its original characteristics tend to persist.

As air masses build up and start to move they are *also* termed *cold* or *warm*, depending on whether they are warmer or colder than the *surface over which they move*. The cold type air mass will be warmed from below and convection currents will form. Some typical characteristics of the cold type air mass are: (1) instability [tendency to overturn as convection currents form within] ; (2) turbulent or rough air up to about 10,000 feet; (3) good visibility, except in showers and duststorms; (4) cumiliform clouds; and (5) precipitation in the form of showers, thunderstorms, hail, sleet, and snow flurries, when enough moisture is available within the air mass.

The warm type of air mass, cooled from below by the surface over which it travels, exhibits different characteristics. This type of air mass tends to maintain its original properties and is modified only in the lower few thousand feet as it moves. Some typical characteristics are: (1) stability [resists vertical movement] ; (2) generally smooth air; (3) poor visibility as smoke and dust are held in the lower few thousand feet; (4) stratiform clouds and fog; and (5) drizzle.

CLOUD FORMATION AND TYPES

To an experienced pilot, clouds are *signposts* that indicate the forces at work in the atmosphere. Their location and appearance (size, shape, and color) can show a weather-wise aviator where turbulence might be found, whether a frontal system is approaching, or where hail might be encountered. It is often possible through experience to read the existing weather situation and how it may change by watching the clouds.

CLASSIFICATIONS OF CLOUDS

One way of classifying clouds is according to how they are formed. Two basic types of clouds are *cumulus* and *stratus*.

Cumulus clouds are formed by rising air currents and are prevalent in unstable air that favors vertical development. The currents of air create cumuliform clouds and give them a piled-up or bunched appearance. (See Fig. 5-9.)

Stratus clouds are formed when a layer of moist air is cooled below its saturation point. Stratiform clouds lie mostly in horizontal layers or sheets, resisting vertical development. The word stratus is derived from a form of the Latin word for layer. (See Fig. 5-10.)

The prefixes and suffixes which are combined to make up the names of clouds tell something about the character of a cloud. Clouds which produce rain or snow contain the term *nimbus*. Broken or fragmented clouds are prefixed by *fracto*. *Lenticular* clouds are formed over mountains during high wind conditions and have a lens-shaped appearance.

Fig. 5-11. Cirrus Clouds

Fig. 5-12. Altostratus Clouds

Clouds are also named according to their characteristic elevation. *Cirrus* clouds are the thin, wispy, high clouds normally found above 25,000 feet. Clouds prefixed *alto* are the middle clouds with bases between 6,500 and 23,000 feet. The low stratus and cumulus clouds, normally found below 6,500 feet, are not prefixed.

HIGH CLOUDS

The high clouds are composed almost entirely of ice crystals due to the extremely cold temperatures at higher altitudes. These clouds include *cirrus, cirrocumulus,* and *cirrostratus.* (See Fig. 5-11.) The bases of the high clouds average about 25,000 feet, but may go as low as 16,500 feet in the polar latitudes and as high as 45,000 feet in the equatorial regions.

Because they are composed of ice crystals, cirrus clouds do not present an icing hazard to aircraft. Cirrostratus clouds are generally so thin that the outline of the sun or moon may be seen through them, producing a halo effect.

MIDDLE CLOUDS

The middle cloud group consists of *altocumulus, altostratus,* and *nimbostratus.* Instead of being made of ice crystals, these clouds are made of very small water droplets. Their bases generally range from 6,500 to 23,000 feet.

Altocumulus clouds can form in several different ways and take on various appearances. Generally, however, they

Fig. 5-13. Stratus Clouds

are patchy layers of puffy, roll-like clouds of a whitish or grayish color. Often they resemble cirrocumulus, but the puffs or rolls are much larger. Precipitation from this type of cloud is rare.

Altostratus clouds are stratus clouds that also form in the middle altitudes. (See Fig. 5-12.) They are generally associated with unfavorable flying weather and precipitation.

Nimbostratus clouds are the true rain or snow clouds. They appear heavily laden with moisture, producing a darker appearance than ordinary stratus clouds. Precipitation usually reaches the ground in the form of continuous rain, snow, or ice pellets.

LOW CLOUDS

The low cloud group consists of *stratus, stratocumulus,* and *fair weather cumulus* clouds. Bases may range from near the surface to about 6,500 feet. Stratus, or low clouds, are of the greatest importance to the aviator since they create low ceilings and visibility restrictions near the surface of the earth. The height of these cloud bases has been known to change rapidly. If any of the low clouds form next to the ground, they are reclassified as *fog*.

The stratus cloud is quite uniform and resembles fog. (See Fig. 5-13.) It has a fairly uniform base and a dull gray appearance. Stratus clouds make the sky appear heavy and will occasionally produce fine drizzle or very light snow with fog. Because there is little or no vertical movement in the stratus clouds, however, they usually do not produce precipitation in the form of heavy rain or snow.

Stratocumulus clouds are irregular masses of clouds spread out in a rolling or puffy layer. These do not produce rain by themselves, but sometimes change to nimbostratus types which do. (See Fig. 5-14.) They are very whitish in color, normally with darker spots, and are usually composed of rounded masses which fuse together and become indistinct when rain appears.

Fair weather cumulus clouds are often formed over land by the rising air currents and, therefore, disappear at night when the lifting action recedes. These are referred to as fair-weather cumulus until they begin to pile up to form cumulonimbus.

CLOUDS WITH VERTICAL DEVELOPMENT

Towering cumulus and cumulonimbus clouds are characterized by vertical development. Cloud bases generally range between 1,000 and 10,000 feet; however, the tops of cumulonimbus clouds may rise to an elevation of 75,000 feet. Their vertical development is caused by some type of lifting action such as convective currents found on hot summer afternoons, or when air is forced to rise up the slope of a mountain, or possibly the lifting action that may be present in a frontal system. The towering cumulus cloud has a puffy and cauliflower-shaped appearance.

Cumulonimbus clouds form the familiar *thunderhead* and produce thunderstorm activity. (See Fig. 5-15.) These clouds are characterized by violent updrafts which carry the tops of the clouds to extreme elevations. Tornadoes, hail, and severe rainstorms are all products of this type of cloud. At the top of the cloud, a flat *anvil-like* form caused by the winds aloft appears as the thunderhead begins to dissipate.

Usually, isolated cumulonimbus clouds present no flight problem since they can be circumnavigated without difficulty. However, should these clouds develop in groups or lines known as *squall lines*, they may be impossible to fly around. Sometimes cumulonimbus clouds are em-

Fig. 5-14. Stratocumulus Clouds

Fig. 5-15. Cumulonimbus Clouds

bedded and hidden in stratiform clouds, resulting in very hazardous conditions for flight in instrument conditions.

ELEMENTS OF WEATHER

MOISTURE

The moisture content of the atmosphere is an important weather determinant. Water enters the atmosphere in a gaseous state called *water vapor*. This vapor is produced from evaporation of water surfaces, mainly the oceans. In addition, some water vapor is derived from plants and from the moist earth. The amount of water vapor present in the atmosphere may vary from a trace to approximately five percent by volume.

A measure of the amount of water vapor present in the atmosphere is called *relative humidity*. The amount of water vapor that an air mass is capable of holding is dependent upon temperature. An air mass with a high temperature has a greater ability to contain water vapor than does an air mass of lower temperature.

An air mass with a relative humidity of 90% means the air is 90% *saturated*, or is holding 90% of the water vapor it is capable of holding. If more water vapor was added to the air or if the temperature was reduced, the relative humidity would increase until condensation would take place and visible moisture would appear. The *dewpoint* is the temperature to which the air mass must be cooled in order for condensation to take place. The dewpoint is dependent upon the amount of water vapor present in the atmosphere.

TEMPERATURE

The temperature of the air is primarily regulated by the surface of the earth. Only 15% of the incoming solar radiation (sun's heat) is absorbed by the atmosphere. Eighty-five percent of the atmospheric heating is caused by heating from the earth's surface below. This accounts for the fact that the temperature of still air decreases approximately 3.5° Fahrenheit or 2° Celsius for each 1,000 foot rise in elevation. This is known as the average or *standard lapse rate*.

STABILITY

Stability refers to the ability of an air mass to *resist vertical development*. A stable air mass will resist vertical lifting; however, an unstable air mass will tend to promote vertical development. When air is forced to rise due to *orographic* (air forced to rise over a land surface such as mountains), or *convectional* (air rising due to heating from below) lifting, it may become warmer than the surrounding air. If this should occur, the rising air has reached the level of free convection and will become unstable and continue to rise even though the initial lifting force is no longer present. This situation will produce unstable air with resultant cumulus-type clouds if moisture is present.

TEMPERATURE INVERSIONS

In cases where the temperature increases with an *increase* in altitude, an inversion is present. (See Fig. 5-16.) Since air is a poor conductor of heat, an *inversion* may persist for days or possibly even weeks before the air is cooled above. This,

Fig. 5-16. Temperature Inversion

of course, is assuming no horizontal movement of the air mass. An inversion may cause smog or fog to lie in an area for days.

Inversions may occur at the surface or above the surface when warm air overlies a colder layer of air. Inversions result in an extremely stable condition since the warmer air on top will tend to rise and the colder air on the bottom will tend to descend, thus allowing very little mixing of air in the vicinity of the inversion layer.

Inversions are often produced on cold, clear nights over snow-covered ground. Because the ground is much colder than the air, the air just above the surface becomes cooler than the air at altitude.

PRESSURES AND WINDS

Wind is simply air in motion caused by differences in pressure from one place to another. In the United States, two types of pressure systems are present, both of which are caused by the *unequal* heating of the earth's surface, including the ocean. These are the semi-permanent high and low systems and the variable day-to-day high and low pressure systems.

Atmospheric pressure is the force exerted by the weight of the atmosphere and is due to the gravitational force of the earth. The weight of the atmosphere over a given point is continually fluctuating. These fluctuations result from air mass motion and changes in the temperature and moisture content of the air. A column of air one square inch across at sea level weighs approximately 14.7 pounds.

A device used to measure atmospheric pressure is a *barometer*, which means weight meter.

The simplest kind of barometer — the mercury type — consists of a dish filled with mercury into which is placed the open end of a glass tube with the air removed. (See Fig. 5-17.) The weight of the

Fig. 5-17. Simple Barometer

atmosphere presses down on the mercury in the dish and supports the column of mercury inside the tube. At sea level, the pressure of the atmosphere on a standard day will cause the mercury in the column to rise to 29.92 inches. This value is accepted as the standard value of atmospheric pressure at sea level. As altitude increases, the weight of the atmosphere decreases. The height of the mercury column will decrease by nearly one inch for each 1,000 foot ascent. This is known as the *pressure lapse rate.*

In scientific work, a convenient unit of measurement of atmospheric pressure is the *millibar.* This unit is used internationally for pressure measurement. The standard atmospheric pressure at sea level is 1013.2 millibars (mb), corresponding to 29.92 inches of mercury or 14.7 pounds per square inch. These pressures are all equal, but are expressed in different units. One inch of mercury is equivalent to approximately 34 millibars. Weather charts normally show barometric pressure in millibars, while teletype weather reports usually express barometric pressure in millibars *and* inches of mercury.

STATION PRESSURE

Station pressure is the actual atmospheric pressure taken at a given place. The pressure observed depends upon the height of the station above sea level, the effect of gravity, and the amount of air above the station. Since air becomes thin-

Pressure at 5,000 Feet
= 24.92 In. Hg.

When Reduced to
Sea Level, Pressure is
24.92 + 5.00 = 29.92 In. Hg.

*Fig. 5-18. Altimeter Setting
Converted to Sea Level*

ner with altitude, the pressure at higher elevations will be less than at lower elevations if standard atmospheric conditions are present at both places.

Station pressure is of little value to the meteorologist, however, since the pressure at higher elevations is normally less than at lower elevations even if standard atmospheric conditions persist at both places. For instance, if the barometric pressure was 29.92 inches of mercury at sea level, the pressure at 5,000 feet would be approximately five inches less, or 24.92 if standard atmospheric conditions existed at both elevations. (See Fig. 5-18.)

If all weather observation stations were located at sea level, then the individual barometric readings would give a correct picture of the amount of pressure exerted on a common level. However, to be meaningful, atmospheric pressure measurements are converted to a standard reference, or the *mean sea level altitude.* This eliminates differences in pressure caused by differences in station elevation.

TYPES OF PRESSURE SYSTEMS

The amount of atmospheric pressure at any given time varies for three main reasons. The first is the passage of a well-developed pressure system. In this situation, it is not uncommon to find a change of atmospheric pressure of one inch of mercury in a day's time. The

second is an actual change in the intensity of the pressure system. An example would be the deepening of a low pressure area. And last, a daily variation can occur where the pressure is lowest during the late evening and early morning hours, and highest from about mid-morning to around 10 p.m. In the United States, a daily variation may amount to as much as 0.04 of an inch of mercury. It is important to realize that the daily variation is normal and does not necessarily indicate the approach of a storm or a change in the pressure system.

Isobars, or lines connecting points of equal pressure, are drawn on weather maps. "Iso" means equal and "bar" means barometric pressure. These lines of equal pressure are drawn at selected intervals, usually four millibars apart, and indicate the configuration of the pressure system over a given area. The isobar pattern is never the same on any two weather maps; however, their patterns are similar and have definite meanings for the aviator. The five types of pressure systems are defined as follows: (See Fig. 5-19.)

1. LOW — a center of low pressure surrounded on all sides by higher pressure. An area of low pressure is like a depression or a valley in the atmosphere.

2. HIGH — a center of high pressure surrounded on all sides by lower pressure. It can be visualized as a mountain surrounded by valleys or areas of low pressure on all sides.

3. TROUGH — an elongated area of low atmospheric pressure, usually extending from the center of a low pressure system.

4. RIDGE — an elongated area of relatively high pressure, extending from the center of a high-pressure system.

5. COL — a neutral area that exists between two high-pressure areas or low-pressure areas.

Fig. 5-19. Pressure Systems

PRESSURE SYSTEM CHARACTERISTICS

Pilots should know the general characteristics associated with different pressure systems in the Northern Hemisphere. In the Northern Hemisphere, the wind flow is counterclockwise around the low pressure system. In addition, unfavorable flying conditions may be present in the form of low clouds, poor visibility, rain or snow, fog, strong gusty winds, and turbulence.

Conversely, the winds around a high-pressure system in the Northern Hemisphere flow clockwise. Flying conditions are generally much more favorable than in low-pressure areas. This is because there are normally fewer clouds, better visibility, and only calm or light winds, and the areas of turbulence are much less severe.

Where a trough is present, the weather is frequently very violent; whereas along a high-pressure ridge, favorable flying weather will generally prevail.

PRESSURE GRADIENT

If it were not for the earth's rotation, air from high-pressure areas would tend to flow directly toward areas of low pressure. The speed at which this wind would blow would be dependent upon the steepness of the *pressure gradient*, or the amount of change of pressure over a given distance. (See Fig. 5-20.)

The spacing of isobars on a surface weather map gives a good impression of the steepness of the pressure gradient. Where the isobars are spread widely apart, the pressure gradient is very *shallow;* however, where isobars are close together, the pressure gradient is very *steep.* The steepness of the pressure gradient gives an indication of wind velocity. A steep pressure gradient will normally produce strong wind, and a shallow pressure gradient will result in a light wind.

In general, upper winds tend to flow parallel to the isobars. This is due to the resultant effects of two opposing forces — centrifugal force and pressure gradient. As air spins counterclockwise around a low, centrifugal force is produced outward from the center of the low. The pressure gradient, on the other hand, directly opposes centrifugal force and the resulting winds flow *parallel* to the isobars. (See Fig. 5-21.)

On weather maps, the upper wind direction can be determined by noting the pattern of the isobars surrounding the high- and low-pressure areas. Remember, winds flow *parallel* to the isobars and *clockwise* around a high and *counterclockwise* around a low-pressure area.

FRICTION EFFECT

Friction between the air masses and the surface of the earth retards the movement of the air. This causes the low-level winds to blow at an angle across the isobars from a high-pressure area to a low-pressure area instead of parallel to the isobars as in the upper atmosphere. The amount which the wind veers due to the friction effect varies with the type of ground surface and velocity of the wind.

Over water, where the friction is slight, the wind will veer only about ten degrees. Over land, however, depending on the roughness of the terrain, the amount of veer may be as much as 30 to 50 degrees from parallel to the isobars. Naturally, the friction effect is greatest near the surface of the earth, but exists up to 1,500 to 2,500 feet above the ground. Above this level, the friction effect decreases

Fig. 5-20. Pressure Gradient

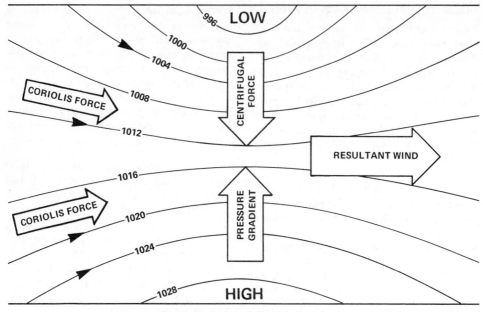

Fig. 5-21. Counterbalancing Forces

very rapidly, and, for all practical purposes, can be considered negligible. Therefore, air about 2,500 feet or more above the surface of the earth will usually tend to flow parallel to the isobars.

LOCAL WIND SYSTEMS

Local wind systems are created by the immediate geographic features in a given area, such as mountains, valleys, or large bodies of water. These systems account for significant weather changes in some localities.

LAND AND SEA BREEZES

Because land and water surfaces absorb heat at different rates, *convection* over the two kinds of surfaces varies and causes local winds. During the daytime, the temperature of the land rises faster than the bordering water and cools faster during the night. This difference between the temperature of the land and of the water produces a corresponding difference in the local pressure gradient. As the earth is heated during the day and convection begins to take place, the pressure over the land becomes lower than over the colder water.

This sets up an air circulation pattern during the day as shown on the left side of figure 5-22. Air moves from the high-pressure area over the cooler sea toward the low-pressure area over the warmer land surface. This creates the characteristic sea breeze that is normally encountered during the daytime hours on the coast. As this air rises over the warmer land surface, it cools and descends again over the water to continue the circulation.

The land breeze, as shown on the right half of figure 5-22, is produced at night from a circulation pattern opposite the circulation pattern which occurs during the day. During the evening hours, the land cools faster than the sea creating a high pressure over the land surface and a lower pressure area over the ocean. Air moving from the "land high" to the "sea low" creates a breeze outward from the land toward the ocean. This is known as a land breeze.

EFFECTS OF ELEMENTS OF WEATHER

After gaining an understanding of the elements producing the earth's weather, the pilot is concerned with the effects these

Fig. 5-22. Land and Sea Breezes

elements have on the atmosphere in which he must fly. Pilots are mainly concerned with two major factors: visibility and ceiling. A ceiling is the height above the earth's surface of the *lowest* layer of clouds or obscuring phenomena that cover more than one-half of the sky. One of the major visibility restrictions that has been a hazard for pilots throughout the history of aviation is *fog*.

FOG

Fog is basically a cloud which is very near or touching the earth's surface. It consists of small water droplets or ice crystals suspended in the atmosphere. Although they may each be too small to see with the naked eye, they are so numerous that visibility is reduced. The existence of fog is a serious problem in terminal areas because of the restricted visibility during the takeoff or landing phase of flight. A knowledge of the different types of fog, how they are formed, when they are most likely to occur, and the dissipation properties is extremely important in the planning of a safe flight.

For fog to form, several conditions must be present. First, a relatively high humidity must exist for condensation to occur. Therefore, it is necessary for a small *temperature/dewpoint spread* to be present. Any time the temperature and dewpoint are within 5° Celsius or less of each other, pilots should expect the possibility of fog. Fog is most frequently encountered, however, when the spread is less than 2°C. The temperature dewpoint spread can be ascertained from surface aviation weather reports which are described later in this chapter.

The high relative humidity necessary for fog formation can occur in two distinct ways: (1) when the air is cooled to its dewpoint; (2) when the moisture is added to the air near the surface.

Generally, a light surface wind is also necessary. Wind provides a mixing action which spreads and increases the thickness of the fog. If no wind is present, the fog will most likely be shallow and close to the ground. Strong surface winds, however, are not conducive to fog formation, since they tend to break up the fog layer.

The third necessary ingredient for the formation of fog is an abundance of *condensation nuclei* such as particles of salt or smoke which are suspended in the atmosphere. These particles provide the nuclei around which moisture can condense.

The different types of fog are named according to the processes by which they are formed.

Radiation fog forms as the earth rapidly loses its heat on clear nights. If the sky is overcast, radiation escaping into the

Fig. 5-23. Radiation Fog

Fig. 5-24. Advection Fog

atmosphere is limited and most of it is reflected back to the earth. When the earth cools on a clear night, however, the temperature near the surface may drop more than 20° Fahrenheit. Although the dewpoint remains constant during the night, the temperature/dewpoint spread decreases as the air is cooled by direct contact with the earth's surface and radiation fog develops.

Radiation fog is sometimes referred to as *ground fog*. Often this fog formation occurs near sunrise when the temperature is at its lowest reading. Radiation fog normally lifts and dissipates as the temperature begins to rise within a few hours after sunrise. (See Fig. 5-23.)

Advection fog is formed when warm, moist air flows over a cold surface. This type of fog is most often found along coastal regions where the temperature of the land and the temperature of the water differ widely. As warm, moist air flows inward over the continent, it is cooled by direct contact with the cold ground. If the temperature of the air reaches the dewpoint temperature, fog forms.

Advection fog can be very persistent during both day and night. Like radiation fog, it deepens as the wind speed is increased up to about 15 knots. If the velocity of the wind is about 15 knots or greater, however, advection fog will usually be lifted to form a layer of low stratus clouds. If advection fog forms

over water and then blows ashore, it is sometimes referred to as *sea fog*. (See Fig. 5-24.)

Upslope fog occurs when moist air flows uphill resulting in a temperature drop through adiabatic cooling or cooling by expansion. In order for upslope fog to form, the pressure gradient must be great to maintain an uphill airflow. This upslope wind is not only necessary for the formation of upslope fog, but also for its continued existence. (See Fig. 5-25.)

Steam fog occurs when cold air moves over water that is much warmer than air. This causes intense evaporation of the moisture into the cold air until it becomes saturated and the excess water vapor condenses as fog. Because steam fog rises upward from the water and looks much like rising smoke, it is sometimes called *sea smoke*.

Steam fog is commonly found over rivers and lakes during the fall and over the ocean during the winter when the wind is blowing from offshore. Since its formation is brought about by the movement of a cold air mass over a warm surface, the air is unstable. Turbulence and icing conditions are frequently encountered in this type of fog.

Rain-induced fog results from the addition of moisture to the air or by the evaporation of cold rain falling from above. This type of fog usually becomes more

Fig. 5-25. Upslope Fog

Fig. 5-26. Rain-Induced Fog

dense as night approaches and the air near the ground cools. (See Fig. 5-26.)

HAZE AND SMOKE

Haze consists of very fine dust or salt particles suspended in the atmosphere. Stable air is necessary in order for haze to become a very serious restriction to visibility since the particles can only be concentrated in stable air. Haze is often a characteristic of an inversion condition. Although it is usually only found at low altitudes, the top of a haze layer can go as high as 15,000 feet above the surface.

Flight visibility on hazy days depends upon several things: the height of the haze layer, its intensity, the position of the sun, and the direction in which the pilot is looking. Visibility is often much less when the sun is low and unobscured by clouds above the haze.

Smoke is usually found near large industrial areas and restricts the forward visibility in much the same way as haze. When smoke is produced by forest fires, it is normally in concentrated layers with generally good visibility above and below these layers.

Smog is technically a mixture of smoke and fog and can produce very poor visibility. Today, however, the term "smog" has been applied to any heavy concentration of atmospheric pollution. Normally present in large industrial areas, flight within a smog area is similar to that in haze or smoke. The amount of visibility depends upon its density and whether an individual is facing toward or away from the sun. When the top layer of smog is well defined, visibility above is usually very good.

VISIBILITY RESTRICTIONS DUE TO WIND

Wind, blowing snow, dust, or sand can produce very low visibility. Blowing snow makes it difficult for the pilot to distinguish objects and sometimes produces optical illusions. Blowing dust occurs in dry areas where the air is unstable and wind speed is high. An optical illusion can result when the pilot tries to top a layer of blowing dust. The pilot may sense that climbing a few hundred feet more will carry him to the top of the dust layer; however, as the climb is continued, he may find that it will be necessary to climb several thousand feet before actually topping the layer.

OBSCURED SKY CONDITIONS

The word *obscured* as used in aviation meteorology means that the sky or clouds are partially or totally hidden from an observer on the ground. An obscuration may extend upward from the surface of the earth and is usually caused by various forms of visibility restrictions such as drizzle, snow, smog, fog, etc. The phrase *total obscuration* means the sky is

Fig. 5-27. Obscured Sky

totally covered to the observer on the ground.

The reported ceiling in this situation is the vertical visibility looking up from the ground. If an observer can see part of the sky or clouds through the obscuring phenomenon, the sky condition is reported as a *partial obscuration*. In this case, the height of clouds above is reported rather than the vertical visibility through the obscuring phenomena. (See Fig. 5-27.)

WEATHER NEAR LARGE BODIES OF WATER

Large bodies of water sometimes have pronounced effects on local weather conditions. For example, during the winter season, the Great Lakes are warmer than the surrounding land areas and the cold air masses that move southward from Canada. Heat and moisture are added to these cold air masses as they pass over the lakes. The resulting convection causes cumulus-type clouds and rain or snow showers and squalls. The areas on the downwind side of large bodies of water are usually affected by this type of weather.

FRONTS

Air masses which have different properties of temperature and/or moisture content do not mix to any appreciable degree. When different air masses collide they form a *front*. A front or frontal zone may be hundreds of miles long and many miles wide.

If a cold air mass is advancing toward a warm air mass, the cold, heavy air attempts to push under and lift up the warm, relatively lighter air. This is known as a *cold front*. Conversely, a warm air mass advancing toward cold, retreating air pushes up over the cold air, thus creating a *warm front*. If the boundary between the two air masses does not move, then a *stationary front* has developed.

In the case of warm and cold fronts, a clash between the two air masses may exist, breeding unsettled and stormy weather. The different types of air masses which may clash were discussed in a previous paragraph. (See Fig. 5-28.)

Fig. 5-28. Front

Fronts are of great importance to pilots since many weather hazards may be present. Usually frontal weather produces clouds and precipitation and in some cases helps to breed thunderstorms.

DISCONTINUITIES ACROSS FRONTS

Fronts are located and classified by the difference in properties between the air masses creating the front. These factors include temperature, moisture, pressure, wind, and type of clouds present. When a front passes, a meteorological change is experienced from the properties of one mass to the properties of another air mass.

This can be very rapid and may occur in a distance of less than a mile. If the change is gradual, however, the transition zone or area of discontinuity may be over 200 miles wide.

The most easily recognized discontinuity across a frontal zone is *temperature*. On the surface of the earth, a notable change in temperature occurs with the passage of a front. With a rapidly-moving front, the rate of temperature change is usually quite rapid. In the case of a slow-moving front, the temperature change is gradual.

Pressure changes will also occur with the passage of a front. Because a front is normally located along a low-pressure trough, the pressure on each side of the front will be higher. When a front is approaching, the pressure will usually be decreasing and, at the point of frontal passage, the pressure will be at its lowest reading. As the front passes, the pressure will begin to rise and the direction of the wind will change. In the Northern Hemisphere, the wind shift is toward the right, or in a clockwise direction as the front passes.

FACTORS WHICH INFLUENCE FRONTAL WEATHER

The factors which influence frontal weather are dependent upon moisture availability, the stability of the air which is being lifted, the frontal slope, the speed of the front, and the amount of temperature and moisture difference between the two air masses.

It should be understood that not all frontal weather is severe or contains hazardous flying conditions. Fronts may be invisible with little or no clouds or precipitation present. They can be extremely hazardous to aviation activities, however, when thunderstorms, low clouds, and poor visibility exist. Where there is sufficient moisture available, the front will have an abundance of clouds and precipitation resulting in poor visibility.

The stability of the air being lifted by the frontal system will determine the type of clouds which will form, either stratiform or cumuliform type. With stratiform clouds, there is little or no turbulence and if precipitation is present, it is steady. Cumuliform clouds possess the shower type of precipitation and are an indication that turbulence may be present.

The slope of the front determines the extent of clouds and precipitation areas. In a shallow frontal surface, there will be large areas of cloudiness and precipitation. With a steep frontal surface moving rapidly, however, there will be narrow bands of cloudiness and showery precipitation. Air masses which are vastly different in their properties will have a steep frontal slope, as illustrated in figure 5-29.

COLD FRONTS

A cold front is a wedge of advancing dense, cold air replacing warm air at the surface. It is called a cold front because the cold air is forcing its way under the warm air. The cold air is capable of doing this because it is more dense. (See Fig. 5-29.) In the Northern Hemisphere, intense cold fronts are normally oriented in a line from the northeast to the southwest and their movement is toward the east or southeast.

Fig. 5-29. Cold Front Profile

Fig. 5-30. Squall Line

Cold fronts are classified as either *fast moving* or *slow moving*. Fast-moving cold fronts may contain winds as high as 60 m.p.h. and can move across the surface at speeds above 30 m.p.h. Generally, their speed is faster in the winter than in the summer, causing the slope to steepen resulting in a narrow band of weather. A thunderstorm may develop ahead of a fast-moving cold front. A line of thunderstorms or a squall line will have cloud tops which may average 40,000 feet or higher. Some of these cloud tops have been observed as high as 75,000 feet.

A squall line may develop between 50 and 300 miles ahead of the front and will lie roughly parallel to the front itself. (See Fig. 5-30.) With a fast-moving cold front, the weather behind will clear rapidly because the air is so much colder than the surface over which it is lying. Gusty and turbulent winds will be present upon passage of a fast-moving cold front.

With a slow-moving cold front, the frontal slope is less steep and the warm air is not lifted as quickly or violently as with the fast-moving cold front. This results in a broad cloud cover extending well over the front. If the warm air is stable as it is being lifted, stratiform clouds will develop. If, however, the warm air is moist and unstable, cumulus-type clouds will normally be present.

WARM FRONTS

A warm front is created when a warm air mass is overtaking and replacing a cold air mass. The leading edge of the advancing warm air is called the warm front. The speed of a warm front is approximately half that of a cold front or about 15 m.p.h., or even slower. The less dense, warm air gradually moves up the slope and does not produce the typical bulge of cold air which is associated with a cold front. This occurs because ground friction drags the bottom edge of the retreating cold air. This, in turn, creates a broad cloud system which typically extends from the surface portion of the front to about 500 to 700 miles in advance of the surface front.

The type of clouds that form are dependent upon the moisture content and the stability of the air as it rises up the slope. (See Fig. 5-31.) If the air is warm, moist, and unstable, however, cumuliform clouds will be mixed with stratiform clouds. When the air is stable, the sequence of clouds encountered with the approach of a warm front is as follows: cirrus, cirrostratus, altostratus, and nimbostratus. Precipitation will increase gradually with the approach of a warm front and will usually continue until after frontal passage.

If the air is unstable, the sequence of the clouds will be as follows: cirrus, cirrocumulus, altocumulus, and cumulonim-

Fig. 5-31. Warm Front Profile

Fig. 5-32. Occluded Front Profile and Plan View

bus. Cumulonimbus clouds are frequently embedded in the cloud masses as the warm front approaches. This is the major hazard for pilots flying in unstable warm front areas.

Showery precipitation will usually occur with the advance of an unstable warm front. Because of the large area of precipitation ahead of the warm front surface, low clouds in the form of stratus and fog will sometimes form creating areas of poor visibility and low ceilings over a great area. If the retreating cold air has temperatures below freezing, the precipitation may be in the form of freezing rain or sleet, another hazard to aircraft flying in the vicinity.

STATIONARY FRONTS

When a front has little or no movement, it is then referred to as a stationary front. This condition exists when opposing air masses are of *equal* pressure. In the case of a stationary front, the surface wind tends to blow parallel to the front instead of against or away from it. The weather phenomena associated with stationary fronts are comparable to those found in a warm front but are usually less intense in nature and cover a much wider area.

OCCLUDED FRONTS

Occluded fronts develop from a complex storm system which consists briefly of a warm front followed by a cold front

both radiating outward from the center of the same low-pressure system. (See Fig. 5-32.) Many times the rain remains in the center of a low-pressure system. They are of two types, cold and warm, designated by the front that develops at the surface.

The occlusion starts at the center of the low and progresses outward as the faster moving cold front overtakes the warm front. This produces the occluded front profile as shown in figure 5-32A. The weather associated with occluded fronts will usually consist of widespread rains and cloud cover with poor visibility and possible icing.

THUNDERSTORMS

Thunderstorms produce the most severe type of weather known to mankind. Tornadoes with winds reaching 350 miles per hour, hailstones the size of baseballs, and extreme turbulence are all conditions which can result from thunderstorm formation.

Thunderstorms are a hazard for all types of flight operation since tops of the cumulonimbus clouds may reach elevations in excess of 75,000 feet. Even jet airliners capable of topping all other types of weather phenomena are subject to thunderstorm hazards.

The hazards that exist with thunderstorm activity are not confined just to the

Fig. 5-33. Thunderstorm Development

storm area itself. Pilots flying outside the thunderstorm cell, but near the storm area, can encounter hail and/or extreme turbulence.

Several factors must exist for the formation of a thunderstorm. First, for the formation of the cumulus cloud and for its continuing build-up, some sort of *lifting action* must be present. This lifting action may be orographic, convectional, or frontal.

Orographic lifting consists of air forced to rise over the surface of the earth, such as air rising over a mountain. *Convectional lifting* occurs when air being heated from below is forced to rise. *Frontal lifting* takes place when moist air is forced aloft by the wedge of an advancing cold front. In addition, the formation of a thunderstorm requires the availability of moisture and unstable air.

STAGES OF THE THUNDERSTORM

There are three stages to the development of a thunderstorm. The first stage is known as the *cumulus stage*. The main feature of this stage is the cumulus cloud and the updraft which may extend from near the earth's surface to several thousand feet above visible cloud tops. Water droplets are very small, but grow into raindrops as the clouds build upward. Many times the raindrops remain in the liquid state even above the freezing level. These raindroplets are suspended by the currents within the clouds. (See Fig. 5-33.)

The second or *mature* stage begins as rain begins to fall at the earth's surface. Raindrops and ice particles by this point have grown to such a size that they can no longer be supported by the updrafts. The mature stage occurs approximately 10 to 15 minutes after the cloud has built beyond the freezing level in the atmosphere. Occasionally, during the mature stage, a cloud may build as high as 50,000 to 60,000 feet, but 25,000 to 30,000 feet is the norm.

Severe up and downdrafts occur in the mature stage. As the raindrops fall, they pull air with them and create downdrafts that may exceed 2,500 feet per minute. This causes gusty winds at the surface as the downdrafts strike the earth and spread outward.

The *dissipating* stage is characterized by the collapse of the cumulonimbus cloud. Downdrafts continue to develop and spread vertically and horizontally while updrafts weaken and finally dissipate completely. Soon the entire thunderstorm becomes an area of downdrafts. Rain decreases, then ceases, and the thunderstorm begins to dissipate. The top of the thunderstorm, at this point, begins to develop the characteristic anvil appearance with the point of the anvil in the direction of the prevailing winds. (See Fig. 5-33.)

WEATHER IN MOUNTAINOUS AREAS

Terrain, as well as fronts, can cause air to be lifted and cooled until cloudiness results. When the wind blows against a mountain barrier, the moisture content of the air and its stability determine the amount and height of clouds, their thickness, and their type. As the air descends on the leeward side of the terrain, it is warmed and clouds disappear.

Fronts and low-pressure systems, moving through mountainous regions, create more cloudiness and precipitation, turbulence, and icing conditions on the windward slopes than occur as the systems move over flat terrain. This is because the terrain lifting effect is added to the frontal lifting forces at work.

Because of the rapid changes of elevation in mountainous areas, weather conditions frequently change rapidly in short distances. Cloud heights above ground level, in particular, vary significantly from place to place even though the mean sea level elevation of clouds may be uniform. Pilots should understand the effects of terrain on weather especially in mountainous areas.

MOUNTAIN WAVE

The movement of air over the mountain ridges also causes turbulence, and may generate a mountain wave. The air, being cooled and forced up over a mountain, has a tendency to roll, or tumble, down the leeward side of the mountain causing tremendous downdrafts and turbulence. It also causes

a wave or ripple in the atmosphere which can extend for miles downwind from the mountain range.

The only way a pilot has of knowing that this tremendous turbulence exists is by noticing the various clouds that form in this area. (See Fig. 5-34.) A lenticular cloud, which is a lens-shaped cloud, is usually found at the top in the crest of one of the standing mountain waves. At about the same level as the mountain peak, or the ridge of the mountain range, roll or rotor clouds are formed. A pilot should be on the lookout for this type of warning in mountainous areas. These downdrafts and turbulence are very severe and could cause an aircraft to go out of control and crash into the mountains.

A mountain wave should be anticipated whenever winds of 40 knots or greater are blowing perpendicular to the mountain range. Aircraft should fly at a level at least 50% greater than the height of the range to avoid mountain turbulence. For example, a pilot should fly at 15,000 feet for a 10,000-foot range of mountains. (See Fig. 5-34.) Small aircraft, whose performance ceiling is close to the suggested height, should not attempt to cross the mountain ranges. Also, an oxygen system should be available to the occupants of the aircraft for extended flight above 10,000 feet.

Fig. 5-34. Mountain Waves

The effects of the mountain wave are dangerous since they can produce downdrafts in excess of 5,000 feet per minute and extreme turbulence. Therefore, pilots should avoid flight in mountainous areas when winds at mountain top level are at high velocities. If moderate or severe turbulence is encountered, however, it is important for the pilot to immediately reduce airspeed to the maneuvering speed and maintain a constant attitude to prevent excessive load factors.

LOW LEVEL WIND SHEAR

Wind shear is a weather phenomenon defined as a sudden, drastic shift in wind speed, direction, or both, in a very short distance and time. Low level wind shear may occur in the vertical as well as the horizontal planes, creating an acute danger during takeoffs and landings. Inadvertent encounters with this phenomenon during approaches and departures may subject an aircraft to sudden updrafts, downdrafts, or extreme horizontal wind components, causing loss of lift, and erratic and sometimes violent changes in vertical velocities and attitudes.

Wind shear hazards should be anticipated when frontal systems and thunderstorms exist in the vicinity of an airport. To predict the presence of low level wind shear prior to takeoff, a detailed analysis of the weather situation should be conducted during preflight planning.

Severe wind shear should be anticipated when any combination of the following exists: the temperature differential across a front is 6° Celsius or greater; the speed of a front is 30 knots or more; the surface temperature is approximately 25° Celsius or higher; the temperature/dewpoint spread is approximately 20° Celsius or more; thunderstorms are forecast or observed; virga is present (precipitation falling from high altitude cumulus clouds but evaporating before reaching the ground); a gust front is observed as evidenced by blowing dust on the surface; and extreme variation of wind velocity and direction are reported or observed.

Although any known severe wind shear should be avoided, the pilot should be prepared to act promptly and positively to control the aircraft if this condition is encountered. With an awareness of impending wind shear, the pilot can take appropriate action to avoid this serious hazard to flight. This may include delaying takeoff until more favorable conditions exist or changing the airport of intended landing.

ICING

Structural icing can occur during flight in areas of visible moisture, when the outside air temperature is below +4° Celsius. Ice can build up on any exposed surface of an aircraft causing a loss of lift, an increase in weight, and control problems. Any aircraft operating in icing conditions should be equipped with anti-icing and de-icing equipment.

Two types of ice — *rime* and *clear* — can form on the aircraft's wings, tail surfaces, propellers, and other components. Rime ice normally is encountered in stratus-type clouds and results from instantaneous freezing of tiny water droplets striking the aircraft surface. Rime ice has a characteristic opaque appearance caused by air being trapped in the water droplets as they freeze instantly. The major hazard of rime ice is its ability to change the shape of an airfoil, and destroy the airfoil's lift. Since rime ice freezes instantly, it builds up on the leading edge of airfoils but does not flow back following the basic curvature of the wing and tail surfaces.

Clear ice normally is found in cumulus-type clouds and is formed by the relatively slow freezing of large water droplets. Clear ice can glaze aircraft surfaces when the large water droplets slowly freeze as they flow over the aircraft structure. Clear ice is the most serious of the various forms of ice because it adheres tenaciously to the aircraft and is more difficult to remove than rime ice.

SECTION B - WEATHER REPORTS AND FORECASTS

WEATHER SERVICES

One of the important steps in learning about weather is becoming acquainted with facilities and services available. The National Weather Service maintains a comprehensive weather observing program and a nationwide aviation weather forecasting service. However, at some locations, the actual weather observations are made by FAA flight service specialists or by FAA traffic controllers associated with airport control towers.

FAA flight service stations are pilot communication centers that provide preflight weather briefings for pilots and scheduled aviation weather broadcasts over enroute navigation aids. These stations are strategically located throughout the nation. If an airport has no flight service station or control tower but does have a Weather Service office, pilot briefing services are provided by the National Weather Service. National Weather Service offices and flight service stations are well equipped with a vast communications system, measuring instruments, maps, charts, and radar information to perform many important services for the pilot.

The National Weather Service has stations throughout the United States and coordinates the use of weather information from Canada and many ships at sea. These stations are the primary means of determining current weather and predicting future weather. At most of these stations, meteorologists are on duty 24 hours a day, making observations and sending hourly reports to central locations. The National Weather Service is responsible for operating the national weather teletypewriter system.

TELETYPE REPORTS

Along the airways and at important points off the airways, weather observations are taken and transmitted at periodic intervals. A series of teletype circuits is used to provide weather stations throughout the country with up-to-date weather information. Each station is part of a circuit which consists of all stations in a geographical region of the United States. Each station in a local circuit sends its own report in assigned order. Monitoring stations on the circuit then relay selected reports from other stations, beginning with nearby stations and following with stations at greater distances. The result is that stations on the local circuit receive reports from all stations on their own circuit and selected reports from other circuits.

SURFACE AVIATION WEATHER REPORTS

Surface aviation weather reports are gathered and sent hourly throughout the day. To help explain this type report, figure 5-35 shows a sample from the teletype machine. A plain-language interpretation of the report is given in the following paragraph. Then, on following pages, surface aviation weather reports are described in detail.

"Wichita . . . special report . . . 300 feet scattered; measured 800 feet broken; 2,000 feet overcast . . . One and one-half miles visibility with thunderstorms and moderate rain showers . . . Barometer reading, in millibars converted to sea level, 1013.2 . . . Temperature 72°F . . . dewpoint 64°F . . . Wind from 020° at 14 knots with gusts to 18 knots . . . Altimeter setting, 29.92 in. Hg.

Fig. 5-35. Sample Surface Aviation Weather Report

. . . Runway 01 visual range is variable from 3,000 to 5,000 feet. A thunderstorm is southwest of the station, moving eastward and has frequent lightning from cloud to cloud. The rain began at 15 minutes after the previous hour.''

STATION IDENTIFICATION

The first part of the surface aviation weather report is the three letter *station identification code.* (See Fig. 5-35, item 1.) The one shown in the sample sequence report is "ICT" which stands for Wichita, Kansas. A list of station codes is usually placed in the flight service station or National Weather Service office along the edges of clipboards or bulletin boards where the reports are mounted to help pilots identify the stations to which the surface aviation weather reports are referring.

An "SP" in the second segment of a surface aviation weather report indicates it is a special report. (See Fig. 5-35, item 2.) This means there was a significant change in the weather since the last report was issued. Sometimes these specials are transmitted on the teletype separately; however, they are usually sent along with other surface aviation weather reports.

SKY COVERAGE

The sky coverage segment of the surface aviation weather report indicates the amount and height of clouds. The abbreviations and symbols indicating the extent of sky coverage are shown in figure 5-36. The sky coverage portion of the sample report (see Fig. 5-35, item 3) indicates scattered clouds at 300 feet, a measured ceiling of broken clouds at 800 feet, and an overcast layer at 2,000 feet. The heights of the clouds are given in hundreds of feet *above ground level* (AGL). Two zeros must be added to the

CLR	Clear: Less than 0.1 sky cover.
SCT	Scattered: 0.1 to 0.5 sky cover.
BKN	Broken: 0.6 to 0.9 sky cover.
OVC	Overcast: More than 0.9 sky cover.
–	Thin (When prefixed to the above symbols.)
–X	Partial obscuration: 0.1 to less than 1.0 sky hidden by precipitation or obstruction to vision (bases at surface).
X	Obscuration: 1.0 sky hidden by precipitation or obstruction to vision (bases at surface).

Fig. 5-36. Sky Cover Abbreviations and Symbols

number given in the report; i.e., 3 designates 300 feet.

CEILING

For all practical purposes, a *ceiling* is the height above the ground of the bases of the lowest layer of clouds or obscuring phenomena aloft that is reported as broken, overcast, or obscured, but is not classified as scattered, thin, or partial. The term *thin* means the cloud cover

Fig. 5-37. Rotating Beam Ceilometer

is predominantly transparent and does not constitute a ceiling. This condition is indicated by a minus sign (-) preceding the sky cover symbol.

The ceiling figures in the aviation weather reports are always preceded by a code letter which indicates how the ceiling was determined. A code letter will not precede a non-ceiling cloud cover. These code letters are:

M - measured
E - estimated
W - indefinite

MEASURED CEILINGS

A *measured ceiling* (M) means that the ceiling was determined through the use of a rotating beam *ceilometer* which is an electronic device used to measure cloud bases. (See Fig. 5-37.) The resultant readings may be remotely indicated in the control tower, the flight service station, and the National Weather Service.

ESTIMATED CEILINGS

Aircraft-estimated ceilings are reported to a local approach controller or FAA radio station and then forwarded to the weather observer. The MSL altitude given by a pilot is converted to an above

ground level (AGL) altitude for reporting cloud *bases.*

A *balloon-estimated ceiling* is determined by releasing a weather balloon and noting the time it requires to reach the cloud base. The accuracy of this method, however, is rather limited because vertical air currents often cause the balloon to rise at speeds other than normal rates. (See Fig. 5-38.)

Fig. 5-38. Ballon-Estimated Ceiling

In the absence of the above methods of determining cloud heights, the meteorologist can estimate the ceiling height by relying on experience and knowledge of cloud forms. Balloon, aircraft, and observer-determined ceilings are collectively termed *estimated* ceilings (E).

INDEFINITE CEILINGS

An *indefinite ceiling* (W) indicates only the maximum vertical visibility into a surface-based obstruction to vision. These obstructions are normally indicated by an "X," which stands for an obscured sky, in the sky coverage portion of surface aviation weather reports. This symbol may be prefixed with a minus (—) sign, meaning *partial obscuration.* Obscured means the overlying sky conditions cannot be observed due to fog, dust, blowing snow, or other restrictions.

If a ceiling is *variable*, the letter "V" will follow the ceiling height. For example, the surface aviation weather report, "ICT E15 VOVC," indicates that there is an estimated ceiling of 1,500 feet overcast with varying ceilings in the area.

The ceiling over an airport is actually determined by the first totally obscured, broken, or overcast layer of clouds prefixed on the weather report by one of the letters indicating the method of determining the ceiling layer. In the Wichita example, shown in figure 5-35, the 800 foot broken layer is prefixed by the letter "M" indicating measurement by ceilometer. Therefore, the ceiling at Wichita is 800 feet broken. A minus sign between the 800 and the broken sky cover abbreviation would have indicated a light or thin cloud cover that did *not* constitute a ceiling. In addition, if the broken layer had been classified as thin, the "M" would not have preceded the number "8."

VISIBILITY

The next segment in the sample surface aviation weather report shows the visibility in statute miles. (See Fig. 5-35, item 4.) In the Wichita example, the visibility is one and one-half statute miles.

WEATHER AND OBSTRUCTIONS TO VISION

The next segment of the surface aviation weather report may consist of one letter or a combination of letters to indicate the weather and obstruction to vision at the station at the time of observation. If the observation was made at a distance from the station, this information would be reported in a remarks section. The "TRW" shown in figure 5-35, item 5, stands for thunderstorms and moderate rain showers. This type of weather information is shown on surface aviation weather reports by one or more of the following codes and symbols.

Weather Symbols

T	— thunderstorm
T+	— severe thunderstorm
R	— rain
RW	— rain shower
L	— drizzle
ZR	— freezing rain
ZL	— freezing drizzle
A	— hail
IP	— ice pellets
IPW	— ice pellet showers
S	— snow
SW	— snow showers
SP	— snow pellets
SG	— snow grains
IC	— ice crystals

Obstructions to Vision Symbols

BD	— blowing dust
BN	— blowing sand
BS	— blowing snow
BY	— blowing spray
D	— dust
F	— fog
GF	— ground fog
H	— haze

IF — ice fog
K — smoke

Intensity Symbols

+ — heavy
No Sign — moderate
— — light

NORTH	**(360°)**	**36**
EAST	**(090°)**	**09**
SOUTH	**(180°)**	**18**
WEST	**(270°)**	**27**
NNW	**(340°)**	**34**

Fig. 5-39. Wind Direction Symbols

ATMOSPHERIC PRESSURE

The next entry in the sample surface aviation weather report (see Fig. 5-35, item 6) is the local atmospheric pressure reading converted to the equivalent sea level pressure and stated in millibars. The numbers given in this report (132) are the last three digits of the pressure reading, 1013.2 millibars. The normal pressure readings range from 960.0 to 1050.0 millibars. The "9" or "10" and the decimal point are omitted for brevity. To decode, the number should be prefixed with a "9" or "10," whichever brings the result closer to 1000.0 millibars.

TEMPERATURE

Next on the report is the surface temperature in degrees Fahrenheit. In the Wichita example, the temperature is 72°F (22°C). (See Fig. 5-35, item 7.)

DEWPOINT

Following the temperature on the sample report is "64" which is the dewpoint in degrees Fahrenheit. (See Fig. 5-35, item 8.) The dewpoint is the temperature to which the air must be cooled before the moisture in the air will condense and become visible. When the temperature and dewpoint difference is small, some restriction to visibility, such as drizzle or fog, can be anticipated.

WIND

The next two digits indicate wind direction reported to the nearest 10°. In the "ICT" example (see Fig. 5-35, item 9), the wind is blowing from 020°. This direction is measured with reference to

true north. A zero is added to the two digit number in the report to obtain the correct wind direction. (See Fig. 5-39.)

Following the wind direction is the wind velocity in knots. At Wichita, the wind velocity is 14 knots with gusts to 18 knots. (See Fig. 5-35, item 9.) A "G" and the numerals following it represent gusts of at least 10 knots between peaks and lulls. A "Q" in lieu of the "G" indicates that squalls are occurring. A squall is a significant wind increase of at least 15 knots to a sustained speed of 20 knots or more, lasting for at least one minute.

Figure 5-40 shows several examples. The left column depicts information as it would appear on a surface aviation weather report and the right column provides a plain language interpretation.

ALTIMETER SETTINGS

The next item in the surface aviation weather report is the altimeter setting in *inches of mercury*. (See Fig. 5-35, item 10.) The information in this segment consists of the last three digits of the altimeter setting. In this example, "992" indicates that the altimeter setting is

ØØØØ	— Calm
3416	— From 340° at 16 knots
2727	— From 270° at 27 knots
3414G28	— From 340° at 14 knots, gusts to 28 knots.

Fig. 5-40. Wind Reports

"29.92." Since the normal range of altimeter settings is from 28.00 inches to 31.00 inches of mercury, the coded value should be prefixed with a 2 or a 3, whichever brings it closer to 30.00 inches.

REMARKS

The next segment of the surface aviation weather report is the remarks section. (See Fig. 5-35, item 11.) Remarks include information concerning runway visual range or RVR. Runway visual range is a visibility value, expressed in feet, that is measured instrumentally at some landing runways. In the example shown in figure 5-41, at the approach end of runway one (indicated by R01), the visual range (VR) is 3,000 feet variable (V) to 5,000 feet. These values are averages recorded during a 10-minute period.

The remarks section may also include information on cloud types, thunderstorms, precipitation, and lightning. Some typical remarks found on surface aviation weather reports are shown in figure 5-42. In the example, "T SW MOVG E FQT LTGCC" means that thunderstorms southwest of the airport are moving east, and there is frequent lightning from cloud to cloud. The final remark on the aviation weather report shows that rain began at 15 minutes past the previous hour.

NOTAMs

NOTAMs (Notices to Airmen) are included after some surface aviation

UA/BKN 55 — pilot weather report (PIREP) indicating that the estimated top of the broken layer is at 5,500 feet MSL

V OVC — cloud layer is broken variable to overcast

BINOVC — breaks in overcast
CB — cumulonimbus clouds
CU FRMG — cumulus forming
OCNL SPKL — occasional sprinkles
RB 48 — rain began 48 minutes past the hour
RE 10 — rain ended 10 minutes past the hour
CIG RGD — ceiling ragged

Fig. 5-42. Standard Remarks Abbreviations

weather reports. Closed or shut down radio or instrument approach facilities, runway construction, and closed runways are all types of information that may be obtained from NOTAMs. This information usually is written in code to save space on the teletype page. An explanation of the code can normally be found at the flight service station next to the display board where surface aviation weather reports are posted.

Figure 5-43 shows a sample NOTAM. The horizontal arrow pointing to the right indicates the beginning of the NOTAM. The letters "ICT" following the arrow denote the reporting station (Wichita). Following the station letters is the NOTAM number (04/021). A "C" may be used in this initial section to indicate cancellation of the notice. The illustrated NOTAM is read as follows:

```
. . . RØ1VR3ØV5Ø/T SW MOVG E FQT LTGCC/RB15
```

Fig. 5-41. Remarks

```
→ICT Ø4/Ø21 PTT 17-35 CLSD NIGHT
```

Fig. 5-43. Sample NOTAM

"Wichita NOTAM No. 4-21: Pratt Airport runway 17-35 is closed at night."

Figure 5-44 shows examples of surface aviation weather reports, including NOTAMs as they come off the teletype; first on a local circuit and then by state. A NOTAM summary, or NOSUM, is printed after the reports from the local teletype circuit.

TERMINAL FORECASTS

Another type of weather information provided in the teletype format is the *terminal forecast*, as illustrated in figure 5-45. This type of forecast is issued three times daily to provide information on future weather for some of the larger air terminals throughout the country. Airport weather is forecast for a 24-hour period. The last six hours is an outlook stated by the terms IFR, LIFR (low IFR), MVFR (marginal VFR), or VFR. The cause of LIFR, IFR, or MVFR is

also given by ceiling or visibility restrictions or both.

The following steps indicate how to analyze the heading for the terminal forecasts in figure 5-45:

1. These FTs (terminal forecasts) were issued for the state of Oregon (OR).
2. These forecasts were issued on the first day of the month.
3. Time of the release was 1040 GMT time, or 0240 Pacific Standard Time. GMT (Greenwich Mean Time) is used as a standard time reference to alleviate the confusion associated with flying through several time zones. The time covered by this terminal forecast is from 1100 Zulu or 3 a.m. Pacific Standard Time on the first day through 1100 Zulu or 3 a.m. Pacific Standard time on the following day.

```
SA27 141200
DEN SA 1151 250 SCT 60 156/49/33/2103/015/ 303 1078
48 RADAT 50116 ASE FINO
RIW SA 1138 50 SCT 15 41/36/0000/015
LAR SA 1145 180 -BJN 50 170/36/30/1206/022/ 207 35
RWL SA 1156 100 SCT E250 BKN 60 167/40/27/1805/019/
103 40
RKS SA 1150 200 -SCT 40 163/44/23/0000/018/ 400 43


→ NOSUM14 1202
→ RIW 05/002 RIW CTLZ 05-2200 LOCAL EXCP HOL
→ RKS 05/011 RKS 3-21 CLSD


CO 141203
ALS SA 1153 CLR 50 214/31/24/1704/030/ 500 1002 46829
COS SA 1155 CLR 65 160/47/25/3106/019/FEW AC CI/
205 1071 44
GJT
→ GJT 05/003 CEZ CTLZ 06-2200 LOCAL EXCP HOL
→ GJT 05/004 DRO CTLZ 05-2200 LOCAL EXCP HOL
```

Fig. 5-44. Sample Surface Aviation Weather Reports

```
FT
OR Ø11Ø4Ø
BKE Ø11111 3Ø SCT 5Ø SCT 3315 5Ø SCT OCNL BKN CHC
  C2Ø OVC 5SW-- TIL ØØZ. Ø5Z VFR..
MFR Ø11111 4Ø SCT 25Ø SCT. 23Z 5Ø BKN. Ø5Z VFR..
OTH Ø11111 CLR 151Ø. 21Z 5Ø SCT 25Ø BKN 3312. Ø5Z
  VFR..
PDX Ø11111 C15 BKN. 18Z 2Ø SCT OCNL BKN. 2ØZ 3Ø
  SCT 25Ø BKN. Ø4Z 5Ø SCT C12Ø BKN. Ø5Z VFR..
RDM Ø11111 25Ø SCT. 21Z 4Ø SCT 25Ø BKN. Ø5Z VFR..
TTD Ø11111 15 SCT. 2ØZ 3Ø SCT 25Ø BKN. Ø4Z 5Ø SCT
  C12Ø BKN. Ø5Z VFR..
```

Fig. 5-45. Terminal Forecast Heading Data

Figure 5-46 shows a series of terminal forecasts which predict marginal VFR and IFR conditions in Colorado. Figure 5-47 shows the decoding of a typical forecast. It is read as follows:

1. Ceiling 3,500 feet broken with scattered rain showers. (The ceiling in a terminal forecast is denoted with the same sky coverage symbols and format as used in the surface aviation weather reports with one major exception. In terminal forecasts, the forecast ceiling is preceded with the letter "C.")

2. The wind is forecast to be 150° true at 15 knots.

3. At 1600 Zulu, the weather is forecast to become 3,500 feet scattered and the visibility is forecast to be seven statute miles.

```
FT
CO 11Ø945
ALS DLAD TIL 112ØZ
COS 111Ø1Ø C3 X 1/2ZL-S-F OCNL C1Ø X 11/2S-F. 15Z C5 X
  1/2S-F OCNL C1Ø X 11/2S-F. Ø4Z IFR CIG VSBY SNW..
DEN 111Ø1Ø 1Ø SCT C2Ø OVC 5F OCNL C5 X 1S-F. 2ØZ -X
  C1Ø OVC 21/2S--F OCNL C5X 3/4S- Ø412. Ø4Z IFR CIG
  VSBY SNW..
GJT 111Ø1Ø 12 SCT 2Ø SCT C4Ø BKN SCT V BKN OCNL S-.
  15Z 2Ø SCT C4Ø BKN CHC C2Ø OVC RW-. 22Z C2Ø BKN
  OCNL S- CHC C1Ø BKN 11/2SW-. Ø4Z MVFR CIG.
PUB 111Ø1Ø C3 X 1S-F OCNL C1Ø X 3S--F. Ø4Z IFR CIG
  VSBY SNW..
```

Fig. 5-46. Terminal Forecasts

Fig. 5-47. Terminal Forecast Explanation

The terminal forecast continues in this manner until a complete forecast of the weather is given for the *valid period* noted in the beginning of the forecast.

The symbols and notations used in terminal forecasts are the same as those used in surface aviation weather reports and appear in the same order. However, the wind forecast is only included when it is expected to be 10 knots or greater. The prevailing visibility appears in a terminal forecast only if it is forecast to be six statute miles or less. Terminal forecasts are originated in one or more forecast centers per state.

AREA FORECASTS

Certain National Weather Service offices are designated as forecast centers to predict aviation weather within their *areas*. These forecasts, called *area forecasts*, are issued every 12 hours and cover a period of 18 hours plus a general outlook for an additional 12 hours. Area forecasts are distributed via teletype and are presented in a standard format.

The normal order of presentation begins with the heading followed by a designation of the forecast area. Then, a synopsis of the weather-producing structures appears, such as fronts, troughs, and airmasses. Statements follow concerning the amount of cloud cover, bases and tops, weather, obstructions to visibility, and surface winds when significant. If icing is anticipated, the freezing level, types of ice, and intensities are specified. Turbulence is not predicted but is *always* implied when thunderstorms are forecast.

The heading identifies the type of forecast, the originating forecast center, the date and the month, the time the forecast was issued, and the period covered by the forecast. All times are in Greenwich Mean Time, as indicated by the letter "Z." For example, in the heading pointed out by item 1 in figure 5-48, "FA" indicates this is an area forecast. "MSY" stands for New Orleans (the forecast center), 13 is the thirteenth day of the month, and 0040 is the time the forecast was issued.

This forecast is valid from 0100Z until 1900Z on Tuesday. Note the forecast period is for 18 hours and the outlook is for 12 hours.

Item 2 of figure 5-48 shows the next three items in the forecast. They include the geographic area covered, a standard notation about heights, and a synopsis of weather-producing conditions. They read as follows: "This forecast is for Tennessee, Arkansas, Louisiana, Mississippi, Alabama, Florida west of 85° west longitude, and the coastal waters. All heights are above sea level unless noted otherwise." The synopsis states: "There is a flat pressure gradient at the surface and a weak trough aloft which will continue over the area."

The next section (see Fig. 5-48, item 3) describes the amount and height of sky cover. It gives cloud tops, surface visibility, state of weather, visibility obstructions, surface winds, and other information needed to describe flying conditions expected during the forecast period. It is read as follows:

"Clouds and weather: Over land, 1,500 to 2,500 feet scattered, ceilings 8,000 to 12,000 broken developing by 1000Z. Some areas, ceilings 300 to 800 feet broken, variable to overcast with visibilities from one to three miles with fog. Cloud tops will be 4,000 feet. Cloud layers will be merging in widely scattered showers or isolated thunderstorms with tops to 35,000 feet. After 1200Z, the ceilings will be 1,000 to 3,000 broken with visibilities from four to six miles in light drizzle and fog, improving by 1600Z. After that time, clouds will be 3,000 feet scattered, ceilings 12,000 broken with widely scattered areas having ceilings of 800 feet overcast and visibility of one

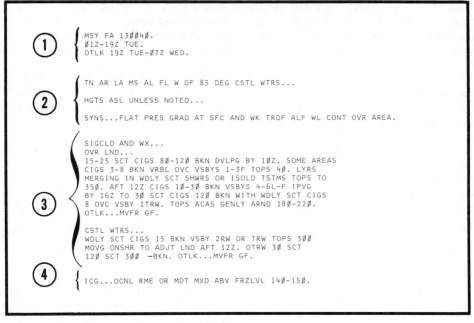

```
①  {  MSY FA 13ØØ4Ø.
      Ø1Z-19Z TUE.
      OTLK 19Z TUE-Ø7Z WED.


②  {  TN AR LA MS AL FL W OF 85 DEG CSTL WTRS...

      HGTS ASL UNLESS NOTED...

      SYNS...FLAT PRES GRAD AT SFC AND WK TROF ALF WL CONT OVR AREA.


      SIGCLD AND WX...
      OVR LND...
      15-25 SCT CIGS 8Ø-12Ø BKN DVLPG BY 1ØZ. SOME AREAS
      CIGS 3-8 BKN VRBL OVC VSBYS 1-3F TOPS 4Ø. LYRS
      MERGING IN WDLY SCT SHWRS OR ISOLD TSTMS TOPS TO
      35Ø. AFT 12Z CIGS 1Ø-3Ø BKN VSBYS 4-6L-F IPVG
      BY 16Z TO 3Ø SCT CIGS 12Ø BKN WITH WDLY SCT CIGS
③     8 OVC VSBY 1TRW. TOPS ACAS GENLY ARND 18Ø-22Ø.
      OTLK...MVFR GF.

      CSTL WTRS...
      WDLY SCT CIGS 15 BKN VSBY 2RW OR TRW TOPS 3ØØ
      MOVG ONSHR TO ADJT LND AFT 12Z. OTRW 3Ø SCT
      12Ø SCT 3ØØ —BKN. OTLK...MVFR GF.


④  {  ICG...OCNL RME OR MDT MXD ABV FRZLVL 14Ø-15Ø.
```

Fig. 5-48. Area Forecast

mile with moderate thunderstorms and rain showers. Tops of altocumulus and altostratus generally around 18,000 to 22,000 feet. Outlook is marginal VFR conditions due to ground fog.

"Over coastal waters, widely scattered ceilings of 1,500 broken, two miles visibility with moderate rain showers or thunderstorms, cloud tops at 30,000 feet moving onshore to adjacent land after 1200Z. Otherwise 3,000 scattered, 12,000 scattered, 30,000 thin broken. Outlook marginal VFR conditions due to ground fog."

Area forecasts include a statement concerning expected icing conditions plus the height of the freezing level. Item 4 in figure 5-48 shows a very brief statement read as follows: "Icing: Occasional rime or moderate mixed icing above freezing level at 14,000 to 15,000 feet." Mixed refers to a combination of rime and clear ice.

WINDS AND TEMPERATURES ALOFT FORECASTS

Another teletype service is the winds and temperatures aloft forecast. Figure 5-49 shows the data time, time of teletype transmission, valid time, and

Data Time	Report Time	Valid Time	For Use (Period)	Heading
0000Z	0545Z	1200Z	0600-1500Z	FDUS1
0000Z	0545Z	1800Z	1500-2100Z	FDUS2*
0000Z	0945Z	0000Z	2100-0300Z	FDUS3*
1200Z	1745Z	0000Z	1800-0300Z	FDUS1
1200Z	1745Z	0600Z	0300-0900Z	FDUS2+
1200Z	1945Z	1200Z	0900-1500Z	FDUS3+

* At 1800Z, discontinue using FD forecasts based on 0000Z data.

+ At 0600Z, discontinue using FD forecasts based on 1200Z data.

Fig. 5-49. Winds and Temperatures Aloft Forecast Times

usable time for each forecast. The *data time* is the actual time the observation of wind velocity and speed is made and on which the forecast is based. The *teletype transmission time* is the time that the winds aloft information was transmitted over the teletype system. The valid time designates the hour at which the winds, as indicated in the forecast, are to be as forecast. This forecast will be usable, however, for winds aloft information during the *use period*.

The winds and temperatures aloft forecasts begin with the heading shown in figure 5-50. The forecast information is printed on the teletype in vertical columns according to altitude and is given for 3,000, 6,000, 9,000, 12,000, 18,000, 24,000, 30,000, 34,000, and 39,000 feet *above sea level* (ASL). The first level for which winds aloft are issued for a particular station is 1,500 feet or more *above the station elevation.* The temperature is forecast in Celsius for all wind levels that are 2,500 feet or more above the level of the station with the exception of the 3,000-foot level. Since temperatures are always below 0°C at 30,000 feet and above, the minus signs are deleted from the temperatures at the 30,000-, 34,000-, and 39,000-foot levels.

The body of the winds and temperatures aloft forecast is fairly simple to read. For

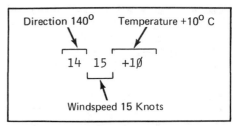

Fig. 5-51. Winds and Temperatures Aloft Segment

example, a segment of a sample forecast is shown in figure 5-51. The first two numbers indicate the true direction from which the wind is blowing. The number "14" indicates the wind direction of 140° (a zero must be added). This direction is given in relation to *true* north.

The next item is the wind velocity, which is 15 knots and can be read as printed. If the wind is five knots or less at a particular altitude, the number "9900" is used to indicate the wind is light and variable. The last item in this segment is the temperature, +10°C.

Forecast winds of 100 to 199 knots are deciphered by subtracting 50 from the two-digit direction and adding 100 to the speed given. For example, 7545 would be read 250° at 145 knots.

IN-FLIGHT ADVISORIES

When it becomes apparent to weather forecasters and flight service station

---

Winds and Temperatures Aloft Forecast

Date   Transmission Time (Zulu)

FDUS3   KWBC   161945
DATA BASED ON 1612ØØZ
VALID 1712ØØZ   FOR USE Ø9ØØ-15ØØZ.   TEMPS NEG ABV 24ØØØ

FT	3ØØØ	6ØØØ	9ØØØ	12ØØØ	18ØØØ	24ØØØ	30ØØØ	34ØØØ	39ØØØ
BOS	2431	2638-Ø3	2646-Ø8	2654-13	2669-24	2783-35	279747	77Ø355	279258
EMI	2619	2728-Ø1	2635-Ø5	2641-Ø9	2654-21	2665-32	268Ø46	269353	269658
JFK	2526	2736-Ø2	2642-Ø6	2649-11	2662-22	2674-33	269Ø46	77Ø154	279858

Fig. 5-50. Sample Winds and Temperatures Aloft Forecast

personnel that weather conditions in a certain area contain hazardous elements or are significantly worse than forecast, in-flight advisories are issued. This is accomplished through the issuance of SIGMETs and AIRMETs. These advisories are broadcast over flight service station navigation frequencies and are an important part of preflight weather briefings.

SIGMETs

SIGMET stands for *significant meteorology*. This category of in-flight advisories includes weather phenomena of particular significance to *all* aircraft. SIGMETs cover severe and extreme turbulence, severe icing, and widespread duststorms or sandstorms which lower visibility below three miles.

CONVECTIVE SIGMETs

Convective SIGMETs are issued for the following phenomena: lines of thunderstorms, tornadoes, embedded thunderstorms, isolated intense thunderstorms, areas of thunderstorms, and hail greater than or equal to 3/4-inch in diameter. If none of these criteria are expected, a negative message ("none") is issued each hour for each of the three coverage areas — *Eastern* (E), *Central* (C), and *Western* (W) United States.

The basic convective SIGMET, shown in figure 5-52, begins with a "header" describing the general area concerned, the issuance number, and the location using two-letter state, Great Lake, and coastal water identifiers. The body of the convective SIGMET contains a *location* statement using VORs to define an area or line, and a *description/movement* statement which includes diameters, tops, hail, and gusts. The *trend*, based on forecaster judgment, usually follows. Cell intensities are given on a scale from one through six, with six being the most severe. A separate paragraph pinpoints most of the more significant cells or groups of cells on a special grid available at most flight service stations.

AIRMETs

AIRMETs are issued for meteorological conditions less severe than for SIGMETs. The conditions are potentially hazardous to aircraft having *limited capabilities* because of lack of equipment or instrumentation, or pilot qualification and are at least of operational interest to *all* aircraft. AIRMETs cover moderate icing, moderate turbulence over an extensive area, large areas where visibility is less than three miles or ceilings less than 1,000 feet including mountain ridges or passes, and sustained winds of 30 knots

```
MKCC WST 221835
CONVECTIVE SIGMET 19
KS OK
FROM 30E GCK TO 20E GAG
LN BKN TSTMS 25 WIDE MOVG FROM 2515 WITH AN INTS LVL5 CELL.
TOPS TO 450...HAIL TO 1 IN...WIND GUSTS TO 55.
CONDS EXPCD TO INTSFY.
```

It is read as follows:
Convective SIGMET number nineteen for Kansas and Oklahoma. From 30 miles east of Garden City, Kansas, to 20 miles east of Gage, Oklahoma, there is a broken line of thunderstorms 25 miles wide moving from 250° at 15 knots. It contains an *intense* (level 5) cell. Tops are as high as 45,000 feet, hail as large as one inch in diameter is occurring, and wind is gusting as high as 55 knots. Conditions are expected to intensify.

Fig. 5-52. Convective SIGMET

```
GSW WA 161210
161210-161400

AIRMET ALFA 1. FLT PRCTN OVR NRN TEX AND OKLA BECAUSE OF STG WNDS
AND LOW CIGS VSBYS. OVR NWRN N CNTRL NERN TEX AND OKLA WNDS 40 KTS
OR MORE WITHIN 2 THSD FT OF SFC. OVR NERN TEX CIGS BLO 1 THSD FT
VSBY OCNLY 2 MIS OR LESS IN FOG. IPVG BY 1400Z. CNL AT 1400Z.
```

It is read as follows:
AIRMET Alpha One: Flight precaution over northern Texas and Oklahoma because of strong winds and low ceilings and visibilities. Over northwestern, north central, and northeastern Texas, and all of Oklahoma; winds at four zero knots or more within two thousand feet of the surface. Over northeastern Texas; ceilings below one thousand feet, visibility occasionally two miles or less in fog. Improving by fourteen hundred ZULU. Cancel this AIRMET at fourteen hundred ZULU.

Fig. 5-53. AIRMET

at or within 2,000 feet of the surface. An example of an AIRMET is shown in figure 5-53.

FAA flight service stations broadcast SIGMETs at 15-minute intervals for the first hour after issuance. Then they are broadcast as alert notices or flight precautions at 15 and 45 minutes past the hour for the remainder of the period for which the SIGMETs are valid. When broadcasting SIGMETs as alert notices, the coded name of the advisory is given and is designated current; i.e., "SIGMET Bravo 2 is current."

AIRMETs are broadcast twice each hour, at 15 and 45 minutes past the hour during the first hour. Thereafter, they are carried as alert notices at 15 and 45 minutes past the hour for the valid period of the advisory.

PIREPs

PIREPs (pilot reports) contain significant weather information reported by pilots in flight. This information can be very valuable since pilots can supply firsthand information on cloud tops, turbulence, etc., that weather forecasters and FSS personnel would be unable to predict. These reports, in turn, are compiled by FSS personnel and made part of pilot weather briefings and broadcast aviation weather reports. Pilots are urged to cooperate and volunteer reports of cloud tops, upper cloud layers, thunderstorms, ice, turbulence, strong winds, and other significant flight condition information.

Pilots usually report height values as above mean sea level since they determine elevations by the altimeter. In the reports disseminated as PIREPs, elevation references are always given the same as received from pilots — above mean sea level. An example of a PIREP at the end of an aviation weather report is shown in figure 5-54. It is read as follows: "Pilot reports tops of overcast at 2,300 feet mean sea level." If the pilot were to report the bottom of an overcast, or other cloud layer, the sky coverage code would appear *after* the elevation figure. When the sky coverage code appears before the altitude figure, tops of clouds have been reported.

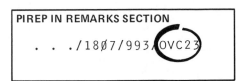

PIREP IN REMARKS SECTION

. . . /1807/993/OVC23

Fig. 5-54. PIREP

Fig. 5-55. Surface Analysis Chart

SECTION C - WEATHER CHARTS

In addition to teletype reports and forecasts, the National Weather Service also has a variety of weather charts that provide valuable meteorological information. By referring to these charts, the pilot is provided with a pictorial representation of the weather across the nation and specifically, along his route of flight. Weather charts are produced by National Weather Service personnel in the National Meteorological Center in Suitland, Maryland, and transmitted to weather stations across the country. These charts are received and reproduced in the various weather stations on facsimile machines like the one shown in figure 5-56, or increasingly, on computer screens similar to television sets. These charts include the surface analysis chart, the weather depiction chart, and the low-level significant weather prognosis chart.

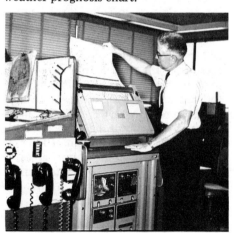

Fig. 5-56. Facsimile Machine

SURFACE ANALYSIS CHART

The *surface analysis chart* is of fundamental importance to the pilot. The velocity and direction of the wind, the temperature and humidity, dewpoint, and other weather data are indicated on the surface weather chart. In addition, this chart provides a general picture of the atmospheric pressure pattern at the surface of the earth by showing the position of highs, lows, and fronts.

A sample chart is shown on the preceding page. (See Fig. 5-55.) The basic unit of information on the chart is the station model. Location identifiers are included on surface charts to assist pilots in briefing themselves. Figure 5-57 shows a close-up of the station model which is read as follows:

1. The station is reporting a wind from the west at 15 knots. The stem of the wind arrow always points in the direction from which the wind is blowing. The velocity of the wind can be determined by the feathers pointing away from the stem. A full-length feather represents 10 knots while a half-length feather is equivalent to five knots. A pennant attached to the wind arrow represents 50 knots of wind.

1. Wind Arrow
   (Direction and Velocity)
2. Sky Coverage
3. Temperature in °F
4. Dewpoint in °F

5. Low Cloud Type
6. High Cloud Type
7. Barometric Pressure (Millibars)
8. Barometric Change
   (Past 3 Hours)
9. Barometric Tendency
10. Location Identifier

Fig. 5-57. Station Model

2. The sky coverage symbol represents the amount of sky covered by clouds in tenths. The symbol shown represents two to three-tenths sky coverage. Other symbols used are shown in figure 5-58.

SKY COVERAGE
(Total Amount)

○	No clouds
◐	Less than one-tenth or one-tenth
◔	Two-tenths or three-tenths
◑	Four-tenths
◑	Five-tenths
◕	Six-tenths
◕	Seven-tenths or eight-tenths
◕	Nine-tenths or over-cast with openings
●	Completely overcast
⊗	Sky obscured

Fig. 5-58. Sky Coverage Symbols

3. The temperatue at the station is 53° F.
4. The dewpoint is 26° F.
5. The station is reporting low stratocumulus clouds. Low clouds are reported by placing the appropriate symbol below the total sky coverage.
6. There are high scattered cirrus clouds, or mare's tails, over the station. The high cloud cover symbol is placed above total sky coverage.
7. The barometric pressure expressed in millibars is 1014.3. The prefix number for the millibar designation is determined in the same way as on aviation weather reports. Thus, barometric pressure is given to the nearest tenth of a millibar.

8. The barometric pressure has risen 1.7 millibars in the past three hours.
9. The barometric tendency in the past three hours is represented by two connected lines. In the example shown in figure 5-57, the barometric pressure has been rising but is now steady. This can be determined from the pattern of the two indicator lines. Notice that the first line rises and is followed by a second line which is level (rising pressure followed by steady pressure). On the other hand, if the pressure had been remaining steady and then dropped, the tendency symbol would be a horizontal line followed by a descending line.
10. The location identifier is placed below the dewpoint figure to complete the typical station model.

Isobars (lines connecting points of equal pressure) are drawn on the surface weather map at four millibar intervals and are labeled with the last two digits of the pressure reading. For example, figure 5-59 shows an isobar that is labeled "08." This represents 1008 millibars. High and low pressure areas are labeled as "H" or "L" on the surface analysis chart. Fronts are shown with conventional symbols as illustrated in figure 5-62. Before reading a surface weather chart, the time the chart was issued should be noted.

Fig. 5-59. 1008 Millibars

RADAR SUMMARY CHART

Another excellent weather briefing aid is the radar summary chart shown in figure 5-60. It is a graphic illustration of weather observed by radar. Special weather service radar is used to detect and track thunderstorms, tornadoes, and hurricanes. These storms contain very heavy concentrations of liquid moisture that reflect radar signals back to the antenna. These "echoes" are then analyzed and plotted on the chart. Weather symbols noted on this chart are important to pilots because the conditions that cause strong echoes are often associated with heavy rain, hail, severe icing, and severe turbulence.

Hourly radar summary facsimile charts and plain language radar summaries are prepared each day. This information is transmitted on service A teletypewriters and to subscribers on the facsimile circuit.

Areas of echoes are surrounded by irregular lines. Speed and direction of movement of the echo areas or individual cells are given. One of the important features of the radar summary chart is that it shows the height of cloud tops. However, some weather phenomena, such as thunderstorms, can change so rapidly that the radar summary cannot be depended on for specific details.

Any important surface precipitation is given in the same terminology as teletype surface aviation reports. For example, "RW" means "rain showers," "S" means "snow," and "A" means "hail." Numbers may precede these symbols to indicate how much of the area is affected. A notation of "3RW," for instance, indicates that 3/10 of the area is covered by rain showers.

RADAR SUMMARY CHART	
Symbol	**Meaning**
(echo symbol)	Intensity 1 Light and moderate
(echo symbol)	Intensity 3 (Second Contour) Heavy and very heavy
(echo symbol)	Intensity 5 (Dark Area) Intense and extreme
(dashed box)	dashed lines define areas of severe weather
→ 20	echoes are moving at 20 knots
(barb line)	line or area is moving at 20 knots (10 knot barbs)
240 / 80	echo top 24,000' MSL echo base 8,000' MSL
INTENSITY AND TREND OF PRECIPITATION	
+	increasing precipitation
−	decreasing precipitation
ECHO COVERAGE	
Symbol	**Meaning**
SLD	solid, over 9/10 coverage
BKN	broken, 6/10 to 9/10 coverage
SCT	scattered 1/10 to 5/10 coverage
NE	No echo — Equipment operating but no echoes
NA	Observation not available
OM	equipment out for maintenance
●	Strong cell identified by one station

Fig. 5-60. Radar Summary Chart

Fig. 5-61. Weather Depiction Chart

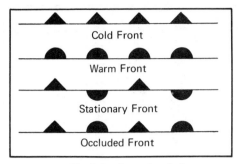

Fig. 5-62. Front Symbols

WEATHER DEPICTION CHART

Another very important weather chart for pilots is the weather depiction chart which is issued every three hours in the National Meteorological Center and reproduced on facsimile machines in various National Weather Service Offices. (See Fig. 5-61 on preceding page.) An *abbreviated* station model is used on a weather depiction chart to show visibility, type of weather, amount of sky cover, and the height of the cloud base. A typical station model is shown in figure 5-63. It is read as follows:

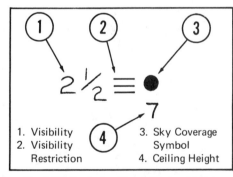

1. Visibility
2. Visibility Restriction
3. Sky Coverage Symbol
4. Ceiling Height

Fig. 5-63. Depiction Chart Station Model

1. The visibility is two and one-half miles. The visibility value is included when it is less than seven miles.
2. The present weather is fog. For other symbols, refer to figure 5-64.
3. The sky coverage symbol indicates the sky is completely overcast. Other sky coverage

symbols used on weather depiction charts are shown in figure 5-64.

4. The height of the ceiling is given below the cloud cover symbol in hundreds of feet. If the cover does not constitute a ceiling, the height then refers to the altitude of the lowest layer of clouds. Item 4 indicates 700 feet.

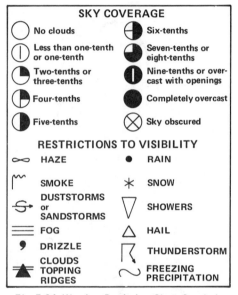

Fig. 5-64. Weather Depiction Chart Symbols

A *scalloped* boundary line is drawn around areas in which the ceiling height is between 1,000 and 3,000 feet and/or the visibility is three to five miles. (See Fig. 5-65.) A *smooth* boundary line is drawn around areas in which the visibility is below three miles *and/or* the

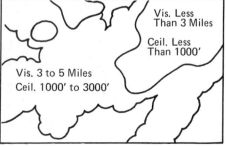

Fig. 5-65. Visibility and Ceiling Boundary Codes

Fig. 5-66. Low Level Significant Weather Prognostic Chart

ceiling is less than 1,000 feet. These conditions indicated by the smooth line would require a pilot to have an instrument clearance to fly in the area outlined. By observing the smooth and scalloped lines, the pilot can see at a glance marginal VFR and IFR weather areas across the nation. The scalloped and solid line designations are always explained in the lower, right-hand corner of the weather depiction chart. (See Fig. 5-61.)

LOW-LEVEL SIGNIFICANT WEATHER PROGNOSIS CHARTS

The low level significant weather prognostic chart shown in figure 5-66 is divided into *two* forecast periods. The two panels on the left show the weather prognosis for a 12-hour period and those on the right for a 24-hour period. The valid times and titles for each panel are shown.

The panels on the top are the forecaster's best estimate of where low or middle clouds will exist. Also depicted are freezing levels, plus areas and altitudes of turbulence. The lower panels are the forecaster's best estimate of the location of frontal and pressure systems as well as the areas and types of precipitation. The two panels on the right (valid for 24 hours) will contain the same information as the two panels on the left (valid for 12 hours), but will indicate the movement *expected between* the two time frames.

Low level prognostic charts are issued four times a day or every six hours. The valid time of each panel appears on the lower left-hand corner of that panel. For example, the weather "picture" on the left-hand panel containing "1800 WED APR 26" represents a prediction of the weather situation that is expected to exist at 1800 Zulu time on Wednesday, April 26th.

On the two upper panels, as shown by item 1 of figure 5-66, the smooth lines

enclose areas where the ceiling is expected to be below 1,000 feet AGL and/or visibility of less than three miles.

Those areas with expected ceilings from 1,000 to 3,000 feet AGL and/or visibilities of three to five miles are enclosed in scalloped lines drawn around the area, as shown by item 2.

A dotted line broken only by the notation "32°F," illustrated by item 3, indicates the predicted location of the freezing isotherm at the surface. An isotherm is a line of equal temperature (just as isobar is a line of equal pressure).

The broken lines represent heights in hundreds of feet of lowest forecast freezing level. As shown by item 4, a line broken by "40" shows the freezing level would be at 4,000 feet MSL. All temperatures will be above freezing at altitudes below 4,000 feet at all locations along the broken line. A pilot in the vicinity of 4,000 feet from that line northward should expect to encounter icing.

Various symbols are used to portray forecast fog or low stratus clouds and also to depict areas of turbulence. A spike, as shown by item 5 of figure 5-66, with the underlined number "80" means that moderate turbulence is predicted below 8,000 feet MSL in that region.

On the lower panels, those areas which are expected to have showers are enclosed by a broken line of dots and dashes. If the precipitation is expected to be more *persistent* (continuous or intermittent), the area will be shaded, as shown by item 6. Various symbols may be used within the precipitation areas to indicate rain showers, snow showers, or thunderstorms. These symbols may be found in figure 5-67.

Arrows may be used to show the predicted direction of movement of the pressure system, as shown by item 7 of figure 5-66. The speed of the low pressure area (15 knots in this example) is often shown near the arrows. The predicted atmospheric pressure in millibars is depicted near the major pressure systems. For example, as shown in item 8, 26 stands for 1026 millibars. The rule previously discussed for prefixing a 9 or 10 still applies.

While verification of these charts has improved greatly over the past decade, the pilot should remember that these charts are *still forecasts.* If the pilot compares an *actual* synoptic chart for a particular time period with the *prognostic*

chart for the same time period, they will probably look quite different. For example, if a weather system decelerates and deepens, it could bring more widespread weather. Conversely, if the weather system accelerates and diminishes in size, the bad weather area would be less extensive.

The individual position of the freezing levels on these two prognostic charts can be helpful to the pilot in planning his flight. For example, the freezing level ordinarily *lowers* behind a cold front. This chart will indicate how much it is expected to lower.

Fig. 5-67. Low Level Prognostic Chart Symbols

chapter 6

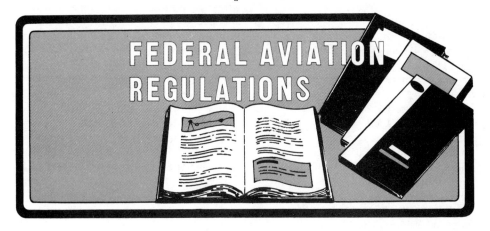

INTRODUCTION

Just as the driver must learn the laws concerning the operation of an automobile, the pilot must know the Federal Aviation Regulations that pertain to the operation of aircraft. In this chapter, excerpts from Parts 1, 61, and 91 have been included that are considered most pertinent to student and private pilots. Also included is the National Transportation Safety Board Part 830 which contains rules pertaining to aircraft accidents, incidents and overdue aircraft. A small airplane silhouette is used to denote those regulations of particular interest to the private pilot applicant.

SECTION A-TOPICAL LISTING OF FARs

SECTION B-FAR PART 1

Part 1 of the FAR(s) alphabetically lists the definitions of terms used in the subsequent regulations. In addition, any abbreviations or symbols used in the FARs are defined and explained in Part 1. Only those definitions of significant importance or of general interest to the student and private pilot have been included.

1.1 GENERAL DEFINITIONS

AIR CARRIER means a person who undertakes directly by lease, or other arrangement, to engage in air transportation.

AIRCRAFT means a device that is used or intended to be used for flight in the air.

AIRCRAFT ENGINE means an engine that is used or intended to be used in propelling aircraft. It includes engine appurtenances and accessories necessary for its functioning, but does not include propellers.

AIRFRAME means the fuselage, booms, nacelles, cowlings, fairings, airfoil surfaces (including rotors but excluding propellers and rotating airfoils of engines), and landing gear of an aircraft and their accessories or controls.

AIRPLANE means an engine-driven fixed-wing aircraft heavier than air that is supported in flight by the dynamic reaction of the air against its wings.

AIRPORT means an area of land or water that is used or intended to be used for the landing and takeoff of aircraft, and includes its buildings and facilities, if any.

AIRPORT TRAFFIC AREA means, unless otherwise specifically designated in Part 93, that airspace within a horizontal radius of 5 statute miles from the geographical center of any airport at which a control tower is operating, extending from the surface up to, but not including, 3,000 feet above the elevation of the airport.

AIRSHIP means an engine-driven, lighter-than-air aircraft that can be steered.

AIR TRAFFIC means aircraft operating in the air or on an airport surface, exclusive of loading ramps and parking areas.

AIR TRAFFIC CLEARANCE means an authorization by air traffic control for the purpose of preventing collision between known aircraft, for an aircraft to proceed under specified traffic conditions within controlled airspace.

AIR TRAFFIC CONTROL means a service operated by appropriate authority to promote the safe, orderly, and expeditious flow of air traffic.

AIR TRANSPORTATION means interstate, overseas, or foreign air transportation or the transportation of mail by aircraft.

ALTERNATE AIRPORT means an airport at which an aircraft may land if a landing at the intended airport becomes inadvisable.

AREA NAVIGATION (RNAV) means a method of navigation that permits aircraft operations on any desired course within the coverage of station-referenced navigation signals or within the limits of self-contained system capability.

BALLOON means a lighter-than-air aircraft that is not engine-driven.

BRAKE HORSEPOWER means the power delivered to the propeller shaft (main drive or main output) of an aircraft engine.

CALIBRATED AIRSPEED means indicated airspeed of an aircraft, corrected for position and instrument error. Cali-

Fig. 6-1. Examples of Airman Certification Categories

brated airspeed is equal to true airspeed in standard atmosphere at sea level.

CATEGORY:

(1) As used with respect to the certification, ratings, privileges, and limitations of airmen, means a broad classification of aircraft. Examples include: airplane; rotorcraft; glider; and lighter-than-air; and

(2) As used with respect to the certification of aircraft means a grouping of aircraft based upon intended use or operating limitations. Examples include: transport; normal; utility; acrobatic; limited; restricted; and provisional.

It is important to distinguish between the term "category" as it pertains to pilot certificates (1) and as it refers to aircraft certification (2). When a pilot receives an airman's certificate, it is endorsed with a category limitation. If the pilot learns to fly a glider only, then his pilot certificate is endorsed and only valid for piloting gliders. The four category ratings for pilot certificates are specified in the regulation.

Aircraft category certification refers to the type of flying and structural strength requirements of the aircraft. For instance, an airplane certified in the acrobatic category must have certain extra structural strength requirements over an airplane certified in the normal category. Restricted category airplanes include aerial application aircraft (agricultural spray planes). Utility category airplanes, although not acrobatic, have greater structural integrity than normal category airplanes. Examples of aircraft categories are given in the regulation.

CLASS:

(1) As used with respect to the certification, ratings, privileges, and limitations of airmen, means a classification of aircraft within a category having similar operating characteristics. Examples include: single-engine; multi-engine; land, water; gyroplane; helicopter; airship; and free balloon; and

(2) As used with respect to the certification of aircraft, means a broad

Fig. 6-2. Examples of Aircraft Certification Categories

grouping of aircraft having similar characteristics of propulsion, flight or landing. Examples include: airplane; rotorcraft; glider; balloon; landplane; and seaplane.

COMMERCIAL OPERATOR means a person who, for compensation or hire, engages in the carriage by aircraft in air commerce of persons or property, other than as an air carrier or foreign air carrier or under the authority of Part 375 of this Title. Where it is doubtful that an operation is for "compensation or hire," the test applied is whether the carriage by air is merely incidental to the person's other business or is, in itself, a major enterprise for profit.

CONTROLLED AIRSPACE means airspace, designated as continental control area, control area, control zone, terminal control area, or transition area, within which some or all aircraft may be subject to air traffic control.

CRITICAL ENGINE means the engine whose failure would most adversely affect the performance or handling qualities of an aircraft.

EXTENDED OVER-WATER OPERATION means an operation over water at a horizontal distance of more than 50 nautical miles from the nearest shore line.

FLAP EXTENDED SPEED means the highest speed permissible with wing flaps in a prescribed extended position.

FLIGHT CREWMEMBER means a pilot, flight engineer, or flight navigator assigned to duty in an aircraft during flight time.

FLIGHT LEVEL means a level of constant atmospheric pressure related to a reference datum of 29.92 inches of mercury. Each is stated in three digits that represent hundreds of feet. For example, flight level 250 represents a barometric altimeter indication of 25,000 feet; flight level 255, an indication of 25,500 feet.

FLIGHT PLAN means specified information, relating to the intended flight of an aircraft, that is filed orally or in writing with air traffic control.

FLIGHT TIME means the time from the moment the aircraft first moves under its own power for the purpose of flight until the moment it comes to rest at the next point of landing. ("Block-to-block" time.)

FLIGHT VISIBILITY means the average forward horizontal distance, from the cockpit of an aircraft in flight, at which prominent unlighted objects may be seen and identified by day and prominent lighted objects may be seen and identified by night.

GLIDER means a heavier-than-air aircraft, that is supported in flight by the dynamic reaction of the air against its lifting surfaces and whose free flight does not depend principally on an engine.

GROUND VISIBILITY means prevailing horizontal visibility near the earth's surface as reported by the United States Weather Bureau or an accredited observer.

GYROPLANE means a rotorcraft whose rotors are not engine-driven except for initial starting, but are made to rotate by action of the air when the rotorcraft is moving; and whose means of propulsion, consisting usually of conventional propellers, is independent of the rotor system.

HELICOPTER means a rotorcraft that, for its horizontal motion, depends principally on its engine-driven rotors.

HELIPORT means an area of land, water, or structure used or intended to be used for the landing and takeoff of helicopters.

IFR CONDITIONS means weather conditions below the minimum for flight under visual flight rules.

INDICATED AIRSPEED means the speed of an aircraft as shown or its pitot static airspeed indicator calibrated to reflect standard atmosphere adiabatic compressible flow at sea level uncorrected for airspeed system errors.

INSTRUMENT means a device using an internal mechanism to show visually or aurally the attitude, altitude, or operation of an aircraft or aircraft part. It includes electronic devices for automatically controlling an aircraft in flight.

KITE means a framework, covered with paper, cloth, metal, or other material, intended to be flown at the end of a rope or cable, and having as its only support the force of the wind moving past its surfaces.

LANDING GEAR EXTENDED SPEED means the maximum speed at which an aircraft can be safely flown with the landing gear extended.

LANDING GEAR OPERATING SPEED means the maximum speed at which the landing gear can be safely extended or retracted.

Both the landing gear extension speed and landing gear operating speeds are calibrated airspeeds and are found in the owner's handbook or airplane flight manual. The landing gear extension speed refers to the maximum speed at which the airplane can be flown with the gear "down and locked," while landing gear operating speed refers to the maximum speed at which the gear can be retracted or extended. Exceeding either of these speeds may cause damage to the landing gear mechanism.

LARGE AIRCRAFT means aircraft of more than 12,500 pounds, maximum certificated takeoff weight.

LIGHTER - THAN - AIR AIRCRAFT means aircraft that can rise and remain

suspended by using contained gas weighing less than the air that is displaced by the gas.

LOAD FACTOR means the ratio of a specified load to the total weight of the aircraft. The specified load is expressed in terms of any of the following: aerodynamic forces, inertia forces, or ground or water reactions.

Load factor is usually expressed in terms of "G-Loading." One "G" refers to the weight of the airplane when sitting on the ground. If certain maneuvers increase the effective weight of an airplane to twice its weight, however, the load factor would be two "G's."

MACH NUMBER means the ratio of true airspeed to the speed of sound.

MAJOR ALTERATION means an alteration not listed in the aircraft, aircraft engine, or propeller specifications that might appreciably affect weight, balance, structural strength, performance, powerplant operation, flight characteristics, or other qualities affecting airworthiness.

MANIFOLD PRESSURE means absolute pressure as measured at the appropriate point in the induction system and usually expressed in inches of mercury.

MEDICAL CERTIFICATE means acceptable evidence of physical fitness on a form prescribed by the Administrator.

NIGHT means the time between the end of evening civil twilight and the beginning of morning civil twilight, as published in the American Air Almanac, converted to local time.

PARACHUTE means a device used or intended to be used to retard the fall of a body or object through the air.

PILOTAGE means navigation by visual reference to landmarks.

PILOT IN COMMAND means the pilot responsible for the operation and safety of an aircraft during flight time.

PITCH SETTING means the propeller blade setting as determined by the blade angle measured in a manner, and at a radius, specified by the instruction manual for the propeller.

POSITIVE CONTROL means control of all air traffic, within designated airspace, by air traffic control.

PROHIBITED AREA means designated airspace within which the flight of aircraft is prohibited.

PROPELLER means a device for propelling an aircraft that has blades on an engine-driven shaft and that, when rotated, produces by its action on the air, a thrust approximately perpendicular to its plane of rotation. It includes control components normally supplied by its manufacturer, but does not include main and auxiliary rotors or rotating airfoils of engines.

RATING means a statement that, as a part of a certificate, sets forth special conditions, privileges, or limitations.

REPORTING POINT means a geographical location in relation to which the position of an aircraft is reported.

RESTRICTED AREA means airspace designated under Part 91 (present Part 608) of this chapter within which the flight of aircraft, while not wholly prohibited, is subject to restriction.

ROCKET means an aircraft propelled by ejected expanding gases generated in the engine from self-contained propellants and not dependent on the intake of outside substances. It includes any part which becomes separated during the operation.

ROTORCRAFT means a heavier-than-air aircraft that depends principally for its support in flight on the lift generated by one or more rotors.

SMALL AIRCRAFT means aircraft of 12,500 pounds or less, maximum certificated takeoff weight.

STANDARD ATMOSPHERE means the atmosphere defined in U.S. Standard Atmosphere, 1962 (Geopotential altitude tables).

TAKEOFF POWER:
(1) With respect to reciprocating engines, means the brake horsepower that is developed under standard sea level conditions, and under the maximum conditions of crankshaft rotational speed and engine manifold pressure approved for the normal takeoff, and limited in continuous use to the period of time shown in the approved engine specifications; and
(2) With respect to turbine engines, means the brake horsepower that is developed under static conditions at a specified altitude and atmospheric temperature, and under the maximum conditions of rotorshaft rotational speed and gas temperature approved for the normal takeoff, and limited in continuous use to the period of time shown in the approved engine specifications.

TRUE AIRSPEED means the airspeed of an aircraft relative to undisturbed air.

TYPE:
(1) As used with respect to the certification, ratings, privileges, and limitations of airmen, means a specific make and basic model of aircraft, including modifications thereto that do not change its handling or flight characteristics. Examples include: DC-7; 1049; and F-27; and
(2) As used with respect to the certification of aircraft, means those aircraft which are similar in design. Examples include: DC-7 and DC-7C, 1049G and 1049H, and F-27 and F-27F.

VFR OVER-THE-TOP, with respect to the operation of aircraft, means the operation of an aircraft over-the-top under VFR when it is not being operated on an IFR flight plan.

1.2 ABBREVIATIONS AND SYMBOLS

ALS means approach light system.

ASR means airport surveillance radar.

ATC means air traffic control.

CAS means calibrated airspeed.

DME means distance measuring equipment compatible with TACAN.

FAA means Federal Aviation Administration.

FM means fan marker.

GS means glide slope.

HIRL means high-intensity runway light system.

ICAO means International Civil Aviation Organization.

IFR means instrument flight rules.

ILS means instrument landing system.

LMM means compass locator at middle marker.

M means mach number.

NDB(ADF) means nondirectional beacon (automatic direction finder).

OM means ILS outer marker

PAR means precision approach radar.

RAIL means runway alignment indicator light system.

RBN means radio beacon.

REIL means runway end identification lights.

TVOR means very high frequency terminal omnirange station.

The following designations are commonly called "V-speeds." V stands for velocity and the small letter designators next to the V refer to the specific type of speed. These "V-speeds" are simply shorthand methods of indicating the various speeds associated with today's modern aircraft.

V_A *means design maneuvering speed.*

V_B *means design speed for maximum gust intensity.*

V_C *means design cruising speed.*

V_F *means design flap speed*

V_{FE} *means maximum flap extended speed.*

V_{LE} *means maximum landing gear extended speed.*

V_{LO} *means maximum landing gear operating speed.*

V_{LOF} *means lift-off speed.*

V_{MC} *means minimum control speed with the critical engine inoperative.*

V_{NE} *means never-exceed speed.*

V_{S_0} *means the stalling speed or the minimum steady flight speed in the landing configuration.*

V_{S_1} *means the stalling speed or the minimum steady flight speed obtained in a specified configuration.*

V_X *means speed for best angle of climb.*

V_Y *means speed for best rate of climb.*

VFR means visual flight rules.

VHF means very high frequency.

VOR means very high frequency omnirange station.

VORTAC means co-located VOR and TACAN.

SECTION C - FAR PART 61

Part 61 is important because it prescribes the requirements for the issuance of the student, private, commercial, airline transport pilot, flight instructor certificates, instrument ratings, and aircraft type ratings. In addition, Part 61 lists the requirements for medical certificates and pilot logbooks. An understanding of Part 61 is especially important to the beginning pilot and any pilot wishing to upgrade his certificate or add a new rating to his license. The prospective private pilot should be especially interested in those sections dealing with student and private pilot qualifications, privileges, and limitations, and the medical certificate requirements.

SUBPART A — GENERAL

61.1 APPLICABILITY.

(a) This part prescribes the requirements for issuing pilot and flight instructor certificates and ratings, the conditions under which those certificates and ratings are necessary, and the privileges and limitations of those certificates and ratings.

(b) Except as provided in section 61.71 of this part, an applicant for a certificate or rating may, until November 1, 1974, meet either the requirements of this part, or the requirements in effect immediately before November 1, 1973. However, the applicant for a private pilot certificate with a free balloon class rating must meet the requirements of this part.

61.3 REQUIREMENT FOR CERTIFICATES, RATING, AND AUTHORIZATIONS. ✈

(a) *Pilot certificate.* No person may act as pilot in command or in any other capacity as a required pilot flight crewmember of a civil aircraft of United States registry unless he has in his personal possession a current pilot certificate issued to him under this part. However, when the aircraft is operated within a foreign country a current pilot license issued by the country in which the aircraft is operated may be used.

(b) *Pilot certificate: foreign aircraft.* No person may, within the United States, act as pilot in command or in any other capacity as a required pilot flight crewmember of a civil aircraft of foreign registry unless he has in his personal possession a current pilot certificate issued to him under this part, or a pilot license issued to him or validated for him by the country in which the aircraft is registered.

(c) *Medical certificate.* Except for free balloon pilots piloting balloons and glider pilots piloting gliders, no person may act as pilot in command or in any other capacity as a required pilot flight crewmember of an aircraft under a certificate issued to him under this part, unless he has in his personal possession an appropriate current medical certificate issued under Part 67. However, when the aircraft is operated within a foreign country with a current pilot license issued by that country, evidence of current medical qualification for that license, issued by that country, may be used. In the case of a pilot certificate issued on the basis of a foreign pilot license under 61.75, evidence of current medical qualification accepted for the issue of that license is used in place of a medical certificate.

(e) *Instrument rating.* No person may act as pilot in command of a civil aircraft under instrument flight rules, or in weather conditions less than the minimums prescribed for VFR flight unless —

(1) In the case of an airplane, he holds an instrument rating or an airline transport pilot certificate with an airplane category rating on it;

(h) *Inspection of certificate.* Each person who holds a pilot certificate, flight instructor certificate, medical certificate, authorization, or license required by this part shall present it for inspection upon the request of the Administrator, an authorized representative of the National Transportation Safety Board, or any Federal, State, or local law enforcement officer.

61.5 CERTIFICATES AND RATINGS ISSUED UNDER THIS PART ✈

(a) The following certificates are issued under this part:
(1) Pilot certificates:
(i) Student pilot.
(ii) Private pilot.
(iii) Commercial pilot.
(iv) Airline transport pilot.
(2) Flight instructor certificates.
(b) The following ratings are placed on pilot certificates (other than student pilot) where applicable:
(1) Aircraft category ratings:
(i) Airplane.
(ii) Rotorcraft.
(iii) Glider.
(iv) Lighter-than-air.
(2) Airplane class ratings:
(i) Single-engine land.
(ii) Multiengine land.
(iii) Single-engine sea.
(iv) Multiengine sea.
(3) Rotorcraft class ratings:
(i) Helicopter.
(ii) Gyroplane.

(4) Lighter-than-air class ratings:
(i) Airship.
(ii) Free balloon.
(5) Aircraft type ratings are listed in Advisory Circular 61-1 entitled "Aircraft Type Ratings." This list includes ratings for the following:
(i) Large aircraft, other than lighter-than-air.
(ii) Small turbojet-powered airplanes.
(iii) Small helicopters for operations requiring an airline transport pilot certificate.
(iv) Other aircraft type ratings specified by the Administrator through aircraft type certificate procedures.
(6) Instrument ratings (on private and commercial pilot certificates only):
(i) Instrument — airplanes.
(ii) Instrument — helicopter.

(c) The following ratings are placed on flight instructor certificates where applicable:
(1) Aircraft category ratings:
(i) Airplane.
(ii) Rotorcraft.
(iii) Glider.
(2) Airplane class ratings:
(i) Single-engine.
(ii) Multiengine.
(3) Rotorcraft class ratings:
(i) Helicopter.
(ii) Gyroplane.
(4) Instrument ratings:
(i) Instrument — airplane.
(ii) Instrument — helicopter.

61.11 EXPIRED PILOT CERTIFICATES AND REISSUANCE

(a) No person who holds an expired pilot certificate or rating may exercise the privileges of that pilot certificate, or rating.

(c) A private or commercial pilot certificate or a special purpose pilot certificate, issued on the basis of a foreign pilot license, expires on the expiration date stated thereon. A certificate without an expiration date is issued to the holder of the expired certificate only if he meets the requirements of 61.75 for the issue of a pilot certificate based on a foreign pilot license.

61.13 APPLICATION AND QUALIFICATION.

(a) Application for a certificate and rating, or for an additional rating under this part is made on a form and in a manner prescribed by the Administrator.

(b) An applicant who meets the requirements of this part is entitled to an appropriate pilot certificate with aircraft ratings. Additional aircraft category, class, type and other ratings, for which the applicant is qualified, are added to his certificate. However, the Administrator may refuse to issue certificates to persons who are not citizens of the United States and who do not reside in the United States.

(c) An applicant who cannot comply with all of the flight proficiency requirements prescribed by this part because the aircraft used by him for his flight training or flight test is characteristically incapable of performing a required pilot operation, but who meets all other requirements for the certificate or rating sought, is issued the certificate or rating with appropriate limitations.

(d) An applicant for a pilot certificate who holds a medical certificate under 67.19 with special limitations on it, but who meets all other requirements for that pilot certificate, is issued a pilot certificate containing such operating

limitations as the Administrator determines are necessary because of the applicant's medical deficiency.

(f) Unless authorized by the Administrator—
(1) A person whose pilot certificate is suspended may not apply for any pilot or flight instructor certificate or rating during the period of suspension;

(g) Unless the order of revocation provides otherwise—
(1) A person whose pilot certificate is revoked may not apply for any pilot or flight instructor certificate or rating for 1 year after the date of revocation.

61.15 OFFENSES INVOLVING NARCOTIC DRUGS, MARIHUANA, AND DEPRESSANT OR STIMULANT DRUGS OR SUBSTANCES.

(a) No person who is convicted of violating any Federal or State statute relating to the growing, processing, manufacture, sale, disposition, posession, transportation, or importation of narcotic drugs, marihuana, and depressant or stimulant drugs or substances, is eligible for any certificate or rating issued under this Part for a period of 1 year after the date of final conviction.

(b) No person who commits an act prohibited by 91.12(a) of this chapter is eligible for any certificate or rating issued under this part for a period of 1 year after the date of that act.

(c) Any conviction specified in paragraph (a) of this section or the commission of the act referenced in paragraph (b) of this section, is grounds for suspending or revoking any certificate or rating issued under this part.

61.17 TEMPORARY CERTIFICATE

(a) A temporary pilot or flight instructor certificate, or a rating, effective for a period of not more than 120 days, is issued to a qualified applicant pending a review of his qualifications and the issuance of a permanent certificate or rating by the Administrator. The permanent certificate or rating is issued to an applicant found qualified and a denial thereof is issued to an applicant found not qualified.

(b) A temporary certificate issued under paragraph (a) of this section expires—
  (1) At the end of the expiration date stated thereon; or
  (2) Upon receipt by the applicant of—
    (i) The certificate or rating sought; or
    (ii) Notice that the certificate or rating sought is denied.

61.19 DURATION OF PILOT AND FLIGHT INSTRUCTOR CERTIFICATES ✈

(a) *General.* The holder of a certificate with an expiration date may not, after that date, exercise the privileges of that certificate.

(b) *Student pilot certificate.* A student pilot certificate expires at the end of the 24th month after the month in which it is issued.

(c) *Other pilot certificates.* Any pilot certificate (other than a student pilot certificate) issued under this part is issued without a specific expiration date. However, the holder of a pilot certificate issued on the basis of a foreign pilot license may exercise the privileges of that certificate only while the foreign pilot license on which that certificate is based is effective.

(e) *Surrender, suspension, or revocation.* Any pilot certificate or flight instructor certificate issued under this part ceases to be effective if it is surrendered, suspended, or revoked.

(f) *Return of certificate.* The holder of any certificate issued under this part that is suspended or revoked shall, upon the Administrator's request, return it to the Administrator.

61.23 DURATION OF MEDICAL CERTIFICATES ✈

(a) A first-class medical certificate expires at the end of the last day of—
  (1) The sixth month after the month of the date of examination shown on the certificate, for operations requiring an airline transport pilot certificate;
  (2) The 12th month after the month of the date of examination shown on the certificate, for operations requiring only a commercial pilot certificate; and
  (3) The 24th month after the month of the date of examination shown on the certificate, for operations requiring only a private or student pilot certificate.

(b) A second-class medical certificate expires at the end of the last day of—
  (1) The 12th month after the month of the date of examination shown on the certificate, for operations requiring a commercial pilot certificate; and
  (2) The 24th month after the month of the date of examination shown on the certificate, for operations requiring only a private or student pilot certificate.

(c) A third-class medical certificate expires at the end of the last day of the 24th month after the month of the date of examination shown on the certificate, for operations requiring a private or student pilot certificate.

61.25 CHANGE OF NAME.

An application for the change of a name on a certificate issued under this part must be accompanied by the applicant's current certificate and a copy of the marriage license, court order, or other document verifying the change. The documents are returned to the applicant after inspection.

61.27 VOLUNTARY SURRENDER OR EXCHANGE OF CERTIFICATE.

The holder of a certificate issued under this part may voluntarily surrender it for cancellation, or for the issue of a certificate of lower grade, or another certificate with specific ratings deleted. If he so requests, he must include the following signed statement or its equivalent:

This request is made for my own reasons, with full knowledge that my (insert name of certificate or rating, as appropriate) may not be reissued to me unless I again pass the tests prescribed for its issue.

61.29 REPLACEMENT OF LOST OR DESTROYED CERTIFICATE.

(a) An application for the replacement of a lost or destroyed airman certificate issued under this part is made by letter to the Department of Transportation, Federal Aviation Administration, Airman Certification Branch, Post Office Box 25082, Oklahoma City, OK 73125. The letter must—

(1) State the name of the person to whom the certificate was issued, the permanent mailing address (including zip code), social security number (if any), date and place of birth of the certificate holder, and any available information regarding the grade, number, and date of issue of the certificate, and the ratings on it; and

(2) Be accompanied by a check or money order for $2, payable to the Federal Aviation Administration.

(b) An application for the replacement of a lost or destroyed medical certificate is made by letter to the Department of Transportation, Federal Aviation Administration, Aeromedical Certification Branch, Post Office Box 25082, Oklahoma City, OK 73125, accompanied by a check or money order for $2.

(c) A person who has lost a certificate issued under this part, or a medical certificate issued under Part 67 or both, may obtain a telegram from the FAA confirming that it was issued. The telegram may be carried as a certificate for a period not to exceed 60 days pending his receipt of a duplicate certificate under paragraph (a) or (b) of this section, unless he has been notified that the certificate has been suspended or revoked. The request for such a telegram may be made by letter or prepaid telegram, including the date upon which a duplicate certificate was previously requested, if a request had been made, and a money order for the cost of the duplicate certificate. The request for a telegraphic certificate is sent to the office listed in paragraph (a) or (b) of this section, as appropriate. However, a request for both airman and medical certificates at the same time must be sent to the office prescribed in paragraph (a) of this section.

61.31 GENERAL LIMITATIONS.

(a) *Type ratings required.* A person may not act as pilot in command of any of the following aircraft unless he holds a type rating for that aircraft:

(1) A large aircraft (except lighter-than-air).

(2) A helicopter, for operations requiring an airline transport pilot certificate.

(3) A turbojet powered airplane.

(4) Other aircraft specified by the Administrator through aircraft type certificate procedures.

(b) *Authorization in lieu of a type rating.*

(1) In lieu of a type rating required under paragraphs (a) (1), (3), and (4) of this section, an aircraft may be operated under an authorization issued by the Administrator, for a flight or series of flights within the United States, if—

(i) The particular operation for which the authorization is requested involves a ferry flight, a practice or training flight, a flight test for a pilot type rating, or a test flight of an aircraft, for a period that does not exceed 60 days;

(ii) The applicant shows that compliance with paragraph (a) of this section is impracticable for the particular operations; and

(iii) The Administrator finds that an equivalent level of safety may be achieved through operating limitations on the authorization.

(2) Aircraft operated under an authorization issued under this paragraph—

(i) May not be operated for compensation or hire; and

(ii) May carry only flight crewmembers necessary for the flight.

(3) An authorization issued under this paragraph may be reissued for an additional 60-day period for the same operation if the applicant shows that he was prevented from carrying out the purpose of the particular operation before his authorization expired.

The prohibition of paragraph (b)(2)(i) of this section does not prohibit compensation for the use of an aircraft by a pilot solely to prepare for or take a flight test for a type rating.

(c) *Category and class rating: Carrying another person or operating for compensation or hire.* Unless he holds a category and class rating for that aircraft, a person may not act as pilot in command of an aircraft that is carrying another person or is operated for compensation or hire. In addition, he may not act as pilot in command of that aircraft for compensation or hire.

(d) *Category and class rating: Other operations.* No person may act as pilot in command of an aircraft in solo flight in operations not subject to paragraph (c) of this section, unless he meets at least one of the following:

(1) He holds a category and class rating appropriate to that aircraft.

(2) He has received flight instruction in the pilot operations required by this part, appropriate to the category and class of aircraft for first solo, given to him by a certificated flight instructor who found him competent to solo that category and class of aircraft and has so endorsed his pilot logbook.

(3) He has soloed and logged pilot-in-command time in that category and class of aircraft before November 1, 1973.

(e) *High performance airplanes.* A person holding a private or commercial pilot certificate may not act as pilot in command of an air-

FEDERAL AVIATION REGULATIONS

plane that has more than 200 horsepower, or that has a retractable landing gear, flaps, and a controllable propeller, unless he has received flight instruction from an authorized flight instructor who has certified in his logbook that he is competent to pilot an airplane that has more than 200 horsepower, or that has a retractable landing gear, flaps, and a controllable propeller, as the case may be. However, this instruction is not required if he has logged flight time as pilot in command in high performance airplanes before November 1, 1973.

(f) *Exception.* This section does not require a class rating for gliders, or category and class ratings for aircraft that are not type certificated as airplanes, rotorcraft, or lighter-than-air aircraft. In addition, the rating limitations of this section do not apply to—

  (1) The holder of a student pilot certificate;

  (2) The holder of a pilot certificate when operating an aircraft under the authority of an experimental or provisional type certificate;

  (3) An applicant when taking a flight test given by the Administrator; or

  (4) The holder of a pilot certificate with a lighter-than-air category rating when operating a hot air balloon without an airborne heater.

61.33 TESTS: GENERAL PROCEDURE.

Tests prescribed by or under this part are given at times and places, and by persons, designated by the Administrator.

61.35 WRITTEN TEST: PREREQUISITES AND PASSING GRADES.

(a) An applicant for a written test must—

  (1) Show that he has satisfactorily completed the ground instruction or home study course required by this part for the certificate or rating sought:

  (2) Present as personal identification an airman certificate, driver's license, or other official document; and

  (3) Present a birth certificate or other official document showing that he meets the age requirement prescribed in this part for the certificate sought not later than 2 years from the date of application for the test.

(b) The minimum passing grade is specified by the Administrator on each written test sheet or booklet furnished to the applicant.

This section does not apply to the written test for an airline transport pilot certificate or a rating associated with that certificate.

61.37 WRITTEN TESTS: CHEATING OR OTHER UNAUTHORIZED CONDUCT.

(a) Except as authorized by the Administrator, no person may—

  (1) Copy, or intentionally remove, a written test under this part;

  (2) Give to another, or receive from another, any part or copy of that test;

  (3) Give help on that test to, or receive help on that test from, any person during the period that test is being given;

  (4) Take any part of that test in behalf of another person;

  (5) Use any material or aid during the period that test is being given; or

  (6) Intentionally cause, assist, or participate in any act prohibited by this paragraph.

(b) No person whom the Administrator finds to have committed an act prohibited by paragraph (a) of this section is eligible for any airman or ground instructor certificate or rating, or to take any test therefor, under this chapter for a period of 1 year after the date of that act. In addition, the commission of that act is a basis for suspending or revoking any airman or ground instructor certificate or rating held by that person.

61.39 PREREQUISITES FOR FLIGHT TESTS.

(a) To be eligible for a flight test for a certificate, or an aircraft or instrument rating issued under this part, the applicant must—

    (1) Have passed any required written test since the beginning of the 24th month before the month in which he takes the flight test;

    (2) Have the applicable instruction and aeronautical experience prescribed in this part;

    (3) Hold a current medical certificate appropriate to the certificate he seeks or, in the case of a rating to be added to his pilot certificate, at least a third-class medical certificate issued since the beginning of the 24th month before the month in which he takes the flight test;

    (4) Except for a flight test for an airline transport pilot certificate, meet the age requirement for the issuance of the certificate or rating he seeks; and

    (5) Have a written statement from an appropriately certificated flight instructor certifying that he has given the applicant flight instruction in preparation for the flight test within 60 days preceding the date of application, and finds him competent to pass the test and to have satisfactory knowledge of the subject areas in which he is shown to be deficient by his FAA airman written test report. However, an applicant need not have this written statement if he—

    (i) Holds a foreign pilot license issued by a contracting State to the Convention on International Civil Aviation that authorizes at least the pilot privileges of the airman certificate sought by him;

    (ii) Is applying for a type rating only, or a class rating with an associated type rating; or

    (iii) Is applying for an airline transport pilot certificate or an additional aircraft rating on that certificate.

(b) Notwithstanding paragraph (a)(1) of this section, an applicant for an airline transport pilot certificate or an additional aircraft rating on that certificate who has been since passing the written examination, continuously employed as a pilot, or as a pilot assigned to flight engineer duties by, and is participating in an approved pilot training program of a U.S. air carrier or commercial operator, or who is rated as a pilot by, and is participating in a pilot training program of a U.S. scheduled military air transportation service, may take the flight test for that certificate or rating.

61.41 FLIGHT INSTRUCTION RECEIVED FROM FLIGHT INSTRUCTORS NOT CERTIFICATED BY FAA.

Flight instruction may be credited toward the requirements for a pilot certificate or rating issued under this part if it is received from—

(a) An Armed Force of either the United States or a foreign contracting State to the Convention on International Civil Aviation in a program for training military pilots; or

(b) A flight instructor who is authorized to give that flight instruction by the licensing authority of a foreign contracting State to the Convention on International Civil Aviation and the flight instruction is given outside the United States.

61.43 FLIGHT TESTS: GENERAL PROCEDURES.

(a) The ability of an applicant for a private or commercial pilot certificate, or for an aircraft or instrument rating on that certificate to perform the required pilot operations is based on the following:

(1) Executing procedures and maneuvers within the aircraft's performance capabilities and limitations, including use of the aircraft's systems.

(2) Executing emergency procedures and maneuvers appropriate to the aircraft.

(3) Piloting the aircraft with smoothness and accuracy.

(4) Exercising judgment.

(5) Applying his aeronautical knowledge.

(6) Showing that he is the master of the aircraft, with the successful outcome of a procedure or maneuver never seriously in doubt.

(b) If the applicant fails any of the required pilot operations in accordance with the applicable provisions of paragraph (a) of this section, the applicant fails the flight test. The applicant is not eligible for the certificate or rating sought until he passes any pilot operations he has failed.

(c) The examiner or the applicant may discontinue the test at any time when the failure of a required pilot operation makes the applicant ineligible for the certificate or rating sought. If the test is discontinued the applicant is entitled to credit for only those entire pilot operations that he has successfully performed.

61.45 FLIGHT TESTS: REQUIRED AIRCRAFT AND EQUIPMENT.

(a) *General.* An applicant for a certificate or rating under this part must furnish, for each flight test that he is required to take, an appropriate aircraft of United States registry that has a current standard or limited airworthiness certificate. However, the applicant may, at the discretion of the inspector or examiner conducting the test, furnish an aircraft of U.S. registry that has a current airworthiness certificate other than standard or limited, an aircraft of foreign registry that is properly certificated by the country of registry, or a military aircraft in an operational status if its use is allowed by an appropriate military authority.

(b) *Required equipment (other than controls).* Aircraft furnished for a flight test must have—

(1) The equipment for each pilot operation required for the flight test;

(2) No prescribed operating limitations that prohibit its use in any pilot operation required on the test;

(3) Pilot seats with adequate visibility for each pilot to operate the aircraft safely, except

as provided in paragraph (d) of this section; and

(4) Cockpit and outside visibility adequate to evaluate the performance of the applicant, where an additional jump seat is provided for the examiner.

(c) *Required controls.* An aircraft (other than lighter-than-air) furnished under paragraph (a) of this section for any pilot flight test must have engine power controls and flight controls that are easily reached and operable in a normal manner by both pilots, unless after considering all the factors, the examiner determines that the flight test can be conducted safely without them. However, an aircraft having other controls such as nose-wheel steering, brakes, switches, fuel selectors, and engine air flow controls that are not easily reached and operable in a normal manner by both pilots may be used, if more than one pilot is required under its airworthiness certificate, or if the examiner determines that the flight can be conducted safely.

(d) *Simulated instrument flight equipment.* An applicant for any flight test involving flight maneuvers solely by reference to instruments must furnish equipment satisfactory to the examiner that excludes the visual reference of the applicant outside of the aircraft.

(e) *Aircraft with single controls.* At the discretion of the examiner, an aircraft furnished under paragraph (a) of this section for a flight test may, in the cases listed herein, have a single set of controls. In such case, the examiner determines the competence of the applicant by observation from the ground or from another aircraft.

(1) A flight test for addition of a class or type rating, not involving demonstration of instrument skills, to a private or commercial pilot certificate.

61.47 FLIGHT TESTS: STATUS OF FAA INSPECTORS AND OTHER AUTHORIZED FLIGHT EXAMINERS.

An FAA inspector or other authorized flight examiner conducts the flight test of an applicant for a pilot certificate or rating for the purpose of observing the applicant's ability to perform satisfactorily the procedures and maneuvers on the flight test. The inspector or other examiner is not pilot in command of the aircraft during the flight test unless he acts in that capacity for the flight, or portion of the flight, by prior arrangement with the applicant or other person who would otherwise act as pilot in command of the flight, or portion of the flight. Notwithstanding the type of aircraft used during a flight test, the applicant and the inspector or other examiner are not, with respect to each other (or other occupants authorized by the inspector or other examiner), subject to the requirements or limitations for the carriage of passengers specified in this chapter.

61.49 RETESTING AFTER FAILURE.

An applicant for a written or flight test who fails that test may not apply for retesting until after 30 days after the date he failed the test. However, in the case of his first failure he may apply for retesting before the 30 days have expired upon presenting a written statement from an authorized instructor certifying that he has given flight or ground instruction as appropriate to the applicant and finds him competent to pass the test.

61.51 PILOT LOGBOOKS.

(a) The aeronautical training and experience used to meet the requirements for a certificate or rating, or the recent flight experience requirements of this part must be shown by a reliable record. The logging of other flight time is not required.

(b) *Logbook entries.* Each pilot shall enter the following information for each flight or lesson logged:

(1) *General.*
(i) Date.
(ii) Total time of flight.
(iii) Place, or points of departure and arrival.
(iv) Type and identification of aircraft.

(2) *Type of pilot experience or training.*
(i) Pilot in command or solo.
(ii) Second in command.
(iii) Flight instruction received from an authorized flight instructor.
(iv) Instrument flight instruction from an authorized flight instructor.
(v) Pilot ground trainer instruction.
(vi) Participating crew (lighter-than-air).
(vii) Other pilot time.

(3) *Conditions of flight.*
(i) Day or night.
(ii) Actual instrument.
(iii) Simulated instrument conditions.

(c) *Logging of pilot time —*

(1) *Solo flight time.* A pilot may log as solo flight time only that flight time when he is the sole occupant of the aircraft. However, a student pilot may also log as solo flight time that time during which he acts as the pilot in command of an airship requiring more than one flight crewmember.

(2) *Pilot-in-command flight time.*
(i) A private or commercial pilot may log as pilot in command time only that flight time during which he is the sole manipulator of the controls of an aircraft for which he is rated, or when he is the sole occupant of the aircraft, or when he acts as pilot in command of an aircraft on which more than one pilot is required under the type certification of the aircraft, or the regulations under which the flight is conducted.

(3) *Second-in-command flight time.* A pilot may log as second in command time all flight time during which he acts as second in command of an aircraft on which more than one pilot is required under the type certification of the aircraft, or the regulations under which the flight is conducted.

(4) *Instrument flight time.* A pilot may log as instrument flight time only that time during which he operates the aircraft solely by reference to instruments, under actual or simulated instrument flight conditions. Each entry must include the place and type of each instrument approach completed, and the name of the safety pilot for each simulated instrument flight. An instrument flight instructor may log as instrument time that time during which he acts as instrument flight instructor in actual instrument weather conditions.

(5) *Instruction time.* All time logged as flight instruction, instrument flight instruction, pilot ground trainer instruction, or ground instruction time must be certified by the appropriately rated and certificated instructor from whom it was received.

(d) *Presentation of logbook.*

(1) A pilot must present his logbook (or other record required by this section) for in-

spection upon reasonable request by the Administrator, an authorized representative of the National Transportation Safety Board, or any State or local law enforcement officer.

(2) A student pilot must carry his logbook (or other record required by this section) with him on all solo cross-country flights, as evidence of the required instructor clearances and endorsements.

61.53 OPERATIONS DURING MEDICAL DEFICIENCY. ✈

No person may act as pilot in command, or in any other capacity as a required pilot flight crewmember while he has a known medical deficiency, or increase of a known medical deficiency, that would make him unable to meet the requirements for his current medical certificate.

61.57 RECENT FLIGHT EXPERIENCE: PILOT IN COMMAND. ✈

(a) *Flight review.* After November 1, 1974, no person may act as pilot in command of an aircraft unless, within the preceding 24 months, he has—

(1) Accomplished a flight review given to him, in an aircraft for which he is rated, by an appropriately certificated instructor or other person designated by the Administrator; and

(2) Had his logbook endorsed by the person who gave him the review certifying that he has satisfactorily accomplished the flight review.

However, a person who has, within the preceding 24 months, satisfactorily completed a pilot proficiency check conducted by the FAA, an approved pilot check airman or a U.S. armed force

for a pilot certificate, rating or operating privilege, need not accomplish the flight review required by this section.

(b) *Meaning of flight review.* As used in this section, a flight review consists of—

(1) A review of the current general operating and flight rules of Part 91; and

(2) A review of those maneuvers and procedures which in the discretion of the person giving the review are necessary for the pilot to demonstrate that he can safely exercise the privileges of his pilot certificate.

(c) *General experience.* No person may act as pilot in command of an aircraft carrying passengers, nor of an aircraft certificated for more than one required pilot flight crewmember, unless within the preceding 90 days, he has made three takeoffs and three landings as the sole manipulator of the flight controls in an aircraft of the same category and class and, if a type rating is required, of the same type. If the aircraft is a tailwheel airplane, the landings must have been made to a full stop in a tailwheel airplane. For the purpose of meeting the requirements of the paragraph a person may act as pilot in command of a flight under day VFR or day IFR if no persons or property other than as necessary for his compliance thereunder, are carried. This paragraph does not apply to operations requiring an airline transport pilot certificate, or to operations conducted under Part 135.

(d) *Night experience.* No person may act as pilot in command of an aircraft carrying passengers during the period beginning 1 hour after sunset and ending 1 hour before sunrise (as published in the American Air Almanac) unless, within the preceding 90 days, he has made at least three takeoffs and three landings to a full stop during that period in the category and class of aircraft to be used. This paragraph does not apply to operations requiring an airline transport pilot certificate.

61.59 FALSIFICATION, REPRODUCTION, OR ALTERATION OF APPLICATIONS, CERTIFICATES, LOGBOOKS, REPORTS, OR RECORDS.

(a) No person may make or cause to be made—
   (1) Any fraudulent or intentionally false statement on any application for a certificate, rating, or duplicate thereof, issued under this part;
   (2) Any fraudulent or intentionally false entry in any logbook, record, or report that is required to be kept, made, or used, to show compliance with any requirement for the issuance, or exercise of the privileges, or any certificate or rating under this part;
   (3) Any reproduction, for fraudulent purpose, of any certificate or rating under this part; or
   (4) Any alteration of any certificate or rating under this part.

(b) The commission by any person of an act prohibited under paragraph (a) of this section is a basis for suspending or revoking any airman or ground instructor certificate or rating held by that person.

61.60 CHANGE OF ADDRESS.

The holder of a pilot or flight instructor certificate who has made a change in his permanent mailing address may not after 30 days from the date he moved, exercise the privileges of his certificate unless he has notified in writing the Department of Transportation, Federal Aviation Administration, Airman Certification Branch, Box 25082, Oklahoma City, OK 73125, of his new address.

SUBPART B — AIRCRAFT RATINGS AND SPECIAL CERTIFICATES

61.61 APPLICABILITY.

This subpart prescribes the requirements for the issuance of additional aircraft ratings after a pilot or instructor certificate is issued, and the requirements and limitations for special pilot certificates and ratings issued by the Administrator.

61.63 ADDITIONAL AIRCRAFT RATINGS (OTHER THAN AIRLINE TRANSPORT PILOT).

(a) *General.* To be eligible for an aircraft rating after his certificate is issued to him an applicant must meet the requirements of paragraphs (b) through (d) of this section, as appropriate to the rating sought.

(b) *Category rating.* An applicant for a category rating to be added on his pilot certificate must meet the requirements of this Part for the issue of the pilot certificate appropriate to the privileges for which the category rating is sought. However, the holder of a category rating for powered aircraft is not required to take a written test for the addition of a category rating on his pilot certificate.

(c) *Class rating.* An applicant for an aircraft class rating to be added on his pilot certificate must—
   (1) Present a logbook record certified by an authorized flight instructor showing that the applicant has received flight instruction in the class of aircraft for which a rating is sought and has been found competent in the pilot operations appropriate to the pilot certificate to which his category rating applies; and

(2) Pass a flight test appropriate to his pilot certificate and applicable to the aircraft category and class rating sought.

A person who holds a lighter-than-air category rating with a free balloon class rating, who seeks an airship class rating, must meet the requirements of paragraph (b) of this section as though seeking a lighter-than-air category rating.

(d) *Type rating.* An applicant for a type rating to be added on his pilot certificate must meet the following requirements:

(1) He must hold, or concurrently obtain, an instrument rating appropriate to the aircraft for which a type rating is sought.

(2) He must pass a flight test showing competence in pilot operations appropriate to the pilot certificate he holds and to the type rating sought.

(3) He must pass a flight test showing competence in pilot operations under instrument flight rules in an aircraft of the type for which the type rating is sought or, in the case of a single pilot station airplane, meet the requirements of paragraph (d)(3)(i) or (ii) of this section, whichever is applicable.

(i) The applicant must have met the requirements of this subparagraph in a multiengine airplane for which the type rating is required.

(ii) If he does not meet the requirements of paragraph (d)(3)(i) of this section and he seeks a type rating for a single-engine airplane, he must meet the requirements of this subparagraph in either a single or multiengine air-

plane, and have the recent instrument experience set forth in 61.57 (e), when he applies for the flight test under paragraph (d)(2) of this section.

(4) An applicant who does not meet the requirements of paragraphs (d)(1) and (3) of this section may obtain a type rating limited to "VFR only." Upon meeting these instrument requirements or the requirements of 61.73 (e)(2), the "VFR only" limitation may be removed for the particular type of aircraft in which competence is shown.

(5) When an instrument rating is issued to the holder of one or more type ratings, the type ratings on the amended certificate bear the limitation described in paragraph (d)(4) of this section for each airplane type rating for which he has not shown his instrument competency under this paragraph.

61.69 GLIDER TOWING: EXPERIENCE AND INSTRUCTION REQUIREMENTS.

No person may act as pilot in command of an aircraft towing a glider unless he meets the following requirements:

(a) He holds a current pilot certificate (other than a student pilot certificate) issued under this part.

(b) He has an endorsement in his pilot logbook from a person authorized to give flight instruction in gliders, certifying that he has received ground and flight instruction in gliders and is familiar with the techniques and procedures essential to the safe towing of gliders, including airspeed limitations, emergency procedures, signals used, and maximum angles of bank.

(c) He has made and entered in his pilot logbook —

(1) At least three flights as sole manipulator of the controls of an aircraft towing a glider while accompanied by a pilot who has met the requirements of this section and made and logged at least 10 flights as pilot-in-command of an aircraft towing a glider; or

(2) At least three flights as sole manipulator of the controls of an aircraft simulating glider towing flight procedures (while accompanied by a pilot who meets the requirements of this section), and at least three flights as pilot or observer in a glider being towed by an aircraft.

However, any person who, before May 17, 1967, made, and entered in his pilot logbook, 10 or more flights as pilot in command of an aircraft towing a glider in accordance with a certificate of waiver need not comply with paragraphs (c)(1) and (2) of this section.

(d) If he holds only a private pilot certificate he must have had, and entered in his pilot logbook at least—

(1) 100 hours of pilot flight time in powered aircraft; or

(2) 200 total hours of pilot flight time in powered or other aircraft.

(e) Within the preceding 12 months he has —

(1) Made at least three actual or simulated glider tows while accompanied by a qualified pilot who meets the requirements of this section; or

(2) Made at least three flights as pilot in command of a glider towed by an aircraft.

61.71 GRADUATES OF CERTIFICATED FLYING SCHOOLS: SPECIAL RULES

(a) A graduate of a flying school that is certificated under Part 141 of this chapter is considered to meet the applicable aeronautical experience requirments of this part if he presents an appropriate graduation certificate within 60 days after the date he is graduated. However, if he applies for a flight test for an instrument rating he must hold a commercial pilot certificate, or hold a private pilot certificate and meet the requirements of 61.65(e)(1) and 61.123 (except paragraphs (d) and (e) thereof). In addition, if he applies for a flight instructor certificate he must hold a commercial pilot certificate.

(b) An applicant for a certificate or rating under this part is considered to meet the aeronautical knowledge and skill requirements, or both, applicable to that certificate or rating, if he applies within 90 days after graduation from an appropriate course given by a flying school that is certificated under Part 141 of this chapter and is authorized to test applicants on aeronautical knowledge or skill, or both.

However, until January 1, 1977, a graduate of a flying school certificated and operated under the provisions of 141.29 of this chapter, is considered to meet the aeronautical experience requirements of this part, and may be tested under the requirements of Part 61 that were in effect prior to November 1, 1973.

61.73 MILITARY PILOTS OR FORMER MILITARY PILOTS: SPECIAL RULES

(a) *General.* A rated military pilot or former rated military pilot who applies for a private or commercial pilot certificate, or an aircraft or instrument rating, is entitled to that certificate with appropriate ratings or to the addition of a rating on the pilot certificate he holds, if he meets the applicable requirements of this section. This section does not apply to a military pilot or former military pilot who has been removed from flying status for lack of proficiency or because of disciplinary action involving aircraft operations.

61.75 PILOT CERTIFICATE ISSUED ON BASIS OF A FOREIGN PILOT LICENSE

(a) *Purpose.* The holder of a current private, commercial, senior commercial, or airline transport pilot license issued by a foreign contracting State to the Convention on International Civil Aviation may apply for a pilot certificate under this section authorizing him to act as a pilot of a civil aircraft of U.S. registry.

The remainder of 61.73 and 61.75 has been omitted from this publication. For additional information, refer to the complete regulation.

SUBPART C — STUDENT PILOTS

61.81 APPLICABILITY

This subpart prescribes the requirements for the issuance of student pilot certificates, the conditions under which those certificates are necessary, and the general operating rules for the holders of those certificates.

61.83 ELIGIBILITY REQUIREMENTS: GENERAL ✈

To be eligible for a student pilot certificate, a person must —
(a) Be at least 16 years of age, or at least 14 years of age for a student pilot certificate limited to the

operation of a glider or free balloon;
(b) Be able to read, speak, and understand the English language, or have such operating limitations placed on his pilot certificate as are necessary for the safe operation of aircraft, to be removed when he shows that he can read, speak, and understand the English language; and
(c) Hold at least a current third-class medical certificate issued under Part 67 of this chapter, or, in the case of glider or free balloon operations, certify that he has no known medical defect that makes him unable to pilot a glider or a free balloon.

61.85 APPLICATION

An application for a student pilot certificate is made on a form and in a manner provided by the Administrator and is submitted to —
(a) A designated aviation medical examiner when applying for an FAA medical certificate; or
(b) An FAA operations inspector or designated pilot examiner, accompanied by a current FAA medical certificate, or in the case of an application for a glider or free balloon pilot certificate it may be accompanied by a certification by the applicant that he has no known medical defect that makes him unable to pilot a glider or free balloon.

61.87 REQUIREMENTS FOR SOLO FLIGHT ✈

(a) *General.* A student pilot may not operate an aircraft in solo flight until he has complied with the requirements of this section. As used in this subpart the term solo flight means that flight time during which a student pilot is the sole occupant of the aircraft, or that flight time during which he acts as pilot in command of an airship requiring more than one flight crewmember.

(b) *Aeronautical knowledge.* He must have demonstrated to an authorized instructor that he is familiar with the flight rules of Part 91 of this chapter which are pertinent to student solo flights.

(c) *Flight proficiency training.* He must have received ground and flight instruction in at least the following procedures and operations:

(1) *In airplanes.*

    (i) Flight preparation procedures, including preflight inspection and powerplant operation;

    (ii) Ground maneuvering and runups;

    (iii) Straight and level flight, climbs, turns, and descents;

    (iv) Flight at minimum controllable airspeeds, and stall recognition and recovery;

    (v) Normal takeoffs and landings;

    (vi) Airport traffic patterns, including collision avoidance precautions and wake turbulence; and

    (vii) Emergencies, including elementary emergency landings.

Instruction must be given by a flight instructor who is authorized to give instruction in airplanes.

(d) *Flight instructor endorsements.* A student pilot may not operate an aircraft in solo flight unless his student pilot certificate is endorsed, and unless within the preceeding 90 days his pilot logbook has been endorsed by an authorized flight instructor who—

(1) Has given him instruction in the make and model of aircraft in which the solo flight is made;

(2) Finds that he has met the requirements of this section; and

(3) Finds that he is competent to make a safe solo flight in that aircraft.

61.89 GENERAL LIMITATIONS. ✈

(a) A student pilot may not act as pilot in command of an aircraft—

(1) That is carrying a passenger;

(2) That is carrying property for compensation or hire;

(3) For compensation or hire;

(4) In furtherance of a business; or

(5) On an international flight, except that a student pilot may make solo training flights from Haines, Gustavus, or Juneau, Alaska, to White Horse, Yukon, Canada, and return, over the province of British Columbia.

(b) A student pilot may not act as a required pilot flight crewmember on any aircraft for which more than one pilot is required, except when receiving flight instruction from an authorized flight instructor on board an airship and no person other than a required flight crewmember is carried on the aircraft.

61.91 AIRCRAFT LIMITATIONS: PILOT IN COMMAND.

A student pilot may not serve as pilot in command of any airship requiring more than one flight crewmember unless he has met the pertinent requirements prescribed in 61.87.

61.93 CROSS-COUNTRY FLIGHT REQUIREMENTS. ✈

(a) *General.* A student pilot may not operate an aircraft in a solo cross-country flight, nor may he, except in an emergency, make a solo flight landing at any point other than the airport of takeoff, until he meets the requirements prescribed in this section. However, an authorized flight instructor may allow a student pilot to practice solo landings and takeoffs at another airport within 25 nautical miles from the airport at which the student pilot receives instruction if he finds that the student pilot is competent to make those landings and takeoffs. As used in this section the term cross-country flight means a flight beyond a radius of 25 nautical miles from the point of takeoff.

(b) *Flight training.* A student pilot must receive instruction from an authorized instructor in at least the following pilot operations pertinent to the aircraft to be operated in a solo cross-country flight:
(1) For solo cross-country in airplanes—
    (i) The use of aeronautical charts, pilotage, and elementary dead reckoning using the magnetic compass;
    (ii) The use of radio for VFR navigation, and for two-way communication;
    (iii) Control of an airplane by reference to flight instruments;
    (iv) Short field and soft field procedures, and crosswind takeoffs and landings;
    (v) Recognition of critical weather situations, estimating visibility while in flight, and the procurement and use of aeronautical weather reports and forecasts; and
    (vi) Cross-country emergency procedures.

(c) *Flight instructor endorsements.* A student pilot must have the following endorsements from an authorized flight instructor:
(1) An endorsement on his student pilot certificate stating that he has received instruc-

tion in solo cross-country flying and the applicable training requirements of this section, and is competent to make cross-country solo flights in the category of aircraft involved.
(2) An endorsement in his pilot logbook that the instructor has reviewed the preflight planning and preparation for each solo cross-country flight, and he is prepared to make the flight safely under the known circumstances and the conditions listed by the instructor in the logbook. The instructor may also endorse the logbook for repeated solo cross-country flights under stipulated conditions over a course not more than 50 nautical miles from the point of departure if he has given the student flight instruction in both directions over the route, including takeoffs and landings at the airports to be used.

SUBPART D — PRIVATE PILOTS

61.101 APPLICABILITY.

This subpart prescribes the requirements for the issuance of private pilot certificates and ratings, the conditions under which those certificates and ratings are necessary, and the general operating rules for the holders of those certificates and ratings.

61.103 ELIGIBILITY REQUIREMENTS: GENERAL. ✚

To be eligible for a private pilot certificate, a person must—
(a) Be at least 17 years of age, except that a private pilot certificate with a free balloon or a glider rating only may be issued to a qualified applicant who is at least 16 years of age;
(b) Be able to read, speak, and understand the English language, or

have such operating limitations placed on his pilot certificate as are necessary for the safe operation of aircraft, to be removed when he shows that he can read, speak, and understand the English language;

(c) Hold at least a current third-class medical certificate issued under Part 67 of this chapter, or, in the case of a glider or free balloon rating, certify that he has no known medical defect that makes him unable to pilot a glider or free balloon, as appropriate;

(d) Pass a written test on the subject areas on which instruction or home study is required by 61.105;

(e) Pass an oral and flight test on procedures and maneuvers selected by an FAA inspector or examiner to determine the applicant's competency in the flight operations on which instruction is required by the flight proficiency provisions of 61.107; and

(f) Comply with the sections of this part that apply to the rating he seeks.

61.105 AERONAUTICAL KNOWLEDGE.

An applicant for a private pilot certificate must have logged ground instruction from an authorized instructor, or must present evidence showing that he has satisfactorily completed a course of instruction or home study in at least the following areas of aeronautical knowledge appropriate to the category of aircraft for which a rating is sought.

(a) *Airplanes.*

    (1) The Federal Aviation Regulations applicable to private pilot privileges, limitations, and flight operations, accident reporting requirements of the National Transportation Safety Board, and the use of the "Airman's Information Manu-

al" and the FAA Advisory Circulars;

    (2) VFR navigation, using pilotage, dead reckoning, and radio aids;

    (3) The recognition of critical weather situations from the ground and in flight and the procurement and use of aeronautical weather reports and forecasts; and

    (4) The safe and efficient operation of airplanes, including high density airport operations, collision avoidance precautions, and radio communication procedures.

61.107 FLIGHT PROFICIENCY.

The applicant for a private pilot certificate must have logged instruction from an authorized flight instructor in at least the following pilot operations. In addition, his logbook must contain an endorsement by an authorized flight instructor who has found him competent to perform each of those operations safely as a private pilot.

(a) *In airplanes.*

    (1) Preflight operations, including weight and balance determination, line inspection, and airplane servicing;

    (2) Airport and traffic pattern operations, including operations at controlled airports, radio communications, and collision avoidance precautions;

    (3) Flight maneuvering by reference to ground objects;

    (4) Flight at critically slow airspeeds, and the recognition of and recovery from imminent and full stalls entered from straight flight and from turns;

    (5) Normal and crosswind takeoffs and landings;

    (6) Control and maneuvering an airplane solely by reference to instruments, including descents

and climbs using radio aids or radar directives;

(7) Cross-country flying, using pilotage, dead reckoning, and radio aids, including one 2-hour flight:

(8) Maximum performance take-offs and landings;

(9) Night flying, including take-offs, landings, and VFR navigation; and

(10) Emergency operations, including simulated aircraft and equipment malfunctions.

61.109 AIRPLANE RATING: AERONAUTICAL EXPERIENCE. ✈

An applicant for a private pilot certificate with an airplane rating must have had at least a total of 40 hours of flight instruction and solo flight time which must include the following:

(a) Twenty hours of flight instruction from an authorized flight instructor, including at least—

(1) Three hours of cross country;

(2) Three hours at night, including 10 takeoffs and landings for applicants seeking night flying privileges, and

(3) Three hours in airplanes in preparation for the private pilot flight test within 60 days prior to that test.

An applicant who does not meet the night flying requirement in paragraph (a)(2) of this section is issued a private pilot certificate bearing the limitation "Night flying prohibited." This limitation may be removed if the holder of the certificate shows that he has met the requirements of paragraph (a)(2) of this section.

(b) Twenty hours of solo flight time, including at least—

(1) Ten hours in airplanes;

(2) Ten hours of cross-country flights, each flight with a landing more than 50 nautical miles from the point of departure, and one with landings at three points, each of which is more than 100 nautical miles from each of the other two points; and

(3) Three solo takeoffs and landings to a full stop at an airport with an operating control tower.

61.111 CROSS-COUNTRY FLIGHTS: PILOTS BASED ON SMALL ISLANDS.

(a) An applicant who shows that he is located on an island from which the required flights cannot be accomplished without flying over water more than 10 nautical miles from the nearest shoreline need not comply with paragraph (b)(2) of 61.109. However, if other airports that permit civil operations are available to which a flight may be made without flying over water more than 10 nautical miles from the nearest shoreline, he must show that he has completed two round trip solo flights between those two airports that are farthest apart, including a landing at each airport on both flights.

(b) The pilot certificate issued to a person under paragraph (a) of this section contains an endorsement with the following limitation which may be subsequently amended to include another island if the applicant complies with paragraph (a) of this section with respect to that island:
Passenger carrying prohibited on flights more than 10 nautical miles from (appropriate island).

(c) If an applicant for a private pilot certificate under paragraph (a) of this section does not have at least 3 hours of solo cross-country flight time, including a round trip flight to an airport at least 50 nautical miles from the place of departure with at least two full stop landings at different points along the route, his pilot certificate is also endorsed as follows:

Holder does not meet the cross-country flight requirements of ICAO.

(d) The holder of a private pilot certificate with an endorsement described in paragraph (b) or (c) of this section, is entitled to a removal of the endorsement, if he presents satisfactory evidence to an FAA inspector or designated pilot examiner that he has complied with the applicable solo cross-country flight requirements and has passed a practical test on cross-country flying.

61.118 PRIVATE PILOT PRIVILEGES AND LIMITATIONS: PILOT IN COMMAND.

Except as provided in paragraphs (a) through (d) of this section, a private pilot may not act as pilot in command of an aircraft that is carrying passengers or property for compensation or hire; nor may he, for compensation or hire, act as pilot in command of an aircraft.

(a) A private pilot may, for compensation or hire, act as pilot in command of an aircraft in connection with any business or employment if the flight is only incidental to that business or employment and the aircraft does not carry passengers or property for compensation or hire.

(b) A private pilot may share the operating expenses of a flight with his passengers.

(c) A private pilot who is an aircraft salesman and who has at least 200 hours of logged flight time may demonstrate an aircraft in flight to a prospective buyer.

(d) A private pilot may act as pilot in command of an aircraft used in a passenger-carrying airlift sponsored by a charitable organization, and for which the passengers make a donation to the organization, if—

(1) The sponsor of the airlift notifies the FAA General Aviation District Office having jurisdiction over the area concerned, at least 7 days before the flight, and furnishes any essential information that the office requests;

(2) The flight is conducted from a public airport adequate for the aircraft used, or from another airport that has been approved for the operation by an FAA inspector;

(3) He has logged at least 200 hours of flight time;

(4) No acrobatic or formation flights are conducted;

(5) Each aircraft used is certificated in the standard category and complies with the 100-hour inspection requirement of 91.169 of this chapter; and

(6) The flight is made under VFR during the day.

For the purpose of paragraph (d) of this section, a "charitable organization" means an organization listed in Publication No. 78 of the Department of the Treasury called the "Cumulative List of Organizations described in section 170(c) of the Internal Revenue Code of 1954," as amended from time to time by published supplemental lists.

61.120 PRIVATE PILOT PRIVILEGES AND LIMITATIONS: SECOND IN COMMAND OF AIRCRAFT REQUIRING MORE THAN ONE REQUIRED PILOT.

Except as provided in paragraphs (a) through (d) of 61.118 a private pilot may not, for compensation or hire, act as second in command of an aircraft that is type certificated for more than one required pilot, nor may he act as second in command of such an aircraft that is carrying passengers or property for compensation or hire.

SECTION D - FAR PART 91

Part 91 contains the general operating and flight rules for aircraft operating within the United States. Since changes and amendments are often made to Part 91, it is important for aviators to remain abreast of such revisions.

SUBPART A — GENERAL

91.1 APPLICABILITY

(a) Except as provided in paragraph (b) of this section, this Part prescribes rules governing the operation of aircraft (other than moored balloons, kites, unmanned rockets and unmanned free balloons) within the United States.

(b) Each person operating a civil aircraft of U.S. registry outside of the United States shall —

  (1) When over the high seas, comply with Annex 2 (Rules of the Air) to the Convention on International Civil Aviation and with 91.70(c) and 91.90 of Subpart B;

  (2) When within a foreign country, comply with the regulations relating to the flight and maneuver of aircraft there in force.

  (3) Except for 91.15(b), 91.17, 91.38 and 91.43, comply with Subparts A, C and D of this Part so far as they are not inconsistent with applicable regulations of the foreign country where the aircraft is operated or Annex 2 to the Convention on International Civil Aviation.

91.3 RESPONSIBILITY AND AUTHORITY OF THE PILOT IN COMMAND ✛

(a) The pilot in command of an aircraft is directly responsible for, and is the final authority as to, the operation of that aircraft.

(b) In an emergency requiring immediate action, the pilot in command may deviate from any rule of this Subpart or of Subpart B to the extent required to meet that emergency.

(c) Each pilot in command who deviates from a rule under paragraph (b) of this section shall, upon the request of the Administrator, send a written report of that deviation to the Administrator.

This is one of the more important regulations for all pilots to be aware of. This regulation gives the pilot in command of an airplane authority to deviate from any regulation in this part to the extent required to safely meet an emergency. This is known as the emergency authority of a pilot in command.

91.5 PREFLIGHT ACTION ✛

Each pilot in command shall, before beginning a flight, familiarize himself with all available information concerning that flight. This information must include:

(a) For a flight under IFR or a flight not in the vicinity of an airport, weather reports and forecasts, fuel requirements, alternatives available if the planned flight cannot be completed, and any known traffic delays of which he has been advised by ATC.

(b) For any flight, runway lengths at airports of intended use, and the following takeoff and landing distance information;

  (1) For civil aircraft for which an approved airplane or rotorcraft flight manual containing takeoff and landing distance data is required, the takeoff and landing

distance data contained therein; and

(2) For civil aircraft other than those specified in subparagraph (1) of this paragraph, other reliable information appropriate to the aircraft, relating to aircraft performance under expected values of airport elevation and runway slope, aircraft gross weight, and wind and temperature.

91.8 PROHIBITION AGAINST INTERFERENCE WITH CREW-MEMBERS

No person may assault, threaten, intimidate, or interfere with a crewmember in the performance of the crewmember's duties aboard an aircraft being operated.

91.9 CARELESS OR RECKLESS OPERATION

No person may operate an aircraft in a careless or reckless manner so as to endanger the life or property of another.

91.10 CARELESS OR RECKLESS OPERATION OTHER THAN FOR THE PURPOSE OF AIR NAVIGATION

No person may operate an aircraft other than for the purpose of air navigation, on any part of the surface of an airport used by aircraft for air commerce (including areas used by those aircraft for receiving or discharging persons or cargo), in a careless or reckless manner so as to endanger the life or property of another.

91.11 LIQUOR AND DRUGS

(a) No person may act as a crewmember of a civil aircraft —
 (1) Within 8 hours after the consumption of any alcoholic beverage;
 (2) While under the influence of alcohol; or
 (3) While using any drug that affects his faculties in any way contrary to safety.

(b) Except in an emergency, no pilot of a civil aircraft may allow a person who is obviously under the influence of intoxicating liquors or drugs (except a medical patient under proper care) to be carried in that aircraft.

91.12 CARRIAGE OF NARCOTIC DRUGS, MARIHUANA, AND DE-PRESSANT OR STIMULANT DRUGS OR SUBSTANCES

(a) Except as provided in paragraph (b) of this section, no person may operate a civil aircraft within the United States with knowledge that narcotic drugs, marihuana, and depressant or stimulant drugs or substances as defined in Federal or State statutes are carried in the aircraft.

(b) Paragraph (a) of this section does not apply to any carriage of narcotic drugs, marihuana, and depressant or stimulant drugs or substances authorized by or under any Federal or State statute or by any Federal or State agency.

91.13 DROPPING OBJECTS

No pilot in command of a civil aircraft may allow any object to be dropped from that aircraft in flight that creates a hazard to persons or property. However, this section does not prohibit the dropping of any object if reasonable precautions are taken to avoid injury or damage to persons or property.

91.14 USE OF SAFETY BELTS

(a) Unless otherwise authorized by the Administrator —
 (1) No pilot may take off a U.S. registered civil aircraft (except a free balloon that incorporates a basket or gondola and an airship) unless the pilot in command of that aircraft ensures that each person on board is briefed on how to fasten and unfasten that person's safety belt.

(2) No pilot may take off or land a U.S. registered civil aircraft (except free balloons that incorporate baskets or gondolas and airships) unless the pilot in command of that aircraft ensures that each person on board has been notified to fasten his safety belt.

(3) During the takeoff and landing of U.S. registered civil aircraft (except free balloons that incorporate baskets or gondolas and airships), each person on board that aircraft must occupy a seat or berth with a safety belt properly secured about him. However, a person who has not reached his second birthday may be held by an adult who is occupying a seat or berth, and a person on board for the purpose of engaging in sport parachuting may use the floor of the aircraft as a seat.

(b) This section does not apply to operations conducted under Part 121, 123, or 127 of this chapter. Paragraph (a)(3) of this section does not apply to persons subject to 91.7.

91.15 PARACHUTES AND PARACHUTING ✛

(a) No pilot of a civil aircraft may allow a parachute that is available for emergency use to be carried in that aircraft unless it is an approved type and—

(1) If a chair type (canopy in back), it has been packed by a certificated and appropriately rated parachute rigger within the preceding 120 days; or

(2) If any other type, it has been packed by a certificated and appropriately rated parachute rigger —

(i) Within the preceding 120 days, if its canopy, shrouds, and harness are composed exclusively of nylon, rayon, or other similar synthetic

fiber or materials that are substantially resistant to damage from mold, mildew, or other fungi and other rotting agents propagated in a moist environment; or

(ii) Within the preceding 60 days, if any part of the parachute is composed of silk, pongee, or other natural fiber, or materials not specified in subdivision (i) of this subparagraph.

(b) Except in an emergency, no pilot in command may allow, and no person may make, a parachute jump from an aircraft within the United States except in accordance with Part 105 (New) of this chapter.

(c) Unless each occupant of the aircraft is wearing an approved parachute, no pilot of a civil aircraft, carrying any person (other than a crewmember) may execute any intentional maneuver that exceeds —

(1) A bank of 60 degrees relative to the horizon; or

(2) A nose-up or nose-down attitude of 30 degrees relative to the horizon.

(d) Paragraph (c) of this section does not apply to —

(1) Flight tests for pilot certification or rating; or

(2) Spins and other flight maneuvers required by the regulations for any certificate or rating when given by

(i) A certificated flight instructor; or

(ii) An airline transport pilot instructing in accordance with 61.169 of this chapter.

91.21 FLIGHT INSTRUCTION; SIMULATED INSTRUMENT FLIGHT AND CERTAIN FLIGHT TESTS

(a) No person may operate a civil aircraft (except a manned free balloon) that is being used for flight instruction unless that aircraft has fully functioning, dual controls.

(b) No person may operate a civil aircraft in simulated instrument flight unless —

(1) An appropriately rated pilot occupies the other control seat as a safety pilot;

(2) The safety pilot has adequate vision forward and to each side of the aircraft, or a competent observer in the aircraft adequately supplements the vision of the safety pilot; and

(3) Except in the case of lighter-than-air aircraft, that aircraft is equipped with fully functioning dual controls.

91.22 FUEL REQUIREMENTS FOR FLIGHT UNDER VFR ✈

(a) No person may begin a flight in an airplane under VFR unless (considering wind and forecast weather conditions) there is enough fuel to fly to the first point of intended landing and, assuming normal cruising speed —

(1) During the day, to fly after that for at least 30 minutes; or

(2) At night, to fly after that for at least 45 minutes.

(b) No person may begin a flight in a rotorcraft under VFR unless (considering wind and forecast weather conditions) there is enough fuel to fly to the first point of intended landing and, assuming normal cruising speed, to fly after that for at least 20 minutes.

91.24 ATC TRANSPONDER EQUIPMENT

(a) *All airspace: U.S. registered civil aircraft.* For operations not conducted under Parts 121, 123, 127, or 135 of this chapter, ATC transponder equipment installed after January 1, 1974, in U.S. registered civil aircraft not previously equipped with an ATC transponder, and all ATC transponder equipment used in U.S. registered civil aircraft after July 1, 1975, must meet the performance and environmental requirements of any class of TSO-C74b or any class of TSO-C74c as appropriate, except that the Administrator may approve the use of TSO-C74 or TSO-C74a equipment after July 1, 1975, if the applicant submits data showing that such equipment meets the minimum performance standards of the appropriate class of TSO-C74c and environmental conditions of the TSO under which it was manufactured.

(b) *Controlled airspace: all aircraft.* Except for persons operating helicopters in terminal control areas at or below 1,000 feet AGL under the terms of a letter of agreement, and except for persons operating gliders above 12,500 feet MSL but below the floor of the positive control area, no person may operate an aircraft in controlled airspace, after the applicable dates prescribed in paragraphs (b)(1) through (b)(4) of this section, unless that aircraft is equipped with an operable coded radar beacon transponder having a Mode 3/A 4096 code capability, replying to Mode 3/A interrogation with the code specified by ATC, and is equipped with automatic pressure altitude reporting equipment having a Mode C capability that automatically replies to Mode C interrogations by transmitting pressure altitude information in 100-foot increments. This requirement applies —

(1) In Group I Terminal Control Areas governed by 91.90(a);

(2) In Group II Terminal Control Areas governed by 91.90(b), except as provided therein;

(3) In Group III Terminal Control Areas governed by 91.90(c), except as provided therein; and

(4) In all controlled airspace of the 48 contiguous States and the District of Columbia, above

12,500 feet MSL, excluding the airspace at and below 2,500 feet AGL.

(c) *ATC authorized deviations.* ATC may authorize deviations from paragraph (b) of this section.

The remainder of 91.24 has been omitted from this publication. For more data, refer to the complete regulation.

91.27 CIVIL AIRCRAFT: CERTIFICATIONS REQUIRED ✈

(a) Except as provided in 91.28, no person may operate a civil aircraft unless it has within it the following:
   (1) An appropriate and current airworthiness certificate.
   (2) A registration certificate issued to its owner.

(b) No person may operate a civil aircraft unless the airworthiness certificate required by paragraph (a) of this section or a special flight authorization issued under 91.28 is displayed at the cabin or cockpit entrance so that it is legible to passengers or crew.

91.29 CIVIL AIRCRAFT AIRWORTHINESS ✈

(a) No person may operate a civil aircraft unless it is in an airworthy condition.

(b) The pilot in command of a civil aircraft is responsible for determining whether that aircraft is in condition for safe flight. He shall discontinue the flight when unairworthy mechanical or structural conditions occur.

91.31 CIVIL AIRCRAFT OPERATING LIMITATIONS AND MARKING REQUIREMENTS ✈

(a) Except as provided in paragraph (d) of this section, no person may operate a civil aircraft without compliance with the operating limitations for that aircraft prescribed by the certificating authority of the country of registry.

(b) No person may operate a U.S. registered civil aircraft —
   (1) For which an Airplane or Rotorcraft Flight Manual is required by 21.5 unless there is available in the aircraft a current approved Airplane or Rotorcraft Flight Manual or the manual provided for in 121.141(b); and
   (2) For which an Airplane or Rotorcraft Flight Manual is not required by 21.5, unless there is available in the aircraft a current approved Airplane or Rotorcraft Flight Manual, approved manual material, markings, and placards, or any combination thereof.

(c) No person may operate a U.S. registered civil aircraft unless that aircraft is identified in accordance with Part 45 of this chapter.

(d) *Not applicable to airplanes.*

(e) The Airplane or Rotorcraft Flight Manual, or manual material, markings and placards required by paragraph (b) of this section must contain each operating limitation prescribed for that aircraft by the Administrator, including the following:
   (1) Powerplant (e.g., r.p.m., manifold pressure, gas temperature, etc.).
   (2) Airspeeds (e.g., normal operating speed, flaps extended speed, etc.).
   (3) Aircraft weight, center of gravity, and weight distribution, including the composition of the useful load in those combinations and ranges intended to ensure that the weight and center of gravity position will remain within approved limits (e.g., combinations and ranges of crew, oil, fuel, and baggage).
   (4) Minimum flight crew.
   (5) Kinds of operation.
   (6) Maximum operating altitude.

Fig. 6-3. Supplemental Oxygen

(7) Maneuvering flight load factors.

(8) Rotor speed (for rotorcraft).

(9) Limiting height-speed envelope (for rotorcraft).

91.32 SUPPLEMENTAL OXYGEN ✈

(a) *General.* No person may operate a civil aircraft of U.S. registry —

(1) At cabin pressure altitudes above 12,500 feet (MSL) up to and including 14,000 feet (MSL), unless the required minimum flight crew is provided with and uses supplemental oxygen for that part of the flight at those altitudes that is of more than 30 minutes duration;

(2) At cabin pressure altitudes above 14,000 feet (MSL), unless the required minimum flight crew is provided with and uses supplemental oxygen during the entire flight time at those altitudes; and

(3) At cabin pressure altitudes above 15,000 feet (MSL), unless each occupant of the aircraft is provided with supplemental oxygen. (See Fig. 6-3.)

(b) *Pressurized cabin aircraft.*

(1) No person may operate a civil aircraft of U.S. registry with a pressurized cabin —

(i) At flight altitudes above flight level 250, unless at least a 10-minute supply of supplemental oxygen in addition to any oxygen required to satisfy paragraph (a) of this section, is available

for each occupant of the aircraft for use in the event that a descent is necessitated by loss of cabin pressurization.

91.33 POWERED CIVIL AIRCRAFT WITH STANDARD CATEGORY U.S. AIRWORTHINESS CERTIFICATES; INSTRUMENT AND EQUIPMENT REQUIREMENTS ✈

(a) *General.* Except as provided in paragraphs (c)(3) and (e) of this section, no person may operate a powered civil aircraft with a standard category U.S. airworthiness certificate in any operation described in paragraphs (b) through (f) of this section unless that aircraft contains the instruments and equipment specified in those paragraphs (or FAA approved equivalents) for that type of operation, and those instruments and items of equipment are in operable condition.

(b) *Visual flight rules (day).* For VFR flight during the day the following instruments and equipment are required:

(1) Airspeed indicator.

(2) Altimeter.

(3) Magnetic direction indicator.

(4) Tachometer for each engine.

(5) Oil pressure gauge for each engine using pressure system.

(6) Temperature gauge for each liquid-cooled engine.

(7) Oil temperature gauge for each air-cooled engine.

(8) Manifold pressure gauge for each altitude engine.

(9) Fuel gauge indicating the quantity of fuel in each tank.

(10) Landing gear position indicator, if the aircraft has a retractable landing gear.

(11) If the aircraft is operated for hire over water and beyond power-off gliding distance from shore, approved flotation gear readily available to each occupant, and at least one pyrotechnic signaling device.

(12) Except as to airships, an approved safety belt for all occupants who have reached their second birthday. After December 4, 1980, each safety belt must be equipped with an approved metal to metal latching device.

(13) For small civil airplanes manufactured after July 18, 1978, an approved shoulder harness for each front seat. The shoulder harness must be designed to protect the occupant from serious head injury when the occupant experiences the ultimate inertia forces specified in 23.561(b)(2) of this chapter. Each shoulder harness installed at a flight crewmember station must permit the crewmember, when seated and with his safety belt and shoulder harness fastened, to perform all functions necessary for flight operations. For purposes of this paragraph—

  (i) The date of manufacture of an airplane is the date the inspection acceptance records reflect that the airplane is complete and meets the FAA Approved Type Design Data; and

  (ii) A front seat is a seat located at flight crewmember station or any seat located alongside such a seat.

(c) *Visual flight rules (night).* For VFR flight at night the following instruments and equipment are required:

(1) Instruments and equipment specified in paragraph (b) of this section.

(2) Approved position lights.

(3) An approved aviation red or aviation white anti-collision light system on all U.S. registered civil aircraft. Anti-collision light systems initially installed after August 11, 1971, on aircraft for which a type certificate was issued or applied for before August 11, 1971, must at least meet the anti-collision light standards of Parts 23, 25, 27, or 29, as applicable, that were in effect on August 10, 1971, except that the color may be either aviation red or aviation white. In the event of failure of any light of the anti-collision light system, operations with the aircraft may be continued to a stop where repairs or replacement can be made.

(4) If the aircraft is operated for hire, one electric landing light.

(5) An adequate source of electrical energy for all installed electric and radio equipment.

(6) One spare set of fuses, or three spare fuses of each kind required.

(d) and (e) *Not applicable to private pilot.*

91.52 EMERGENCY LOCATOR TRANSMITTERS

(a) Except as provided in paragraph (e) and (f) of this section, no person may operate a U.S. registered civil airplane unless it meets the applicable requirements of paragraphs (b), (c), and (d) of this section.

(b) To comply with paragraph (a) of this section, each U.S. registered civil airplane must be equipped as follows: (1)(2)(3) *Not applicable to private pilot.*

(4) For operations other than those specified in subparagraphs (1),

(2), and (3) of this paragraph, there must be attached to the airplane a personnel type or an automatic type emergency locator transmitter that is in operable condition and meets the applicable requirements of 37.200 of this chapter.

(c) Each emergency locator transmitter required by paragraph (a) and (b) of this section must be attached to the airplane in such a manner that the probability of damage to the transmitter, in the event of crash impact, is minimized. Fixed and deployable automatic type transmitters must be attached to the airplane as far aft as practicable.

(d) Batteries used in the emergency locator transmitters required by paragraphs (a) and (b) of this section must be replaced (or recharged, if the battery is rechargeable) —
  (1) When the transmitter has been in use for more than one cumulative hour; or
  (2) When 50 percent of their useful life (or, for rechargeable batteries, 50 percent of their useful life of charge), as established by the transmitter manufacturer under 37.200(g)(2) of this chapter, has expired.

The new expiration date for the replacement (or recharge) of the battery must be legibly marked on the outside of the transmitter and entered in the aircraft maintenance record. Subparagraph (2) of this paragraph does not apply to batteries (such as water-activated batteries) that are essentially unaffected during probable storage intervals.

(e) *Pertains only to ferry operations*
No person other than required crewmembers may be carried aboard an airplane being ferried pursuant to paragraph (e) of this section.

(f) Paragraphs (a) and (b) of this section do not apply to —

(1) Turbojet-powered aircraft;
(2) Aircraft while engaged in scheduled flights by scheduled air carriers certificated by the Civil Aeronautics Board;
(3) Aircraft while engaged in training operations conducted entirely within a 50-mile radius of the airport from which such local flight operations began;
(4) Aircraft while engaged in flight operations incident to design and testing;
(5) New aircraft while engaged in flight operations incident to their manufacture, preparation, and delivery;
(6) Aircraft while engaged in flight operations incident to the aerial application of chemicals and other substances for agricultural purposes;
(7) Aircraft certificated by the Administrator for research and development purposes;
(8) Aircraft while used for showing compliance with regulations, crew training, exhibition, air racing, or market surveys;
(9) Aircraft equipped to carry not more than one person; and
(10) An aircraft during any period for which the transmitter has been temporarily removed for inspection, repair, modification or replacement, subject to the following:
  (i) No person may operate the aircraft unless the aircraft records contain an entry which includes the date of initial removal, the make, model, serial number and reason for removal of the transmitter, and a placard is located in view of the pilot to show "ELT not installed."
  (ii) No person may operate the aircraft more than 90 days after the ELT is initially removed from the aircraft.

SUBPART B—FLIGHT RULES: GENERAL

91.61 APPLICABILITY

This subpart prescribes flight rules governing the operation of aircraft within the United States.

91.63 WAIVERS

(a) The Administrator may issue a certificate of waiver authorizing the operation of aircraft in deviation of any rule of this subpart if he finds that the proposed operation can be safely conducted under the terms of the certificate of waiver.

(b) An application for a certificate of waiver under this section is made on a form and in a manner prescribed by the Administrator and may be submitted to any FAA office.

(c) A certificate of waiver is effective as specified on that certificate.

91.65 OPERATING NEAR OTHER AIRCRAFT ✈

(a) No person may operate an aircraft so close to another aircraft as to create a collision hazard.

(b) No person may operate an aircraft in formation flight except by arrangement with the pilot in command of each aircraft in the formation.

(c) No person may operate an aircraft, carrying passengers for hire, in formation flight.

(d) Unless otherwise authorized by ATC, no person operating an aircraft may operate his aircraft in accordance with any clearance or instruction that has been issued to the pilot of another aircraft for radar Air Traffic Control purposes.

91.67 RIGHT-OF-WAY: EXCEPT WATER OPERATIONS ✈

(a) *General.* When weather conditions permit, regardless of whether an operation is conducted under Instrument Flight Rules, vigilance shall be maintained by each person operating an aircraft so as to see and avoid other aircraft in compliance with this section. When a rule of this section gives another aircraft right-of-way, he shall give way to that aircraft and may not pass over, under, or ahead of it, unless well clear.

(b) *In distress.* An aircraft in distress has the right-of-way over all other air traffic.

(c) *Converging.* When aircraft of the same category are converging at approximately the same altitude (except head-on, or nearly so), the aircraft to the other's right has the right-of-way. If the aircraft are of different categories:

(1) A balloon has the right-of-way over any other category of aircraft;

(2) A glider has the right-of-way over an airship, airplane or rotorcraft; and

(3) An airship has the right-of-way over an airplane or rotorcraft.

However, an aircraft towing or refueling other aircraft has the right-of-way over all other engine-driven aircraft.

(d) *Approaching head-on.* When aircraft are approaching each other head-on, or nearly so, each pilot of each aircraft shall alter course to the right to pass well clear.

(e) *Overtaking.* Each aircraft that is being overtaken has the right-of-way and each pilot of an overtaking aircraft shall alter course to the right to pass well clear.

(f) *Landing.* Aircraft, while on final approach to land, or while landing, have the right-of-way over other aircraft in flight or operating on the surface. When two or more aircraft are approaching an airport for the purpose of landing, the aircraft at the lower altitude has the right-of-way, but it shall not take advantage of this rule to cut in front of another which is on final approach to land, or to overtake that aircraft.

(g) *Inapplicability.* This section does not apply to the operation of an aircraft on water.

91.69 RIGHT-OF-WAY RULES: WATER OPERATIONS

(a) *General.* Each person operating an aircraft on the water shall, insofar as possible, keep well clear of all vessels and avoid impeding their navigation, and shall give way to any vessel or other aircraft that is given the right-of-way by any rule of this section.

(b) *Crossing.* When aircraft, or an aircraft and a vessel, are on crossing courses, the aircraft or vessel to the other's right has the right-of-way.

(c) *Approaching head-on.* When aircraft, or an aircraft and a vessel, are approaching head-on or nearly so, each shall alter its course to the right to keep well clear.

(d) *Overtaking.* Each aircraft or vessel that is being overtaken has the right-of-way, and the one overtaking shall alter course to keep well clear.

(e) *Special circumstances.* When aircraft, or an aircraft and a vessel, approach so as to involve risk of collision, each aircraft or vessel shall proceed with careful regard to existing circumstances, including the limitations of the respective craft.

91.70 AIRCRAFT SPEED

(a) Unless otherwise authorized by the Administrator, no person may operate an aircraft below 10,000 feet MSL at an indicated airspeed of more than 250 knots (288 MPH).

(b) Unless otherwise authorized or required by ATC, no person may operate an aircraft within an airport traffic area at an indicated airspeed of more than:

(1) In the case of a reciprocating engine aircraft, 156 knots (180 MPH); or

(2) In the case of a turbine-powered aircraft, 200 knots (230 MPH).

Paragraph (b) of this section does not apply to any operations within a Terminal Control Area. Such operations shall comply with paragraph (a) of this section.

(c) No person may operate an aircraft in the airspace underlying a terminal control area, or in a VFR corridor designated through a terminal control area, at an indicated airspeed of more than 200 knots (230 m.p.h.).

However, if the minimum safe airspeed for any particular operation is greater than the maximum speed prescribed in this section, the aircraft may be operated at that minimum speed.

91.71 ACROBATIC FLIGHT ✈

No person may operate an aircraft in acrobatic flight —
(a) Over any congested area of a city, town, or settlement;
(b) Over an open air assembly of persons;
(c) Within a control zone or Federal airway;
(d) Below an altitude of 1,500 feet above the surface; or
(e) When flight visibility is less than three miles.

For the purposes of this section, acrobatic flight means an intentional maneuver involving an abrupt change in an aircraft's attitude, an abnormal attitude, or abnormal acceleration, not necessary for normal flight.

91.73 AIRCRAFT LIGHTS ✈

No person may, during the period from sunset to sunrise (or, in Alaska, during the period a prominent unlighted object cannot be seen from a distance of three statute miles or the sun is more than six degrees below the horizon) —
(a) Operate an aircraft unless it has lighted position lights;
(b) Park or move an aircraft in, or in dangerous proximity to, a night flight operations area of an airport unless the aircraft —
  (1) Is clearly illuminated;
  (2) Has lighted position lights; or
  (3) Is in an area which is marked by obstruction lights.
(c) *Not applicable to private pilot.*
(d) Operate an aircraft, required by 91.33(c)(3) to be equipped with an anticollision light system, unless it has approved and lighted aviation red or aviation white anticollision lights. However, the anticollision lights need not be lighted when the pilot in command determines that, because of operating conditions, it

would be in the interest of safety to turn the lights off.

91.75 COMPLIANCE WITH ATC CLEARANCES AND INSTRUCTIONS ✈

(a) When an ATC clearance has been obtained, no pilot in command may deviate from that clearance, except in an emergency, unless he obtains an amended clearance. However, except in positive controlled airspace, this paragraph does not prohibit him from cancelling an IFR flight plan if he is operating in VFR weather conditions. If a pilot is uncertain of the meaning of an ATC clearance, he shall immediately request clarification from ATC.
(b) Except in an emergency, no person may, in an area in which air traffic control is exercised, operate an aircraft contrary to an ATC instruction.
(c) Each pilot in command who deviates, in an emergency, from an ATC clearance or instruction shall notify ATC of that deviation as soon as possible.
(d) Each pilot in command who (though not deviating from a rule of this subpart) is given priority by ATC in an emergency, shall, if requested by ATC, submit a detailed report of that emergency within 48 hours to the chief of that ATC facility.

91.77 ATC LIGHT SIGNALS ✈
See Fig. 6-4

91.79 MINIMUM SAFE ALTITUDES; GENERAL ✈

Except when necessary for takeoff or landing, no person may operate an aircraft below the following altitudes:
(a) *Anywhere.* An altitude allowing, if a power unit fails, an emergency landing without undue hazard to persons or property on the surface.
(b) *Over congested areas.* Over any congested area of a city, town, or settlement, or over an open air assembly of persons, an altitude of 1,000 feet above the highest

Color and type of signal	Meaning with respect to aircraft on the surface	Meaning with respect to aircraft in flight
Steady green	Cleared for takeoff	Cleared to land
Flashing green	Cleared to taxi	Return for landing (to be followed by steady green at proper time)
Steady red	Stop	Give way to other aircraft and continue circling
Flashing red	Taxi clear of runway in use	Airport unsafe — do not land
Flashing white	Return to starting point on airport	Not applicable
Alternating red and green	Exercise extreme caution	Exercise extreme caution

Fig. 6-4. ATC Light Signals

obstacle within a horizontal radius of 2,000 feet of the aircraft.

(c) *Over other than congested areas.* An altitude of 500 feet above the surface, except* over open water or sparsely populated areas. In that case, the aircraft may not be operated closer than 500 feet to any person, vessel, vehicle, or structure.

(d) *Helicopters.* Helicopters may be operated at less than the minimums prescribed in paragraph (b) or (c) of this section if the operation is conducted without hazard to persons or property on the surface. In addition, each person operating a helicopter shall comply with routes or altitudes specifically prescribed for helicopters by the Administrator.

91.81 ALTIMETER SETTINGS +

(a) Each person operating an aircraft shall maintain the cruising altitude or flight level of that aircraft, as the case may be, by reference to an altimeter that is set, when operating:
  (1) Below 18,000 feet MSL, to:
    (i) The current reported altimeter setting of a sta-

tion along the route and within 100 nautical miles of the aircraft;
    (ii) If there is no station within the area prescribed in subdivision (i) of this subparagraph, the current reported altimeter setting of an appropriate available station; or
    (iii) In the case of an aircraft not equipped with a radio, the elevation of the departure airport or an appropriate altimeter setting available before departure; or
  (2) at or above 18,000 feet MSL, to 29.92" Hg.

Above 18,000 feet, flight levels begin for all aircraft operating VFR or IFR. The pilot will set his altimeter to 29.92 in. regardless of the local station pressure. Altitudes are then referred to as flight levels. For instance, 23,000 feet would be flight level 230.

91.83 FLIGHT PLAN: INFORMATION REQUIRED +

(a) Unless otherwise authorized by ATC, each person filing an IFR or VFR flight plan shall include in it the following information:

(1) The aircraft identification number and, if necessary, its radio call sign.

(2) The type of the aircraft or, in the case of a formation flight, the type of each aircraft and the number of aircraft, in the formation.

(3) The full name and address of the pilot in command or, in the case of a formation flight, the formation commander.

(4) The point and proposed time of departure.

(5) The proposed route, cruising altitude (or flight level), and true airspeed at that altitude.

(6) The point of first intended landing and the estimated elapsed time until over that point.

(7) The radio frequencies to be used.

(8) The amount of fuel on board (in hours).

(9) In the case of an IFR flight plan, an alternate airport, except as provided in paragraph (b) of this section.

(10) In the case of an international flight, the number of persons in the aircraft.

(11) Any other information the pilot in command or ATC believes is necessary for ATC purposes.

(d) *Cancellation.* When a flight plan has been activated, the pilot in command, upon cancelling or completing the flight under the flight plan, shall notify an FAA Flight Service Station or ATC facility.

Even though the filing of a flight plan is not required by regulation, in the event of an emergency landing, it could save your life by making rescue easier.

91.84 FLIGHTS BETWEEN MEXICO OR CANADA AND THE UNITED STATES

Unless otherwise authorized by ATC, no person may operate a civil aircraft between Mexico and Canada and the United States without filing an IFR or VFR flight plan, as appropriate.

91.85 OPERATING ON OR IN THE VICINITY OF AN AIRPORT; GENERAL RULES ✈

(a) Unless otherwise required by Part 93 of this chapter, each person operating an aircraft on or in the vicinity of an airport shall comply with the requirements of this section and of 91.87 and 91.89.

(b) Unless otherwise authorized or required by ATC, no person may operate an aircraft within an airport traffic area except for the purpose of landing at, or taking off from, an airport within that area. ATC authorizations may be given as individual approval of specific operations or may be contained in written agreements between airport users and the tower concerned.

91.87 OPERATION AT AIRPORTS WITH OPERATING CONTROL TOWERS ✈

(a) *General.* Unless otherwise authorized or required by ATC, each person operating an aircraft to, from, or on an airport with an operating control tower shall comply with the applicable provisions of this section.

(b) *Communications with control towers operated by the United States.* No person may, within an airport traffic area, operate an aircraft to, from, or on an airport having a control tower operated by the United States unless two-way radio communications are maintained between that aircraft and the control tower. However, if the aircraft radio fails in flight, he may operate that aircraft and land if weather conditions are at or above basic VFR weather minimums, he maintains visual contact with the tower, and he receives clearance to land.

(c) *Communications with other control towers.* No person may, within an airport traffic area, operate an aircraft to, from, or on an airport having a control tower that is operated by any person other than the United States unless:

    (1) If that aircraft's radio equipment so allows, two-way radio communications are maintained between the aircraft and the tower; or

    (2) If that aircraft's radio equipment allows only reception from the tower, the pilot has the tower's frequency monitored.

(d) *Minimum Altitudes.* When operating to an airport with an operating control tower, each pilot of— *(1) and (2) Not applicable to private pilot operations.*

    (3) An airplane approaching to land on a runway served by a visual approach slope indicator, shall maintain an altitude at or above the glide slope until a lower altitude is necessary for a safe landing.

However, subparagraphs (2) and (3) of this paragraph do not prohibit normal bracketing maneuvers above or below the glide slope that are conducted for the purpose of remaining on the glide slope.

(e) *Approaches.* When approaching to land at an airport with an operating control tower, each pilot of:

    (1) An airplane, shall circle the airport to the left; and

    (2) A helicopter, shall avoid the flow of fixed-wing aircraft.

(f) *Departures.* No person may operate an aircraft taking off from an airport with an operating control tower except in compliance with the following:

    (1) Each pilot shall comply with any departure procedures established for that airport by the FAA.

    (2) Unless otherwise required by the departure procedure or the applicable distance from clouds criteria, each pilot of a turbine-powered airplane and each pilot of a large airplane shall climb to an altitude of 1,500 feet above the surface as rapidly as practicable.

(h) *Clearances required.* No pilot may, at an airport with an operating control tower, taxi an aircraft on a runway, or take off or land an aircraft, unless he has received an appropriate clearance from ATC. A clearance to "taxi to" the runway is a clearance to cross all intersecting runways but is not a clearance to "taxi on" the assigned runway.

91.89 OPERATION AT AIRPORTS WITHOUT CONTROL TOWERS

(a) Each person operating an aircraft to or from an airport without an operating control tower shall:

    (1) In the case of an airplane approaching to land, make all turns of that airplane to the left unless the airport displays approved light signals or visual markings indicating that turns should be made to the right, in which case the pilot shall make all turns to the right.

    (2) In the case of a helicopter approaching to land, avoid the flow of fixed-wing aircraft; and

    (3) In the case of an aircraft departing the airport, comply with any FAA traffic pattern for that airport.

91.90 TERMINAL CONTROL AREAS.

(a) *Group I terminal control areas.*

   (1) *Operating rules.* No person may operate an aircraft within a Group I terminal control area designated in Part 71 of this chapter except in compliance with the following rules:

      (i) No person may operate an aircraft within a Group I terminal control area unless he has received an appropriate authorization from ATC prior to the operation of that aircraft in that area.

      (ii) Unless otherwise authorized by ATC, each person operating a large turbine engine powered airplane to or from a primary airport shall operate at or above the designated floors while within the lateral limits of the terminal control area.

   (2) *Pilot requirements.* The pilot in command of a civil aircraft may not land or take off that aircraft from an airport within a Group I terminal control area unless he holds at least a private pilot certificate.

   (3) *Equipment requirements.* Unless otherwise authorized by ATC in the case of in-flight VOR, TACAN, or two-way radio failure; or unless otherwise authorized by ATC in the case of a transponder failure occurring at any time, no person may operate an aircraft within a Group I terminal control area unless that aircraft is equipped with—

      (i) An operable VOR or TACAN receiver (except in the case of helicopters);

      (ii) An operable two-way radio capable of communicating with ATC on appropriate frequencies for that terminal control area; and

      (iii) The applicable equipment specified in 91.24.

(b) *Group II terminal control areas.*

   (1) *Operating rules.* No person may operate an aircraft within a Group II terminal control area designated in Part 71 of this chapter except in compliance with the following rules:

(i) No person may operate an aircraft within a Group II Terminal Control Area unless he has received an appropriate authorization from ATC prior to operation of that aircraft in that area, and unless two-way radio communications are maintained within that area, between that aircraft and the ATC facility.

(ii) Unless otherwise authorized by ATC, each person operating a large turbine engine powered airplane to or from a primary airport shall operate at or above the designated floors while within the lateral limits of the terminal control area.

(2) *Equipment requirements.* Unless otherwise authorized by ATC in the case of in-flight VOR, TACAN, or two-way radio failure; or unless otherwise authorized by ATC in the case of a transponder failure occurring at any time, no person may operate an aircraft within a Group II terminal control area unless that aircraft is equipped with—

(i) An operable VOR or TACAN receiver (except in the case of helicopters);

(ii) An operable two-way radio capable of communicating with ATC on the appropriate frequencies for that terminal control area; and

(iii) The applicable equipment specified in 91.24, except that automatic pressure altitude reporting equipment is not required for any operation within the terminal control area, and a transponder is not required for IFR flights operating to or from an airport outside of but in close proximity to the terminal control area, when the commonly used transition, approach, or departure procedures to such airport require flight within the terminal control area.

NOTE:
The FAA has proposed that the regulatory provisions for the designation of Group III Terminal Control Areas be eliminated. If the proposal is adopted, FAR Part 91.24 and 91.90 will be modified accordingly.

(c) *Group III terminal control areas.* After the date specified in 91.24(b)(3), no person may operate an aircraft within a Group III Terminal Control Area designated in Part 71 unless the applicable provisions of 91.24(b) are complied with, except that such compliance is not required if two-way radio communications are maintained, within the TCA, between the aircraft and the ATC facility, and the pilot provides position, altitude, and proposed flight path prior to entry.

91.91 TEMPORARY FLIGHT RESTRICTIONS ✈

(a) Whenever the Administrator determines it to be necessary in order to prevent an unsafe congestion of sight-seeing aircraft above an incident or event which may generate a high degree of public interest, or to provide a safe environment for the operation of disaster relief aircraft, a Notice to Airmen will be issued designating an area within which temporary flight restrictions apply.

(b) When a Notice to Airmen has been issued under this Section, no person may operate an aircraft within the designated area unless:

(1) That aircraft is participating in disaster relief activities and is being operated under the

direction of the agency responsible for relief activities;

(2) That aircraft is being operated to or from an airport within the area and is operated so as not to hamper or endanger relief activities;

(3) That operation is specifically authorized under an IFR ATC clearance;

(4) VFR flight around or above the area is impracticable due to weather, terrain, or other considerations, prior notice is given to the Air Traffic Service facility specified in the Notice to Airmen, and en route operation through the area is conducted so as not to hamper or endanger relief activities; or

(5) That aircraft is carrying properly accredited news representatives, or persons on official business concerning the incident or event which generated the Notice to Airmen; the operation is conducted in accordance with 91.79; the operation is conducted above the altitudes being used by relief aircraft unless otherwise authorized by the agency responsible for relief activities; and further, in connection with this type of operation, prior to entering the area the operator has filed with the Air Traffic Service facility specified in the Notice to Airmen a flight plan which includes the following information:

(i) Aircraft identification, type, and color;

(ii) Radio communications frequencies to be used;

(iii) Proposed times of entry and exit of the designated area;

(iv) Name of news media or purpose of flight; and

(v) Any other information deemed necessary by ATC.

91.93 FLIGHT TEST AREAS

No person may flight test an aircraft except over open water, or sparsely populated areas, having light air traffic.

91.104 FLIGHT RESTRICTIONS IN THE PROXIMITY OF THE PRESIDENTIAL AND OTHER PARTIES

No person may operate an aircraft over or in the vicinity of any area to be visited or traveled by the President, the Vice President, or other public figures contrary to the restrictions established by the Administrator and published in Notice to Airmen (NOTAM).

VISUAL FLIGHT RULES

91.105 BASIC VFR WEATHER MINIMUMS

(a) Except as provided in 91.107, no person may operate an aircraft under VFR when the flight visibility is less, or at a distance from clouds that is less, than that prescribed for the corresponding altitude shown in figure 6-5.

(b) When the visiblity is less than one mile, a helicopter may be operated outside controlled airspace at 1,200 feet or less above the surface if operated at a speed that allows the pilot adequate opportunity to see any air traffic or other obstructions in time to avoid a collision.

(c) Except as provided in 91.107, no person may operate an aircraft, under VFR, within a control zone beneath the ceiling when the ceiling is less than 1,000 feet.

(d) Except as provided in 91.107, no person may take off or land an aircraft, or enter the traffic pattern of an airport, under VFR, within a control zone:

(1) Unless ground visibility at that airport is at least 3 statute miles; and

Altitude	Flight visibility	Distance from clouds
1,200 feet or less above the surface (regardless of MSL altitude)		
Within controlled airspace	3 statute miles	500 feet below 1,000 feet above 2,000 feet horizontal
Outside controlled airspace	1 statute mile except as provided in 91.105(b)	Clear of clouds
More than 1,200 feet above the surface but less than 10,000 feet MSL		
Within controlled airspace	3 statute miles	500 feet below 1,000 feet above 2,000 feet horizontal
Outside controlled airspace	1 statute mile	500 feet below 1,000 feet above 2,000 feet horizontal
More than 1,200 feet above the surface and at or above 10,000 feet MSL.	5 statute miles	1,000 feet below 1,000 feet above 1 mile horizontal

Fig. 6-5. Weather Minimum Table

(2) If ground visibility is not reported at that airport, unless flight visibility during landing or takeoff, or while operating in the traffic pattern, is at least 3 statute miles.

(e) For the purposes of this section, an aircraft operating at the base altitude of a transition area or control area is considered to be within the airspace directly below that area.

91.107 SPECIAL VFR WEATHER MINIMUMS

(a) Except as provided in 93.113 of this chapter, when a person has received an appropriate ATC clearance, the special weather minimums of this section instead of those contained in 91.105 apply to the operation of an aircraft by that person in a control zone under VFR.

(b) No person may operate an aircraft in a control zone under VFR except clear of clouds.

(c) No person may operate an aircraft (other than a helicopter) in a control zone under VFR unless flight visibility is at least one statute mile.

(d) No person may take off or land an aircraft (other than a helicopter) at any airport in a control zone under VFR:
(1) Unless ground visibility at that airport is at least 1 statute mile; or
(2) If ground visibility is not reported at that airport, unless flight visibility during landing or takeoff is at least 1 statute mile.

(e) No person may operate an aircraft (other than a helicopter) in a control zone under the special weather minimums of this section, between sunset and sunrise (or in Alaska, when the sun is more than 6 degrees below the horizon) unless:

(1) That person meets the applicable requirements for instru-

ment flight under Part 61 of this chapter; and

  (2) The aircraft is equipped as required in 91.33(d).

Special VFR weather minimums allow non-instrument rated pilots and airplanes not on IFR flight plans to takeoff with ceiling and visibility below basic VFR minimums. An ATC clearance must be received, however, and the pilot must follow all ATC instructions. In addition, to receive such a clearance, a visibility of at least one mile must exist and the pilot must be able to remain clear of clouds. At many major air terminals, special VFR is not authorized, and this information can be obtained from aeronautical charts, the AIM or from FAR Part 93.

91.109 VFR CRUISING ALTITUDE OR FLIGHT LEVEL ✈

Except while holding in a holding pattern of 2 minutes or less, or while turning, each person operating an aircraft under VFR in level cruising flight more than 3,000 feet above the surface shall maintain the appropriate altitude or flight level prescribed below, unless otherwise authorized by ATC.

(a) When operating below 18,000 feet MSL and —

  (1) On a magnetic course of zero degrees through 179 degrees, any odd thousand foot MSL altitude plus 500 feet (such as 3,500, 5,500, or 7,500); or

  (2) On a magnetic course of 180 degrees through 359 degrees, any even thousand foot MSL altitude plus 500 feet (such as 4,500, 6,500 or 8,500).

(b) When operating above 18,000 feet MSL to flight level 290 (inclusive), and —

  (1) On a magnetic course of zero degrees through 179 degrees, any odd flight level plus 500 feet (such as 195, 215 or 235); or

  (2) On a magnetic course of 180 degrees through 359 degrees, any even flight level plus 500 feet (such as 185, 205, or 235).

(c) When operating above flight level 290 and—

  (1) On a magnetic course of zero degrees through 179 degrees, any flight level, at 4,000-foot intervals, beginning at and including flight level 300 (such as flight level 300, 340, or 380); or

  (2) On a magnetic course of 180 degrees through 359 degrees, any flight level at 4,000 foot intervals, beginning at and including flight level 320 (such as flight level 320, 360, or 400).

SUBPART C — MAINTENANCE, PREVENTIVE MAINTENANCE, AND ALTERATIONS

91.161 APPLICABILITY ✈

(a) This subpart prescribes rules governing the maintenance, preventive maintenance, and alteration of U.S. registered civil aircraft operating within or without the United States.

91.163 GENERAL ✈

(a) The owner or operator of an aircraft is primarily responsible for maintaining that aircraft in an airworthy condition, including compliance with Part 39 of this chapter.

(b) No person may perform maintenance, preventive maintenance, or alterations on an aircraft other than as prescribed in this subpart and other applicable regulations, including Part 43 of this chapter.

Part 43 is entitled "Maintenance, Preventive Maintenance, Rebuilding, and Alteration."

(c) No person may operate a rotorcraft for which a Rotorcraft Maintenance

Manual containing an "Airworthiness Limitations" section has been issued unless the replacement times, inspection intervals, and related procedures specified in that section of the manual are complied with.

91.165 MAINTENANCE REQUIRED

Each owner or operator of an aircraft shall have that aircraft inspected as prescribed in Subpart D or 91.169 of this part, as appropriate, and 91.170 of this part and shall, between required inspections, have defects repaired as prescribed in Part 43 of this chapter. In addition, he shall ensure that maintenance personnel make appropriate entries in the aircraft and maintenance records indicating the

91.169 INSPECTIONS

(a) Except as provided in paragraph (c) of this section, no person may operate an aircraft unless, within the preceding 12 calendar months, it has had —
  (1) An annual inspection in accordance with Part 43 of this chapter and has been approved for return to service by a person authorized by 43.7 of this chapter; or
  (2) An inspection for the issue of an airworthiness certificate.
No inspection performed under paragraph (b) of this section may be substituted for any inspection required by this paragraph unless it is performed by a person authorized to perform annual inspections, and is entered as an "annual" inspection in the required maintenance records.
(b) Except as provided in paragraph (c) of this section, no person may operate an aircraft carrying any person (other than a crewmember) for hire, and no person may give flight instruction for hire in an aircraft which that person provides, unless within the preceding 100 hours of

time in service it has received an annual or 100-hour inspection and been approved for return to service in accordance with Part 43 of this chapter, or received an inspection for the issuance of an airworthiness certificate in accordance with Part 21 of this chapter. The 100-hour limitation may be exceeded by not more than 10 hours if necessary to reach a place at which the inspection can be done. The excess time, however, is included in computing the next 100 hours of time in service.
(c) Paragraphs (a) and (b) of this section do not apply to —
  (1) Any aircraft for which its registered owner or operator complies with the progressive inspection requirements of 91.171 and Part 43 of this chapter;
  (2) An aircraft that carries a special flight permit or a current experimental or provisional certificate;
  (3) Any airplane operated by an air travel club that is inspected in accordance with Part 123 of this chapter and the operator's manual and operations specifications; or

Part 123 governs the certification and operation of air travel clubs using large aircraft.

  (4) An aircraft inspected in accordance with an approved aircraft inspection program under Part 135 of this chapter and so identified by the registration number in the operations specifications of the certificate holder having the approved inspection program.

91.173 MAINTENANCE RECORDS

(a) Except for work performed in accordance with 91.170 and 91.177, each registered owner or operator shall keep the following records for the periods specified in paragraph (b) of this section;

(1) Records of the maintenance and alteration, and records of the 100-hour, annual, progressive, and other required or approved inspections as appropriate, for each aircraft (including the airframe) and each engine, propeller, rotor, and appliance of an aircraft. The records must include —

    (i) A description (or reference to data acceptable to the Administrator) of the work performed;

    (ii) The date of completion of the work performed; and

    (iii) The signature and certificate number of the person approving the aircraft for return to service.

(2) Records containing the following information:

    (i) The total time in service of the airframe.

    (ii) The current status of life-limited parts of each airframe, engine, propeller, rotor, and appliance.

    (iii) The time since last overhaul of all items installed on the aircraft which are required to be overhauled on a specified time basis.

    (iv) The identification of the current inspection status of the aircraft, including the times since the last inspections required by the inspection program under which the aircraft and its appliances are maintained.

    (v) The current status of applicable airworthiness directives (AD) including, for each, the method of compliance, the AD number, and revision date. If the AD involves recurring action, the time and date when the next action is required.

    (vi) A list of current major alterations to each airframe, engine, propeller, rotor, and appliance.

(b) The owner or operator shall retain the following records for the periods prescribed:

(1) The records specified in paragraph (a)(1) of this section shall be retained until the work is repeated or superseded by other work or for one year after the work is performed.

(2) The records specified in paragraph (a)(2) of this section shall be retained and transferred with the aircraft at the time the aircraft is sold.

(c) The owner or operator shall make all maintenance records required to be kept by this section available for inspection by the Administrator or any authorized representative of the National Transportation Safety Board (NTSB).

SECTION E - NTSB PART 830

RULES PERTAINING TO THE NOTIFICATION AND REPORTING OF AIRCRAFT ACCIDENTS OR INCIDENTS AND OVERDUE AIRCRAFT, AND PRESERVATION OF AIRCRAFT WRECKAGE, MAIL, CARGO, AND RECORDS

SUBPART A — GENERAL

830.1 APPLICABILITY

This part contains rules pertaining to:

(a) Providing notice of and reporting, aircraft accidents and incidents and certain other occurrences in the operation of aircraft when they involve civil aircraft of the United States wherever they occur, or foreign civil aircraft when such events occur in the United States, its territories or possessions.

(b) Preservation of aircraft wreckage, mail, cargo, and records involving all civil aircraft in the United States, its territories or possessions.

830.2 DEFINITIONS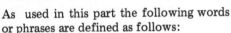

As used in this part the following words or phrases are defined as follows:

AIRCRAFT ACCIDENT means an occurrence associated with the operation of an aircraft which takes place between the time any person boards the aircraft with the intention of flight until such time as all such persons have disembarked, and in which any person suffers death or serious injury as a result of being in or upon the aircraft or by direct contact with the aircraft or anything attached thereto, or in which the aircraft receives substantial damage.

FATAL INJURY means any injury which results in death within 7 days of the accident.

OPERATOR means any person who causes or authorizes the operation of an aircraft, such as the owner, lessee, or bailee of an aircraft.

SERIOUS INJURY means any injury which (1) requires hospitalization for more than 48 hours, commencing within 7 days from the date the injury was received; (2) Results in a fracture of any bone (except simple fractures of fingers, toes, or nose); (3) involves lacerations which cause severe hemorrhages, nerve, muscle, or tendon damage; (4) involves injury to any internal organ; or (5) involves second or third degree burns, or any burns affecting more than 5 percent of the body surface.

SUBSTANTIAL DAMAGE:

(1) Except as provided in subparagraph (2) of this paragraph, substantial damage means damage or structural failure which adversely affects the structural strength, performance, or flight characteristics of the aircraft, and which would normally require major repair or replacement of the affected component.

(2) Engine failure, damage limited to an engine, bent fairings or cowling, dented skin, small punctured holes in the skin or fabric, ground damage to rotor or propeller blades, damage to landing gear, wheels, tires, flaps, engine accessories, brakes, or wing-tips are not considered "substantial damage" for the purpose of this part.

SUBPART B — INITIAL NOTIFICATION OF AIRCRAFT ACCIDENTS, INCIDENTS, AND OVERDUE AIRCRAFT

830.5 IMMEDIATE NOTIFICATION ✈

The operator of an aircraft shall immediately, and by the most expeditious means available, notify the nearest National Transportation Safety Board (Board), Bureau of Aviation Safety field office when:

(a) An aircraft accident or any of the following listed incidents occur:

(1) Flight control system malfunction or failure;

(2) Inability of any required flight crewmember to perform his normal flight duties as a result of injury or illness;

(3) Turbine engine rotor failures excluding compressor blades and turbine buckets;

(4) In-flight fire; or

(5) Aircraft collide in flight.

(b) An aircraft is overdue and is believed to have been involved in an accident.

830.6 INFORMATION TO BE GIVEN IN NOTIFICATION ✈

The notification required in 830.5 shall contain the following information, if available:

(a) Type, nationality, and registration marks of the aircraft;

(b) Name of owner, and operator of the aircraft;

(c) Name of the pilot-in-command;

(d) Date and time of the accident;

(e) Last point of departure and point of intended landing of the aircraft;

(f) Position of the aircraft with reference to some easily defined geographical point;

(g) Number of persons aboard, number killed, and number seriously injured;

(h) Nature of the accident, the weather and the extent of damage to the aircraft, so far as is known; and

(i) A description of any explosives, radioactive materials, or other dangerous articles carried.

SUBPART C — PRESERVATION OF AIRCRAFT WRECKAGE, MAIL, CARGO, AND RECORDS

830.10 PRESERVATION OF AIRCRAFT WRECKAGE, MAIL, CARGO, AND RECORDS ✈

(a) The operator of an aircraft is responsible for preserving to the extent possible any aircraft wreckage, cargo, and mail aboard the aircraft, and all records, including tapes of flight recorders and voice recorders, pertaining to the operation and maintenance of the aircraft and to the airmen involved in an accident or incident for which notification must be given until the Board takes custody thereof or a release is granted pursuant to 831.17.

(b) Prior to the time the Board or its authorized representative takes custody of aircraft wreckage, mail, or cargo, such wreckage, mail or cargo may not be disturbed or moved except to the extent necessary:

(1) To remove persons injured or trapped;

(2) To protect the wreckage from further damage, or

(3) To protect the public from injury.

(c) Where it is necessary to disturb or move aircraft wreckage, mail or cargo, sketches, descriptive notes, and photographs shall be made, if possible, of the accident locale including original position and condition of the wreckage and any significant impact marks.

(d) The operator of an aircraft involved in an accident or incident as defined in this part, shall retain all records and reports, including all internal documents and memoranda dealing with the accident or incident, until authorized by the Board to the contrary.

SUBPART D — REPORTING OF AIRCRAFT ACCIDENTS, INCIDENTS, AND OVERDUE AIRCRAFT

830.15 REPORTS AND STATEMENTS TO BE FILED ✈

(a) *Reports.* The operator of an aircraft shall file a report as provided in paragraph (c) of this section on Board Form 6120.1 or Board Form 6120.2 within 10 days after an accident, or after 7 days if an overdue aircraft is still missing. A report on an incident for which notification is required by 830.5(a) shall be filed only as requested by an authorized representative on the Board.

(b) *Crewmember statement.* Each crewmember, if physically able at the time the report is submitted, shall attach thereto a statement setting forth the facts, conditions, and circumstances relating to the accident or incident as they appear to him to the best of his knowledge and belief. If the crewmember is incapacitated, he shall submit the statement as soon as he is physically able.

(c) *Where to file the reports.* The operator of an aircraft shall file with the field office of the Board nearest the accident or incident any report required by this section.

Forms are obtainable from the Board field offices, the National Transportation Safety Board, Washington, D. C. 20594, and the Federal Aviation Administration, Flight Standards District Office. The National Transportation Safety Board field offices are listed under U.S. Government in the telephone directories in the following cities: Anchorage, Alaska; Chicago, Ill.; Denver, Colo.; Fort Worth, Tex.; Kansas City, Mo.; Los Angeles, Calif.; Miami, Fla.; New York, N.Y.; Oakland, Calif.; Seattle, Wash.; Washington, D. C.

chapter 7

SECTION A - SECTIONAL AND WAC CHARTS

Just as a motorist uses roadmaps when making a long trip, the pilot of an airplane uses aeronautical charts to assist him in finding his way. Knowledge of charts and the ability to use charts, therefore, is another of the skills of an experienced, competent pilot.

PROJECTIONS

If a pilot wanted to carry with him a completely accurate small-scale representation of the surface over which he was flying, he would have to carry a globe or at least a portion of a globe. This procedure, however, would be impractical. Therefore, for the sake of portability and convenience, the representation of the spherical surface of the globe is *flattened* and placed on a chart. In the process of flattening, however, there is a certain amount of *distortion* of the surface represented. This can be illustrated using an orange peel as an example. (See Fig. 7-1.) An orange peel, like the earth, cannot be flattened or mapped without distortion.

The techniques used in converting a portion of the earth's spherical surface to a flat, small-scale representation are known as *projections*. Each projection technique attempts to minimize distortion; however, each has its limitations and advantages. The two principal map projections used in air navigation are the *Mercator* and

Fig. 7-1. Flattening of an Orange Peel Produces Distortion

Lambert Conformal Conic Projections. (See Fig. 7-2.)

The Lambert Conformal Conic is used to a greater extent than the Mercator, especially for flight in the middle latitudes. The sectional and the world aeronautical charts, which are studied and explained in this manual, are Lambert Conformal Conic projections.

Two distinct advantages of the Lambert projection over the Mercator are:

1. A straight line on the chart approximately represents a *great circle* (a great circle is the shortest distance between two points over the earth's surface). This means that a straight-line course drawn on a Lambert chart nearly represents the shortest distance between those two points.

Fig. 7-2. Chart Projections

2. Scale inaccuracies (the ratio of miles on the earth to inches on the chart) are small, so the scale error may be considered negligible over a single chart.

LATITUDE AND LONGITUDE

In order to locate places on the earth's surface, or on any representation of the earth's surface, such as a chart or globe, some method of referencing an exact point must be used. The method accepted worldwide utilizes a system based on lines of *latitude* and *longitude*.

The *Equator* is a line running east and west around the earth midway between the poles. Other lines around the earth parallel to the Equator are called *parallels* or *lines of latitude*. (See Fig. 7-3.) The Equator is labeled as 0° of latitude and the other lines of latitude are numbered in degrees from 0 to 90 north of the Equator. Similarly, parallels of latitude in the Southern Hemisphere are labeled from 0° to 90° south of the Equator. (See Fig. 7-3.)

Other lines called *meridians*, or *lines of longitude*, are drawn from pole to pole; therefore, the direction along these lines is always true north or south. These lines are also numbered starting at the *Prime Meridian*, which is the line of longitude passing through the observatory at Greenwich, England. The Prime Meridian is labeled as 0° of longitude and the other meridians are numbered in degrees east and west of the Prime Meridian.

Fig. 7-3. Parallels and Meridians
(Latitude and Longitude)

There are 360° of longitude; therefore, 180° are labeled east longitude and the remaining 180° are labeled west longitude. Pilots who take their training and fly in the Western Hemisphere will always be dealing with west longitude. The line of longitude labeled 180° is called the *International Date Line* and is on the opposite side of the world from the Prime Meridian.

All charts are laid out with lines of longitude and latitude extending up, down, and across the chart. The lines of longitude and latitude are printed and labeled on the chart for each degree interval. Each degree is divided into 60 equal segments called *minutes*. The minutes, indicated by the symbol ('), are marked along the lines of longitude and latitude in 30 minute, 5 minute, and 1 minute segments. (See Fig. 7-4.)

Fig. 7-4. Chart Reference System

With the system of lines just discussed, the location of objects such as airports and cities may be designated by *geographical coordinates*, or in other words, the intersection of the longitude and latitude lines on the chart. In figure 7-5, the coordinates of the airport are given as 40°15'N, 78°18'W. In this example, the airport is located 40° and 15' north of the zero line of latitude, or Equator, and 78° and 18' west of the Prime Meridian.

The pilot would first locate the parallel labeled 40° north on his chart, then count upward 15' from that line and draw a light line on the chart from the 15' mark parallel to the 40° north latitude line. (See Fig. 7-5, item 1.) Next, he would locate the 78° west longitude line and count 18' to the left, or west, of that line. He would then lightly draw a second

line through the 18' mark and parallel to the 78° west longitude line (item 2). The point where the two lines intersect is the location of the airport. It is not always necessary to actually draw the lines as suggested in this example; however, the procedure outlined should be used in locating places on aeronautical charts when the geographical coordinates are given.

Fig. 7-5. Geographical Coordinates

THE EARTH'S TRUE NORTH POLE AND MAGNETIC NORTH POLE

The position of the earth's True North Pole, or point upon which it would appear to rotate if viewed from space, and the position of the earth's Magnetic North Pole are not the same. In fact, the Magnetic North Pole is located on Prince Wales Island, Canada, approximately 1,000 miles south of the geographic, or True North Pole. The problem introduced into a pilot's navigational planning and piloting technique is simply this: the charts which he uses are oriented toward *true north* and the compass needle in his airplane points to the *Magnetic North Pole*. This angular difference between the direction to true north and the direction to magnetic north is called *magnetic variation*, or simply *variation*. (See Fig. 7-6.)

Figure 7-6 shows that the position of the aircraft relative to the earth's surface will determine whether the compass variation is to the east of true north or to the west of true north. Also, when the aircraft's position on the earth is in alignment with

Fig. 7-6. Magnetic Variation

true north and magnetic north, no variation exists.

Most charts show variation with *isogonic lines*, which are lines connecting points of equal magnetic variation. When flying on a true north heading over the panhandle of Nebraska as seen in figure 7-7, the aircraft compass would read 348° rather than 360° because the magnetic variation is 12° east (of true north). To fly south at the same point, the aircraft compass would read 168° rather than 180° because the variation at any point is always constant regardless of the airplane heading. Figure 7-7 also shows the line of 0° magnetic variation which is termed an *agonic line*.

MEASURING DIRECTION IN DEGREES OF THE COMPASS

Direction is measured in degrees clockwise from north. The *compass rose* in figure 7-8 shows the relationship of the basic points of the compass and direction in degrees. For example, north is 360° (0°), east is 090°, south is 180°, northwest is 315°, and so on. If 0°, or north, is oriented with the True North Pole, then *true* direction is the result. If 0° is oriented with magnetic north, then *magnetic* direction results.

CHARTS

Aeronautical charts are a necessary part of a pilot's equipment for any flight away from the home base or local area. There are two basic types:

　　1. Charts that show all significant

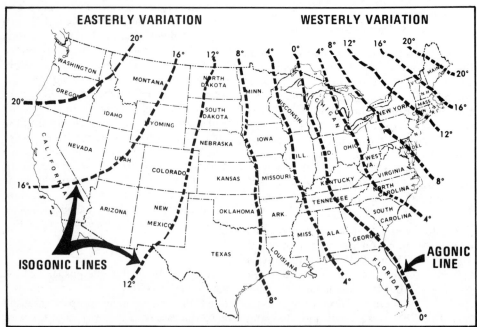

Fig. 7-7. Magnetic Agonic and Isogonic Lines

Fig. 7-8. Compass Rose

Fig. 7-9. Sectional Chart

topography (terrain, natural and man-made features) and most aeronautical information.

2. Charts that show all radio navigation facilities and routes and very little topographical information.

The beginning pilot generally flies "low and slow" and is primarily interested in topographical and some aeronautical information, while pilots of higher performance aircraft flying on airways (the highways of the sky) at high altitudes or in instrument flight conditions are interested in radio navigation and aeronautical information.

Every pilot should be familiar with the charts described in this section. The charts listed here are discussed in the relative order of their importance to the beginning pilot. A detailed discussion of the chart used with this manual appears later in this section.

Sectional charts are the charts most commonly used by private pilots. Each sectional chart shows a portion of the United States and is identified by a name of a principal city. (See Fig. 7-9.) The scale on the sectional chart is 1:500,000, or about eight miles to one inch.

The sectional chart contains topographical information which features the por-

trayal of the terrain relief and also includes visual checkpoints, such as cities, towns, villages, drainages, roads, railroads, and other distinctive landmarks used in VFR flight. The aeronautical information on the sectional chart includes visual and radio aids to navigation, aerodromes (airports, etc.), controlled airspace, special use airspace, obstructions, and related data. The sectional charts are revised and issued every six months.

VFR terminal area charts are large-scale charts (1:250,000) published to assist the private pilot in navigating within or through the terminal control areas, or TCAs, presently established at certain of the nation's airports. (See Fig. 7-10.)

Fig. 7-10. VFR Terminal Area Chart

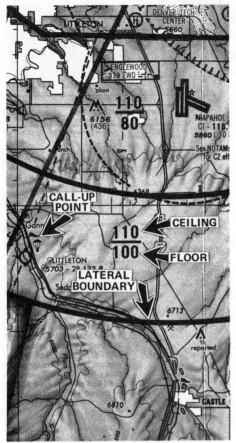

Fig. 7-11. Terminal Area Chart Excerpt

about 16 miles to 1 inch and, therefore, omit some detail. WAC charts are usually used for navigation of higher performance airplanes or for long trips where frequent change of charts en route is bothersome. Each WAC chart is identified by a number. (See Fig. 7-12.) The WAC charts are revised and issued once a year.

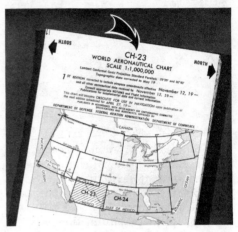

Fig. 7-12. World Aeronautical Chart

TCA charts graphically depict the vertical and lateral limits of the terminal control area. The lateral boundaries of each TCA segment are outlined by heavy blue lines. Each segment has a ceiling and a floor designated by large blue numerals separated by a horizontal line. The vertical limits are depicted in hundreds of feet above mean sea level. Figure 7-11 also illustrates VFR callup points that aid air traffic controllers in identifying VFR aircraft. The VFR terminal area chart is revised and reissued every six months like the sectional chart.

World Aeronautical Charts (WAC) are similar to sectional charts except that WAC charts are drawn to a scale which is one-half that of a sectional chart. WAC charts use a 1:1,000,000 scale, which is

VFR/IFR planning charts are large charts designed to fulfill the requirements of preflight planning for VFR and IFR operations. The planning chart uses a scale of 1:2,333,232 in which 1 inch equals about 36 statute miles. This chart is printed in two parts in such a manner that, when assembled, it forms a composite VFR planning chart on one side and IFR planning chart on the other.

This large chart is often attached to the wall of a ground school classroom, preflight planning area at the local fixed base operator, or in the flight planning area of a flight service station. Information on the VFR chart side includes selected populated areas, large bodies of water, major drainage areas, shaded relief, navigation facilities, airports, special use airspace, and related data.

IFR avigation charts (en route) are radio facility charts. (See Fig. 7-13.) The IFR en route charts include all the information necessary for radio navigation and omit all terrain features except for large

Fig. 7-13. IFR Avigation Chart

SECTIONAL CHARTS

The private pilot must be thoroughly familiar with sectional charts as they are the most popular chart used for VFR flying. Sufficient detail for navigation by pilotage is included on these charts, but much of the aeronautical information is represented by symbols and colors. Their meanings should be memorized because dependence on the legend makes navigation by pilotage awkward.

bodies of water. They are drawn to various scales, depending on the needs of the particular chart. Much of the radio information found on these charts is not available on any other chart series. The en route charts are on a four-week revision cycle; therefore, they are the most current charts available for radio navigation, radio facilities, and communication frequencies.

The name of each sectional chart, derived from a principal city on the chart, is displayed prominently at the top of *both* sides of the chart legend panel. (See Fig. 7-14, item 1.) Both the date at which the chart becomes effective, and also the date at which the chart is considered obsolete for use in navigation are also found on the same panel. (See Fig. 7-14, item 2.) It is important that the dates on the charts be checked so that flight will be made with the most current publication.

Fig. 7-14. Chart Name and Date

The convenient size of the folded sectional chart provides for easy handling, storage, and identification, especially while in flight. The sectionals are printed back to back, making it possible to cover the 48 contiguous (touching or adjacent) states with 37 charts. The arrows marked "NORTH" on the legend margin indicate that the northern half is shown when the chart is extended to the right from the legend margin. (See Fig. 7-15.)

tional chart is shown. The margin is used to list such information as control tower frequencies and data concerning special use airspace.

Some sectional charts include plotting instructions for drawing a course from one side of the chart to the other. Figure 7-17 shows an excerpt from these instructions.

SELECTING CHARTS

The front panel contains a box showing the names of the adjoining charts. (See Fig. 7-18). For example, the San Antonio Chart is used to fly west of the area represented on the Houston Chart. It is wise for the pilot to carry charts of the surrounding area during flight, particularly if the course is near the edge of the chart; otherwise, in the event of an unplanned course change, deteriorating weather, adverse winds, or low fuel supply, the pilot might find himself flying over unfamiliar terrain without the charts necessary for safe navigation.

Fig. 7-15. North Half of Chart Indicators

The arrow labeled "SOUTH" alerts the pilot to turn the chart so the legend on the margin is *upside down*. (See Fig. 7-16.) Then, when the chart is extended to the right, the southern half of the sec-

CHART INTERPRETATION AND USE OF SYMBOLS

Sectional charts are printed in several colors, depending on the range of eleva-

Fig. 7-16. Using South Half of Chart Indicators

Fig. 7-17. Plotting Instructions (Excerpt)

tions encompassed by the chart. Terrain elevations below 1,000 feet are shown by light green; 1,000 to 2,000 feet by darker green; 2,000 to 3,000 feet by yellow; and elevations above 3,000 feet are shown by various shades of brown. (See Fig. 7-19, item 1.) The highest terrain elevation on a particular chart is shown at the top of the color band legend (item 2). The legend for certain elevations is also specified (item 3), and contour intervals are shown (item 4).

Water (lakes, rivers, etc.) is shown in blue, while roads are shown by magenta lines. Heavy lines indicate principal highways, and narrower lines indicate less heavily traveled roads. The relative size and shape of large cities is indicated by a yellow area outlined in black. Yellow squares represent small cities and towns, while villages and hamlets are represented by small circles.

Special use airspace areas, which are explained later in this chapter, are tabulated and defined on the back of the legend panel. Control tower frequencies are also listed here.

SYMBOLS USED ON THE SECTIONAL CHART

To obtain the greatest benefit from the following explanation of sectional chart symbols, the circled numbers on the chart excerpt in figure 7-20 should be referred to each time a new number is encountered in the text. This should help reinforce the meaning of each symbol presented.

1. The information enclosed within the magenta box describes the name, frequency, three-letter identifier, and Morse code for the DeRidder non-directional radio beacon (NDB). Magenta is used *for all* low-frequency radio information.

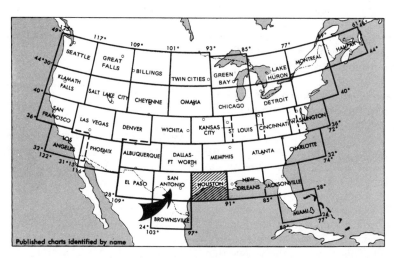

Fig. 7-18. Legend for Adjoining Charts

CONTOUR INTERVAL

500 feet

Intermediate contours shown at 250 feet

―――500――― ―――250―――
Basic Intermediate

HIGHEST TERRAIN elevation is
14433 feet
located at 39°07'N – 106°27'W

Critical elevation - - - - - - - - - - - - - - •4254

Approximate elevation - - - - - - - - - - ×3200

Doubtful locations are indicated by omission
of the point locator (dot or "x")

―――――――― ATTENTION ――――――――
THIS CHART CONTAINS MAXIMUM ELEVATION FIGURES (MEF).
The Maximum Elevation Figures shown in quadrangles bounded by ticked
lines of latitude and longitude are represented in THOUSANDS and
HUNDREDS of feet above mean sea level. The MEF is based on
information available concerning the highest known feature in each
quadrangle, including terrain and obstructions (trees, towers, antennas, etc.).

Example: 12,500 feet . . . . 12^5

14433

12000

9000

7000

5000

3000

Fig. 7-19. Elevation Legend

2. The magenta dot pattern surrounding the Beauregard Parish Airport symbol represents the location of the DeRidder NDB.

3. Maximum elevation figures centered in the quadrangles bounded by *ticked* lines of latitude and longitude are represented in hundreds and thousands of feet above mean sea level. The number 0^8 represents the elevation of 800 feet, which is the highest known feature including terrain and obstructions.

4. A power transmission line and its supporting towers are represented by this symbol.

5. A shaded light blue color represents a body of water. The black line on the southeast end of Bundick Lake represents a man-made dam.

6. The terrain elevation at the location of the dot is 175 feet mean sea level (MSL). This is the highest elevation in the immediate area.

7. The inverted V represents an obstruction whose height at the top is less than 1,000 feet above ground level (AGL). The number 360 represents the elevation of this obstruction above mean sea level, and the number 250 in parentheses represents the elevation above ground level. The student should refer to the chart legend for the symbol used to represent obstructions 1,000 feet and *higher* above ground level.

8. Shaded blue lines represent rivers or streams.

9. The number "100" represents the MSL altitude of the adjacent contour line, or line connecting points of equal elevation.

10. A lookout tower is shown here.

11. The open-air theater symbol is representative of those symbols

Fig. 7-20. Sectional Chart Excerpt

which actually look like the objects they represent.

12. Identifying markers, such as this one for U.S. Highway 171, are shown.

13. This is a *restricted* airport not open to the general public. Notice in the legend by the airport symbol that Longville is a private field.

14. This symbol represents an isogonic line (line of equal magnetic variation) which is 5°30' east on this chart.

15. This line of longitude is 93° west of the Prime Meridian in Greenwich, England, as shown near the bottom of the chart excerpt.

16. The locations of small towns or villages, such as Reeves, are shown with circles.

17. Shaft mines or quarries are represented by a symbol that looks like two crossed pick axes.

18. This line with spaced single crossbars represents a single-track railroad.

19. Interstate freeways and tollways are depicted with a double magenta line.

20. The shape and relative size of the town of Sulphur is represented by the area outlined in yellow.

21. The black dots represent storage tanks which contain oil in this case.

22. The small solid black square is used to represent a variety of prominent landmarks. In this case, a factory is designated.

23. The letters "FSS" indicate that a flight service station is available on the field at the Lake Charles Airport.

24. The Lake Charles Control Tower frequency is 120.7 MHz.

25. The dashed blue line surrounding the Lake Charles Airport defines the boundaries of the control zone. A control zone surrounds airports where there are special weather (ceiling and visibility) requirements. (The details of control zones are discussed in Section B of this chapter.)

26. This symbol represents a VORTAC station, a type of radio navigation station which is discussed in Chapter 8.

27. The dark blue box encloses information regarding the Lake Charles VORTAC such as the VORTAC frequency which is 113.4 MHz. This station has a flight service station which transmits and receives on 122.3 and 122.55 MHz. In addition, it receives on 122.1 MHz.

28. In this case, the solid black square represents a pumping station and is so labeled.

29. Oil wells are represented by the closely-spaced group of circles.

30. The Welsh Airport is 19 feet above sea level, has lighting for night operations, and has a runway that is 2,700 feet long. UNICOM, a non-FAA advisory facility, is available on the frequency 122.8 MHz. The airport information and symbol are printed in *magenta* indicating an airport with no control tower or airport traffic area.

31. An airport symbol with a runway depicted has one runway which is at least 1,500 feet long. The star above the airport symbol indicates the presence of a rotating beacon. The three extensions on the sides and bottom of the airport diagram indicate that facilities such as fuel, maintenance, etc. *are* available.

32. The airway extending northeast from the Lake Charles VORTAC on the 057° radial is V-222/20N. This VHF airway connects two navigational facilities.

33. This large body of water would provide an excellent VFR checkpoint.

34. The numerals indicate that this east-west line of latitude is 30° north of the Equator.

35. Swamps and marshes are depicted by horizontal blue lines interspersed with short vertical dashes suggesting the clumps of marsh grass common in such areas.

SECTION B - AIRSPACE UTILIZATION

Certainly when the Wright brothers made their first flight, and for some time thereafter, all of the airspace was available to all of the users. As aircraft, and particularly airplanes, became more complex and their numbers and types of operations increased, the necessity for implementing regulation of the use of airspace became apparent.

When a portion of the airplanes of those early days of aviation were equipped to operate in what is now known as "instrument conditions," it was necessary to establish basic flight rules and to set aside certain portions of the airspace in which aircraft flying by instrument reference could be controlled and separated from other aircraft. It was also necessary to provide for those aircraft *not* under air traffic control (control by radio). These requirements have generated the necessity for many of the various divisions of airspace existing today.

A study of *uncontrolled* and *controlled* airspace is important to the private pilot so that he may learn the segments of controlled airspace in which he will be subject to air traffic control. A second reason for studying airspace utilization is that different weather minimums (visibility, ceiling, and distance from clouds) apply in the various types of controlled and uncontrolled airspace.

UNCONTROLLED AIRSPACE

Uncontrolled airspace is defined as that portion of airspace within which FAA Air Traffic Control (ATC) does not have authority nor the responsibility to exercise any control over air traffic.

CONTROLLED AIRSPACE

Certain elements of airspace were originally controlled only to prevent collisions of aircraft operating in instrument conditions and to exclude non-instrument equipped aircraft and non-instrument

rated pilots. However, the complexity and density of aircraft movements today have generated the necessity for establishing control functions in other airspace segments; for example, to provide for the orderly and safe flow of traffic around air terminals.

Controlled airspace now consists of those areas designated as positive control areas, continental control areas, control areas, control zones, terminal control areas, and transition areas within which some or all aircraft may be subject to air traffic control.

POSITIVE CONTROL AREA

Positive control area airspace extends from 18,000 feet MSL to flight level (FL) 600 (approximately 60,000 feet MSL), and aircraft within this airspace are required to be operated under instrument flight rules (IFR). Positive control airspace is not shown on sectional charts; however, it is depicted on en route high altitude charts. For operations within positive control areas, aircraft must be:

1. operated under IFR at specified flight levels assigned by air traffic control;
2. equipped with instruments and equipment required for IFR operations and flown by a pilot rated for instrument flight;
3. equipped with a radar beacon transponder; and
4. radio equipped to provide direct pilot-to-controller communications.

Even though non-instrument rated pilots cannot legally operate in positive control airspace, the topic is presented to better acquaint the student with the airspace utilization plan.

CONTINENTAL CONTROL AREA

The continental control area consists of the airspace at and above 14,500 feet MSL over the 48 contiguous states, the

District of Columbia, and that portion of Alaska east of longitude 160° west. The continental control area does not include the airspace less than 1,500 feet above the surface of the earth or prohibited and restricted areas. (See Fig. 7-21.) The definition of the continental control area given in the FAR's implies that there is no upward limit to this airspace.

The continental control area was established to increase the visibility and cloud clearance minimums at the higher altitudes at which high performance airplanes fly. For example, one cannot fly VFR in this airspace unless there is five miles visibility. Also, there must be one mile horizontal separation and 1,000 feet vertical separation from all clouds.

CONTROL AREAS

Control areas consist of the airspace designated as VOR federal airways, additional control areas, and control area extensions which include transition areas. These are depicted on sectional charts as shown in figure 7-22.

VOR FEDERAL AIRWAYS

Each airway is based on a centerline that extends from one radio navigational aid or intersection to another navigational aid specified for that airway. An airway is depicted in figure 7-23. Notice that the airway begins at 1,200 feet above ground level (AGL), intersects the base of the continental control area, and extends up to, but not including, 18,000 feet MSL. The centerline is shown in blue on sectional charts and the magnetic course and the airway identification number are indicated.

Each airway includes airspace within parallel boundary lines, normally four nautical miles each side of the airway centerline. Where airways pass through otherwise uncontrolled airspace, the outer limit of the airway is shown by the darker and more definite edges of the blue tinted boundaries, and the vanishing

Fig. 7-21. Continental Control Area

Fig. 7-22. Typical Control Areas Shown on Sectional Charts

Fig. 7-23. Typical Airway

Fig. 7-24. Airway Boundaries

or feathered edges show the controlled airspace within the airway. (See Fig. 7-24.)

TRANSITION AREAS

Transition areas from airways to airports for which an instrument approach procedure has been prescribed have been established. These transition areas extend upward from 700 feet or 1,200 feet above the surface and enable an instrument pilot to remain within controlled airspace as he descends for an instrument approach to an airport. Transition areas are shown in magenta or in blue. As with other controlled airspace, the outer limit of the transition area is shown by the darker and more definite edge, and the feathered tint shows the side on which the controlled airspace exists. (See Fig. 7-25.)

CONTROL ZONES

Controlled airspace which extends upward from the surface and terminates at the base of the continental control area is called a *control zone*. Control zones that do not underlie the continental control area have no upper limit. A control zone may include one or more airports and is normally a circular area with a radius of

Fig. 7-25. Transition Areas

five statute miles and any extensions necessary to include instrument departure and arrival paths. (See Fig. 7-26.)

The control zone was established in order that air traffic control could be exercised on aircraft taking off or landing when instrument conditions exist within the control zone, and also to exclude possible conflicting VFR traffic when weather conditions are below VFR minimums.

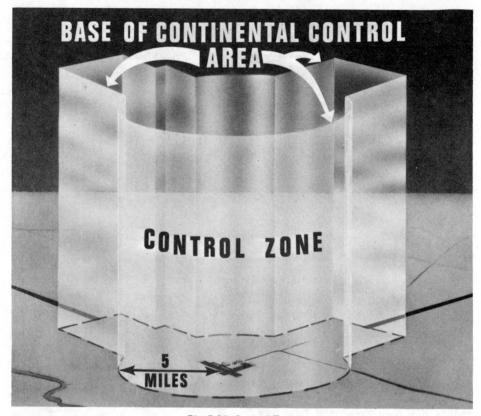

Fig. 7-26. Control Zone

Control zones are depicted on sectional charts with a broken blue line and, if a control zone is effective only during certain hours of the day, this fact will also be noted on the chart. (See Fig. 7-27.) Student pilots often erroneously assume that a control zone exists only where there is a control tower; however, such is not the case. Many control zones, such as the one shown in figure 7-27, exist at airports without control towers.

In order to operate within a control zone, the ceiling must be not less than 1,000 feet and the visibility must be at least three miles at that airport. However, a special VFR clearance may be obtained from the nearest tower, ATC center, or FSS if there is one mile visibility and the aircraft can be maintained clear of clouds.

Some major terminals have experienced such high traffic density that special

Fig. 7-27. Typical Control Zone

VFR clearances were determined to be incompatible with maximum safety and separation of aircraft. Therefore, there are a number of terminals where special VFR clearances are not issued. The control zone outline where special VFR is not authorized is depicted as a series of T's.

AIRPORT TRAFFIC AREA

In order to provide for the separation and orderly flow of traffic around many of the nation's larger airports, control towers and mandatory two-way radio communications were established. The *airport traffic area* is the airspace within which the control of all air traffic is exercised and is normally defined as the airspace within five statute miles of an airport at which a control tower is in operation.

This airspace extends from the ground up to, but not including, 3,000 feet above ground level. (See Fig. 7-28.) Although the boundaries are not depicted on aeronautical charts, the presence of an airport traffic area is indicated when the letters "CT" and control tower radio frequencies are shown in the airport data listing. (See Fig. 7-29.)

AIRPORT ADVISORY AREA

The area within five statute miles of an airport where a control tower is *not* oper-

Fig. 7-28. Airport Traffic Area

ating, but where a flight service station *is* located, is called an *airport advisory area*. At such locations, flight service stations provide advisory service to arriving and departing aircraft. The advisory service usually includes wind direction and velocity, altimeter setting, favored runway or runway in use, and local reported aircraft traffic information.

TERMINAL CONTROL AREAS

Terminal control areas (TCAs) have been established to separate all arriving traffic, both VFR and IFR, at large airports. Although each area is designed to facilitate traffic separation at a particular terminal and, therefore, is different from other terminal control areas, the TCA is generally shaped like an upside-down wedding cake. (See Fig. 7-30.)

Fig. 7-29. Indicators of an Airport Traffic Area

Fig. 7-30. Terminal Control Area

and equipment requirements as specified in Part 91.90 of the FAR's. Each such location includes at least one primary airport enclosed by a TCA.

The Denver TCA, as depicted on the sectional chart, is shown in figure 7-31. Notice that the controlled airspace is divided into ceilings and floors. For instance, the area surrounding Stapleton International is controlled from the surface to 11,000 feet MSL. A pilot wishing to operate through this area without meeting the necessary equipment and pilot requirements could do so only above 11,000 feet.

Within the expanding controlled airspace of the terminal control area, all aircraft are subject to operating rules and pilot

Fig. 7-31. Denver TCA Planview

The National Ocean Survey (NOS) publishes a VFR terminal area chart for each TCA. These charts are drawn to a scale of 1:250,000 to aid in identifying VFR checkpoints within the area.

An overview of the national airspace system is presented on the following pages in figure 7-32. These airspace divisions should be studied carefully.

SPECIAL USE AIRSPACE

Special use airspace consists of those areas where the nature of certain activities within the airspace, or in proximity to the airspace, requires limitations upon aircraft operation. These areas, called prohibited, restricted, warning, and military operations areas, are shown on sectional charts.

The same symbol is used to mark the boundaries of these four types of areas; however, the number or name of each special use airspace area accompanies its designator. For example, P indicates prohibited; R — restricted; W — warning; and MOA — military operations area.

A listing of prohibited, restricted, warning, and military operations areas appearing on the sectional chart is found in the margin. The controlling authority is also listed there. Permission to transit or land in a restricted area, or information regarding dates and times of intense military aircraft training activities can be obtained by contacting the controlling agency or nearest flight service station.

PROHIBITED AREAS

Prohibited areas are portions of the airspace within which the flight of aircraft is not permitted. Such areas are generally established for reasons of national security or national welfare. An example of a prohibited area is the area

Fig. 7-33. Prohibited Area

surrounding the Rocky Mountain Arsenal near Stapleton International Airport, Denver, Colorado. (See Fig. 7-33.)

RESTRICTED AREA

Restricted areas include airspace within which the flight of aircraft, while not wholly prohibited, is subject to certain limitations. Restricted areas denote the existence of unusual, but often invisible, hazards to aircraft, such as artillery firing, aerial gunnery, or flight of guided missiles. Penetration of restricted areas without authorization from the controlling agency may be extremely hazardous.

WARNING AREA

A *warning area* is that airspace which may contain hazards to non-participating aircraft in international airspace; therefore, these warning areas are established beyond the three-mile limit. Although the activities conducted within warning areas may be as hazardous as those in restricted areas, warning areas cannot be legally designated as restricted because they are over international waters.

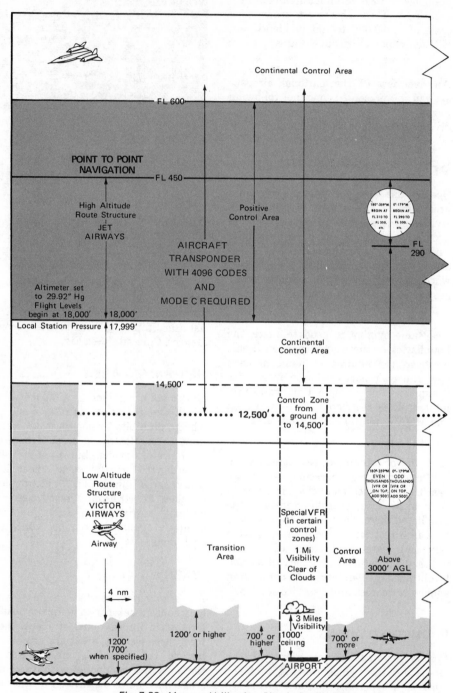

Fig. 7-32. Airspace Utilization Plan in Profile View

AERONAUTICAL CHARTS

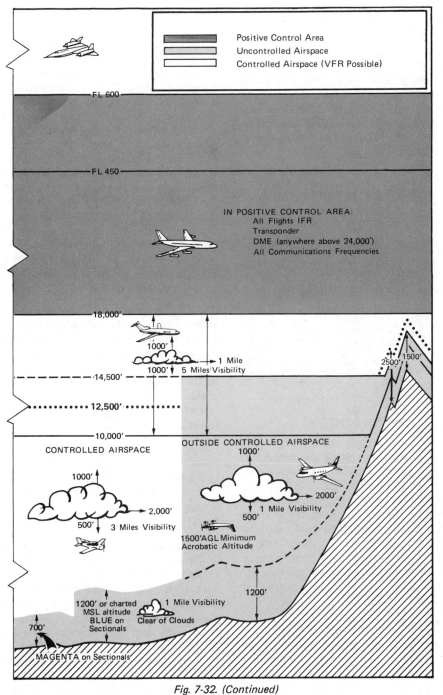

Fig. 7-32. (Continued)

MILITARY OPERATIONS AREAS

Military operations areas are depicted on sectional charts, as shown in figure 7-34, to inform transient or cross-country pilots of areas that may contain a high volume of pilot training or an unusual type of aerial activity. Flight within these areas is not restricted, but pilots are urged to exercise extreme caution. Both the pilots of aircraft participating in activities within the area and pilots transiting the MOA are fully responsible for collision avoidance.

Fig. 7-34. Military Operations Area

VR, IR, AND SR ROUTES

Low altitude, high speed military VFR and IFR training routes are called VR and IR routes Operations are conducted along VRs only in VFR weather conditions, while those along IRs encompass both VFR and IFR. SR routes are low altitude, slow speed (250 knots or less) military training routes. Locations of these routes are charted and nearby flight service stations can provide information on their status (active or inactive).

COLLISION AVOIDANCE

In the VFR flight environment, the responsibility for collision avoidance rests entirely with the pilot. Visual scanning is one of the pilot's most important techniques for practicing collision avoidance. It requires the pilot to concentrate his attention *outside* the airplane, using head and eye movements to make a systematic sweep of the entire area.

Effective collision avoidance techniques are especially important in airport operations, where the volume of traffic usually increases. The pilot should make a point of checking that both the approach and departure paths are clear prior to takeoff. During climbout, the aircraft should be accelerated to cruise climb speed as soon as a safe altitude is reached in order to reduce pitch and increase forward visibility. During operations from an airport without an operating control tower, the pilot should broadcast his intentions on the appropriate frequency. In addition, such aids as airport advisory service and radar traffic information service should be utilized, when available.

An FAA program called "Operation— Lights On" provides an added margin of safety for operations in the vicinity of airports. Under this program, pilots are requested to turn on their landing/taxi lights whenever they are operating within 10 miles of an airport, and to operate their anticollision lights anytime the engine is running.

During all flight operations, the pilot must maintain an awareness of the blind spots inherent in the design of the aircraft. Clearing turns must be employed to expose the airspace hidden by the fuselage and wings.

Another excellent collision avoidance aid is the spot method for determining the collision potential of another aircraft within the pilot's field of vision. For example, if the other aircraft appears to move up in relation to a spot on the windshield, door post, or engine cowling, it will pass above the observer's aircraft. If it moves down, the aircraft will pass below. If there is no movement in relation to the spot, the flight paths of the two aircraft are on converging courses requiring appropriate action.

SECTION C - THE NAVIGATION PLOTTER

CONVENTIONAL NAVIGATION PLOTTER

The navigation plotter, developed to assist the pilot in flight planning, combines the protractor, straightedge, and scales into one convenient and compact device to serve the needs of pilots. The most conventional style of navigation plotter is shown in figure 7-36. It is a precision instrument made of clear plastic so that chart details can be viewed through the plotter. Since it is made of plastic, care should be taken to keep it from being exposed to high temperatures or prolonged exposure to direct sunlight, such as might be encountered if left on top of the airplane instrument panel. Such abuse could cause the plotter to warp out of shape and to shrink in size.

The direction of a course is measured by the protractor or semicircular scale of the plotter. It is labeled from 0° to 180° on the outside scale and 180° to 360° on the inside scale. (See Fig. 7-35.)

The straightedge portion of the plotter is used to measure distance and draw the course line from the center of the departure airport to the center of the

Fig. 7-35. Protractor Portion of Plotter

arrival airport. This line, when measured from true north, is called the *true course*. The plotter shown in figure 7-36 incorporates the following features in the straightedge portion of the plotter:

1. On one side of the straightedge portion of the plotter, the mileage scale matches that of the sectional chart which has a 1:500,000 scale. (See item 1.)

As shown by item 2, the scale along the bottom of the straightedge is

Fig. 7-36. Conventional Navigation Plotter

graduated in statute miles. The scale along the top of the straight-edge is graduated in nautical miles. (See item 3.)

2. The opposite side of the plotter displays both statute and nautical mile scales for the WAC, or world aeronautical charts, which have a scale of 1:1,000,000.

3. Concise instructions on how to use this device are provided in the center area of the plotter. For convenience, these instructions appear on both sides.

USING THE PLOTTER

The plotter is used to measure the true course angle using the following steps, which correspond to the circled numbers in figure 7-37.

1. Place the small hole in the center of the plotter directly over an intersection of the true course line and one of the longitude lines printed on the chart.

2. Next, align the edge of the plotter that is adjacent to the protractor part of the plotter with the true course line, being careful to keep the hole in the plotter over the intersection of the longitude and the true course lines.

3. Read from the scale of the protractor that lies directly over the longitude line. The outside scale is used to measure easterly courses, and the inner scale is used to measure westerly courses. In this case, the true course line is easterly and measures 098°.

The plotter is used to measure the course distance using the following steps, which correspond to the circled numbers in figure 7-38.

1. Determine the correct side of the plotter (in this case the sectional chart side) to use for the measurement.

2. Place the nautical miles scale parallel to the true course line and align the

Fig. 7-37. Measuring the True Course

Fig. 7-38. Measuring Course Distance

zero mile mark with the center of the airport from which the departure is being made.

3. Read the nautical mile mark closest to the center of the airport of arrival. In this example, the distance from Hearne Airport to Huntsville Airport is 54 nautical miles.

USING THE NORTH-SOUTH SCALES

Sometimes in the process of flight planning, a true course is laid out that has an extreme northerly or southerly course which does not cross a meridian. Rather than extend the course until it intersects a meridian, the pilot may use a parallel of latitude instead and apply the special innermost north-south scales provided on the plotter. With a northerly course, as shown in figure 7-39, the edge of the plotter is aligned with the course line. The intersection of the course line and the latitude line is directly under the small index hole of the plotter. The true course of 003° is read at the point where the north scale directly overlies the latitude line. It should be remembered that the outer special scale is used to measure the direction of southerly courses, and the inner special scale in this example is used to determine the direction of northerly courses. Each reading should be checked to be certain that it coincides with the direction of flight.

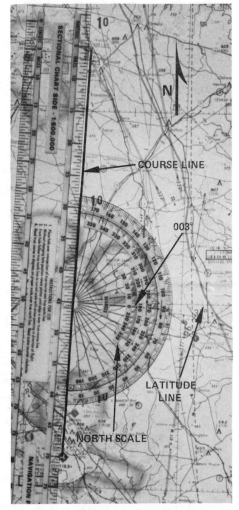

Fig. 7-39. Measuring a North-South True Course Line

ROTATING AZIMUTH PLOTTER

Another type of plotter is shown in figure 7-40. To measure the true course between two points on the chart, use the following steps, which correspond to the circled numbers in figure 7-41.

1. Place an edge of the plotter parallel to the desired course line.
2. While holding the plotter stationary,

rotate the circular protractor until the arrowed lines point north and are parallel to a line of longitude.
3. Read the true course at the "course arrow" which points in the desired direction. The other "course arrow" indicates the reciprocal of the desired course.

Mileages are measured in the same manner as with the conventional plotter; however, the statute mile scale is printed

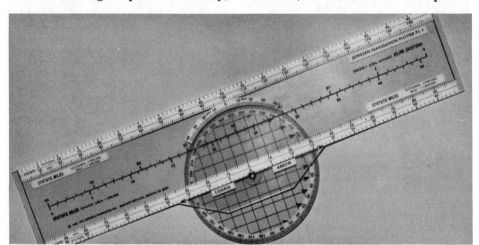

Fig. 7-40. Rotating Azimuth Plotter

Fig. 7-41. Using the Rotating Azimuth Plotter

on one side of the plotter, while the nautical mile scale is printed on the reverse side. Inch and centimeter scales are provided in the center of the plotter.

AERONAUTICAL CHARTS

chapter 8

RADIO
NAVIGATION

INTRODUCTION

In the early days of flying, it became apparent that a system to assist the pilot in navigation would be necessary if the airplane was really going to be useful as a transportational tool. One of the most primitive navigational aids consisted of bonfires built by farmers and ranchers at predetermined times. (See Fig. 8-1.) The pilots would fly from bonfire to bonfire across the country. Obviously, in today's airspace this would be an impossible task.

Another system used in the early days of navigation was a cross-country system of light beacons and emergency airfields. In 1926, these light beacons covered approximately 2,000 miles; by 1929, over 10,000 miles. The biggest disadvantage of this system was that it was only effective at night and only when visibility was good. (See Fig. 8-2.)

Early in 1925, experimental work was begun utilizing a radio beacon which would produce a radio beam for navigational purposes. When put into use, these became known as radio range stations, and some are still in use in Canada, Mexico, and many other countries.

The old radio range stations, however, were destined to give way to the new, more sophisticated VHF omnidirectional range which is the primary mode of navigation in the United States today.

Fig. 8-1. The Bonfire Airway System

Fig. 8-2. Airway Light Beacons

SECTION A - VOR NAVIGATION SYSTEM

In the late 1940's, a system of navigation was developed called the *very high frequency omnidirectional range* (VOR). Approximately 400 VOR stations had been installed by 1953 as the VOR began to take the place of the low frequency airway system. Today, there are hundreds of VOR stations in the United States.

VOR RADIALS

A VOR station transmits beams called *radials* outward in every direction, as shown in figure 8-3. An airborne VOR receiver in the aircraft is used to detect these radiated signals and then to indicate on which radial the aircraft is located, thus enabling a pilot to follow a radial to or from a VOR.

Each radial is numbered according to its *bearing* from the station. A compass rose is drawn around each VOR on a chart, with the 0° radial pointed toward magnetic north. Thus, the 090° radial of a VOR is located 90° clockwise from the 0° radial and represents a magnetic course of 090° away *from* the station. The radials are all magnetic courses and many are used to form the *Victor airways* that connect most VORs.

Fig. 8-3. VOR Radials

TACAN, which stands for tactical air navigation, is a military navigational aid. Civil aviation uses the portion of the TACAN system that deals with distance measuring equipment (DME), which will be discussed later. Since TACAN was developed for the military and VOR was developed for civil aviation, it was determined practical to collocate the civil VOR and the military TACAN at the same site. These integrated facilities are called VORTACs.

A VORTAC facility is comprised of VOR and TACAN, and provides three individual services: VOR azimuth for civil aviation, TACAN azimuth for military aviation, and TACAN distance (DME) which is used by both civil and military aviation. When the term "VOR" is used in this section, "VORTAC" is also implied.

Technically, the VOR station broadcasts an infinite number of radials; however, the airborne receiver is generally calibrated to reflect only 360 separate radials. The VOR is accurate to a tolerance of one full degree — hence 360 radials are assumed. Radials are like spokes of a wheel, as depicted by figure 8-3. *Each radial is a magnetic direction from a VOR station.*

In figure 8-4, a representative VOR station azimuth from a sectional chart is reproduced. A radial of 008° FROM the station is indicated (item 1); other radials shown are 057°, 118°, 167°, 268°, and 325° (items 2 through 6). These are only six of the possible 360 radials available to the pilot from this station.

The aircraft VOR receiver is able to detect each radial and, therefore, can identify the one on which the aircraft is currently located. Thus, if within receiving distance, the pilot is able to determine a bearing or line of position *at any direction from the VOR station.*

VOR NAVIGATION

The VOR is the most popular and easiest to use of the various radio navigational aids, principally because it has the following advantages:

1. MANY POSSIBLE COURSES — Omnidirectional means in all directions — the pilot can navigate on any of 360 courses to or away from a VOR.

2. FREEDOM FROM INTERFERENCE — The VOR frequencies are virtually free from precipitation static and annoying interference caused by electrical storms.

3. ACCURACY — Course accuracy of ±1° is possible when flying VOR.

4. STRAIGHT LINE COURSE — A pilot can fly a straight line, and wind drift is compensated for automatically.

5. MAGNETIC COURSES — All VOR courses are related to magnetic north. Therefore, under a no-wind condition, the magnetic course will be the same as the magnetic heading. When correction for wind is taken into consideration, the difference between the VOR course and the magnetic heading is the *wind correction angle.*

On a sectional or world aeronautical chart, a VOR station symbol (see Fig. 8-4, item 7) is shown in blue and is surrounded by an azimuth ring (item 8). The calibrated azimuth ring surrounding the station is a built-in protractor corrected for local magnetic variation; therefore, all that is needed to plot a course is a straightedge.

Information about the VOR station is given in the small box (see Fig. 8-4, item 9) near the VOR azimuth ring. This box contains the following information:

1. Name of station (item 10).

Fig. 8-4. VOR Information

2. Station frequency in MegaHertz (item 11). Stations without voice facilities will have the station frequency underlined.
3. Station code letters (item 12).
4. Morse code identification of the station (item 13).
5. If the voice over the VOR station is handled by a remote flight service station, brackets (item 14) are placed just under the frequency box.

There is only one positive method of identifying a VOR station. That is by listening to the Morse code identification or the recorded automatic voice identification. Automatic voice identification has been added to numerous VOR stations. When used, it is always indicated by the word "VOR" following the station name. The transmission consists of a voice announcement *"Denver VOR"* alternating with the usual Morse code identification.

VOR identification should never be determined by listening to the voice transmissions aired by flight service stations or any other radio facility. Many FSS stations remotely operate several VORs which have different names and, in some cases, none have the name of the "parent" flight service station. Also, it should be remembered that when maintenance is being performed on a VOR station, the coded identification is removed and the station should not be used for navigation.

VOR stations *with voice facilities* broadcast weather reports and notice-to-airmen information at 15 minutes past each hour *from reporting points within approximately 150 miles of the broadcast station.* In addition, unscheduled broadcasts are made at random times. Consequently, pilots can monitor VOR stations to get current weather information as they fly across the country.

Victor airways are shown on charts with a light blue line. (See Fig. 8-5.) The airway centerlines are VOR radials which are listed on the chart near the VOR station azimuth. Each airway has a certain magnetic direction that is determined by the VOR radial being used. Victor airways are designated with a "V" followed by a number; for example, V222.

Fig. 8-5. Victor (VHF) Airway

THE VOR RECEIVER

Figure 8-6 shows a modern navigation/communication (nav/com) radio and VOR indicator. The radio is crystal-tuned and has separate volume controls and positive-action squelch.

The communications transmitter, which is the left half of this radio, may have either 360 or 720 channels. The 360-channel transmitter uses 50 kHz spacing in a range from 118.00 to 135.95 MHz, while the 720-channel version uses 25 kHz spacing in the range from 118.00 to 135.975 MHz. The navigation receiver, which occupies the right side of the radio, has 200 channels with a frequency range from 108.00 to 117.95 MHz and 50 kHz spacing.

THE VOR INDICATOR

The VOR indicator has three basic components, as illustrated in figure 8-7 and described in the following discussion.

1. COURSE DEVIATION INDICATOR (CDI) — This indicator is shown in the left portion of figure 8-7 The vertical needle, which swings to the left or right, indicates whether the

Fig. 8-6. VOR Receiver and Indicator

**Course Deviation
Indicator (C.D.I.)**　　**TO/FROM
Indicator**　　**Course Selector**

Course Selector Knob

Fig. 8-7. VOR Indicator

aircraft is to the left of course, the right of course, or exactly on course. The CDI is commonly called the "left-right" needle.

2. TO-FROM INDICATOR — The TO-FROM indicator is shown in the center of figure 8-7. This instrument indicates whether the course selected by the pilot will take him TO the station or FROM the station. It also provides positive indications of station passage.

3. COURSE SELECTOR — The right side of figure 8-7 shows a diagram of a course selector, also called the omni bearing selector (OBS). The course selector has an azimuth grad-

uated in 360° which can be rotated to select the desired radial, or to find the aircraft's position. The course is shown at the top of the dial, while the reciprocal or opposite course is on the bottom index.

VOR NAVIGATION PROCEDURES

The procedure for using the VOR receiver is very simple. For example, to fly to a VOR station, a pilot would use the following four steps in sequence:

1. Tune the receiver to the frequency printed on the chart and *identify the station by listening to the Morse*

code identifier. (Either the voice or the Morse code identifier can be selected by the use of the lever on the right tuning knob, as shown in figure 8-6.)

2. Turn the course selector (OBS) until the TO-FROM window indicates a TO.

3. Continue turning the course selector until the course deviation indicator (CDI) is centered.

4. The reading on the course selector is the magnetic course *to the station.* Turn the aircraft until the heading indicator and the course selector correspond; then, with the CDI still centered, the aircraft will proceed directly TO the station on the selected course.

Some very important things to remember are:

1. Directions indicated by the course selector are in relation to the station. That is, the heading of the aircraft has no relationship to the direction indicated by the course selector. Figure 8-8 shows three aircraft on the same radial, but with different headings. The CDI indications would be the same in each case because all of the aircraft are on the 120° radial from the station. The VOR receiver in the aircraft reacts only to transmissions from a VOR station, and *not* to the heading of the aircraft.

2. When the course selected is toward a station, be sure the TO-

Fig. 8-8. VOR – Airplane Positions

FROM indicator reads TO and the course selector and heading indicator are in general agreement. When the course selected is from a station, be sure the TO-FROM indicator reads FROM and the course selector is in general agreement with the heading indicator.

The TO-FROM indicator has two positive indications: TO and FROM. When an OFF or NAV indication is displayed, either the signal is too weak to be used for reliable navigation, or the aircraft is in a position abeam (90° from) the selected course. On some equipment, a red warning flag is used to indicate a poor signal or the abeam position.

VOR INDICATIONS

The pilot of an aircraft approaching Leona VORTAC from the west, with intentions of flying to the station on the 270° radial, should tune the VOR receiver to 110.8 MHz which is the frequency printed on the sectional chart. (See Fig. 8-9.) The Morse code identification of Leona VOR can be received on the *voice facilities* of the VORTAC station.

The course selector should be rotated to 090°, which is the magnetic course *to* the station. The TO-FROM indicator will read TO. Assuming the aircraft in figure 8-9 is on the 270° radial and the course selector is set to 090°, the CDI needle will be centered. This indicates the aircraft is on the selected course. Since the aircraft heading and selected course are in general agreement, if the aircraft deviates from the course northward, the CDI needle will be deflected to the right, telling the pilot the course is to the right. If the pilot deviates to the south of the course, the CDI needle will deflect to the left, indicating the course is to the left.

Assuming a no-wind condition while maintaining a heading of 090°, the aircraft will fly to the Leona VORTAC on the 270° radial and the CDI needle

Fig. 8-9. Correct Needle Sensing and TO-FROM Indications

will be centered. The TO-FROM indicator will continually display a TO indication until the aircraft passes Leona VORTAC.

After crossing Leona VORTAC, the aircraft is outbound *from* the VORTAC station on the 090° radial. With the course selector still set to 090° (as it should be), the TO-FROM indicator will change to a FROM indication since the 090° course will take the pilot away *from* the VORTAC station.

The aircraft proceeding away from Leona VORTAC in figure 8-9 will experience the same CDI deflections as the other aircraft. If, while tracking away from the VORTAC station on the 090° radial, the aircraft deviated north of the course, the CDI would be deflected to the right, indicating the course was to the right of the aircraft. If the aircraft deviated south of the course, the CDI needle would deflect to the left, indicating the course was to the left of the aircraft.

VOR PRACTICE PROBLEMS

To further explain and help visualize how the VOR works, a series of situations is illustrated in figure 8-10. The Mountain VOR station is tuned and identified by the aircraft at position 1 in figure 8-10. To identify the aircraft's position, the course selector is turned until the TO-FROM indicator indicates FROM and the CDI is centered. The course selector is checked and, because of the aircraft's position, 180° is noted. The pilot knows from this information that the aircraft is on the 180° radial from the Mountain VOR.

Assuming the pilot wants to fly to the station, the course selector should be rotated until the TO-FROM indicator indicates TO and the CDI is centered. This will cause the course selector to read 0°, as shown at position 2 in figure 8-10. As the aircraft is flown to the station, the pilot makes course corrections by noting the deflection of the CDI. For example, if the needle moves to the right, the aircraft should be turned to the right to recenter the needle.

As the aircraft nears the station, as shown in position 3, the CDI needle becomes very sensitive. Because the VOR courses are *degrees*, the *distance*

Fig. 8-10. VOR Indications

between courses is very small near the VOR station.

Station passage is determined by noting the change of the TO-FROM indicator from TO to FROM. At position two, the aircraft was flying inbound on the 180° radial. At position four, the aircraft is shown as flying outbound on the 360° radial. If the aircraft were flown to position five with the same settings on the receiver as in position four, the CDI needle would be deflected to the right indicating to the pilot that a right heading correction would be necessary to bring the airplane back to the selected course.

REVERSE NEEDLE SENSING

If the aircraft made a 180° turn and flew to position six in figure 8-10, with the course selector still set on 0°, the CDI needle would still be to the right and the TO-FROM indicator would still indicate FROM.

The heading of the airplane has absolutely no effect on the VOR indications; however, if the airplane heading is the same as the course selector, a right CDI needle indicates the course is to the right. In the case of the airplane at position six, since the heading is 180° and the course selector is 0°, a 180° ambiguity exists. The CDI needle for airplane six will be to the right even though the selected course is to the pilot's left. This could be remedied by turning the course selector to 180°; however, for the sake of instruction, the course selector will remain at 0° for the airplane in positions six, seven, and eight.

With these same settings, the aircraft is flown to position seven where the TO-FROM indicator reflects neither TO nor FROM and the OFF flag is shown because the aircraft is in the area of ambiguity. The airplane at position seven is on a radial which is 90° from the selected course. This is called the *abeam* position. At position eight, with the course selector still set on 0°, the CDI needle still is to the right, and the TO-FROM indicator indicates TO.

INTERCEPTING AN INBOUND COURSE

Now, assuming that the pilot wants to fly inbound on the 200° radial, the inbound course of 020° (reciprocal of 200°) is selected, the TO-FROM indicator is noted to read TO, and the CDI indicator shows a needle deflection to the right. The aircraft, then, is turned to a heading of 050° which is used to intercept the 200° radial, as shown at position nine. When the needle on the CDI moves to center, the aircraft is turned to a heading of 020° as shown at position ten. The pilot then flies to the station. Station passage is noted by the sensitivity of the CDI and the changing of the TO-FROM indicator from TO to FROM.

Assuming that the pilot wants to fly away from the station on the 080° radial, the course selector is turned to 080° and the TO-FROM indicator is noted to read FROM. Since the CDI is to the right, the pilot turns to the right to an intercept heading of 120° as shown at position 11. When the CDI needle comes from the right to center, the aircraft is intercepting the course and the heading of the aircraft, as shown at position 12, should be changed to 080°.

USING THE VOR FOR A CROSSCHECK

If the position of the airplane along the 080° radial was desired, a second VOR station could be used to locate the position. For example, if the airplane at position 13 tuned in the Valley VOR station illustrated in figure 8-10, the course selector should be turned until the TO-FROM indicator indicated FROM and the CDI centered. In this case, the course selector would read 350° indicating that the aircraft was on the 350° radial from the Valley VOR. The 080° radial from the Mountain VOR and the 350° radial from the Valley VOR could be easily plotted on a chart thereby showing the pilot's exact position.

VOR ORIENTATION

To illustrate an example of the many possible combinations of aircraft headings, aircraft locations, and VOR indications, some typical samples are shown in figure 8-11. Airplane "A" is located on the 0° radial of the Cicero VOR and is flying a magnetic heading of 090°. By referring to the indications on the bottom of figure 8-11, it can be seen that with the course selector set to 0°, the VOR indicator in airplane A would have a centered CDI and a FROM indication. (Sample VOR indications are also shown for Airplanes B through I.)

A rule may be used to assist in orientation while solving the problems in figures 8-10 and 8-11: *"When orientation is in doubt, mentally or physically turn the airplane to a heading that coincides with the setting on the course selector; then, the CDI needle will point toward the*

Airplane	A	B	C	D	E	F	G	H	I
Heading	090˚	210˚	090	310˚	0˚	045˚	090˚	270˚	270˚
Course Selector	0˚	180˚	270˚	270˚	130˚	180˚	180˚	270˚	270˚
CDI									
To-From	FR	TO	TO	TO	FR	FR	FR	FR	FR

Fig. 8-11. VOR Orientation

selected course; the TO-FROM needle will read TO if the course will lead toward the station and FROM if the course will take the aircraft away from the station."

Since VOR equipment is VHF, it is subject to line-of-sight restriction. There is some "spillover," however, and reception range at an altitude of 1,000 feet above the ground can be expected to be about 40 to 45 miles. This distance will increase with altitude.

VOR TEST SIGNALS

VOR test facilities (VOTs) at selected locations allow pilots to test the accuracy of their VOR receivers. The VOT will function anywhere on the airport. The frequencies for the radiated test signals are listed in the *Airport/Facility Directory.*

To use the VOT, the pilot first selects the frequency and notes that the aural signal is a steady series of dots. Then, when the course selector is set to 0°, the CDI should be centered and the TO-FROM indicator should read FROM. When 180° is selected on the course selector, the CDI should center and the TO-FROM indicator should read TO.

If the CDI needle does not center, the pilot can determine the exact amount of error. To determine the error, the course selector should be rotated until the CDI centers, and then the number of degrees that the course selector reads should be noted. The difference between the course selector indications and 180° or 360° is the error.

There are means other than the VOT of testing the accuracy of the VOR receiver. The AIM gives instructions for VOR checks that may be made at a point on an airport, or over a prominent landmark *that may be overflown.*

SECTION B - DME AND AREA NAVIGATION

DISTANCE MEASURING EQUIPMENT

Distance measuring equipment, or DME, is a radio ranging system that measures the distance from the aircraft to a VORTAC or VOR-DME station. The system consists of special equipment in the two types of VOR transmitter facilities and a DME transceiver in the aircraft. (See Fig. 8-12.)

During operation, the airborne equipment sends a signal which the ground equipment receives, then automatically transmits it back to the aircraft. The DME equipment in the aircraft measures the elapsed time between the transmission of the original signal and the time the response is received from the ground station. The resultant information is converted into an instrument indication that displays the *distance* from the station in *nautical miles.*

Most DME units also have a ground speed function which indicates the speed in *knots* toward or away from the station. This ground speed indication is accurate only when the aircraft is flying directly to or directly away from the VORTAC station.

The DME, in addition to being useful for en route navigational situations, is also useful in finding an airport, since it indicates the exact mileage from a VORTAC station. Moreover, the combination of VOR and DME is useful in giving air traffic control position reports. For example, a pilot might report on the 120° radial of a VORTAC station at 22 DME miles from the station, thereby giving a positive location of the aircraft.

The DME does have an inherent error that must be taken into consideration, particularly when flying at higher altitudes and close to the station. This error is due to the fact that the DME actually measures *slant distance*, not horizontal distance. For example, the aircraft illustrated in figure 8-13 is 1.7 miles from the VORTAC station. In this case, however, the DME indicator will

Fig. 8-12. Distance Measuring Equipment

Fig. 8-13. DME Slant Range Error

read two miles from the station. The error diminishes as the distance from the station increases.

AREA NAVIGATION

Area navigation has been designed and developed to provide more lateral freedom and, thus, more complete use of available airspace. This mode of navigation does not require a track directly to or away from existing radio navigational aids. Therefore, it will prevent the tunneling effect of aircraft transitioning to or away from heavily used en route navigational aids.

Another advantage is the saving effected by flying direct routes. Figure 8-14 shows a typical comparison of a flight that is made on airways and a flight that uses area navigation. On a long flight, the time and cost advantages of flying with area navigation can be considerable.

Doppler radar, inertial navigation systems, and *course line computers* are typical of area navigation systems presently in use. The Doppler and inertial navigation systems are not dependent upon ground based navigational aids, while the course line computer utilizes VORTAC ground stations.

Fig. 8-14. Area Navigation

A characteristic common to all three types of area navigation is the use of *waypoints.* A waypoint may be described as a predetermined geographical location that may be a desired destination or a checkpoint along the route to a destination. The three systems differ in the manner in which the waypoints are determined.

DOPPLER RADAR SYSTEM

The Doppler system utilizes radar to detect direction and rate of movement of the aircraft across the ground. This information is sent to the computer. The computer in turn relates the aircraft's position and the desired course on the pilot's navigational display.

INERTIAL NAVIGATION SYSTEM

The inertial navigation system utilizes an inertial platform and a computer. The inertial platform contains two gyroscopes and three accelerometers. The gyroscopes maintain their orientation in space, while the accelerometers sense all direction and rate of movement. The information from the inertial platform is sent to the computer. The computer makes corrections in the information to allow for such things as the rotation of the earth, and then sends the information to the pilot's display unit. The inertial platform may also be used in conjunction with the air-

Fig. 8-15. Inertial Navigation Control Panel

craft's attitude instruments. Figure 8-15 shows the control display for a typical inertial navigation system.

The buttons are used to "type" the geographical coordinates of a desired waypoint. The waypoint coordinates shown in the window of the control unit in figure 8-15 would be 34°10.2' North latitude by 118°35.4' West longitude.

COURSE LINE COMPUTER

The course line computer utilizes ground-based VORTAC facilities and a vector analog computer to create a *phantom station* at the desired waypoint. Figure 8-17 shows an aircraft using a course line computer to fly to a waypoint, or phantom station.

The waypoint is established by setting 280° and 54 miles in the course line computer control illustrated in figure 8-16. The computer then creates the phantom station 54 miles from the Midway VOR on the 280° radial. The pilot's VOR and DME indications are exactly the same as if the Midway VOR were actually at the waypoint.

The pilot may fly TO or FROM the waypoint on any desired radial, and the distance relative to the waypoint will be shown in the DME window on the area navigation control panel. (See Fig. 8-16.) The aircraft in this example is 61 nautical miles from the waypoint.

Figure 8-18 shows a Jeppesen VFR RNAV chart with an RNAV route based on waypoints which are defined by radials and distances from specific VORTACs. For example, the Des Moines waypoint is located 22.1 n.m. from DSM on the 270° radial.

Fig. 8-16. Area Navigation Control Panel

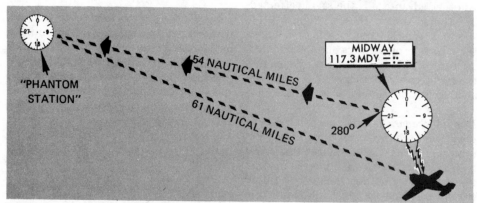

Fig. 8-17. "Phantom Station" or Waypoint

RADIO NAVIGATION

Fig. 8-18. VFR RNAV Chart

SECTION C - AUTOMATIC DIRECTION FINDER

Automatic direction finder (ADF) navigation supplements the VOR navigation system. It is used primarily with non-directional radio beacons (NDBs), but it can also be used with commercial AM broadcast stations.

Unlike VOR signals, the low and medium frequency NDB transmissions are not limited to line-of-sight reception. These signals travel both as ground waves that penetrate obstacles and follow the curvature of the earth, and as sky waves that bounce off the ionosphere. Sky waves can be received at great distances and at low altitudes.

An example of a nondirectional radio facility and the associated information box is shown in figure 8-19. An example of how a standard broadcast station is shown on a chart is depicted in figure 8-20. NDBs are also listed in the *Airport/Facility Directory*.

ADF RECEIVERS

The ADF receiver, shown in figure 8-21, has several functions. The beat frequency oscillator (BFO) is used to tune and identify continuous wave (CW) radio signals which are unmodulated. Receive (REC) is used for tuning and identifying a station or when using the ADF as a

receiver only. The automatic direction finder (ADF) function is used for navigation purposes.

Note that the bearing indicator has a 360° azimuth ring and a needle. On this model, the azimuth is fixed, and zero represents the nose of the aircraft.

When a station is tuned and the function selector knob is set to the ADF position, the needle on the indicator will point to the station, and a bearing, relative to the nose of the aircraft, is noted. If the magnetic heading of the aircraft and the relative bearing on the ADF indicator are added together, the *magnetic bearing to the station* may be determined.

RELATIVE BEARING AND MAGNETIC BEARING

For example, if the aircraft in figure 8-22 is on a magnetic heading of 200° and the ADF is tuned to the Kedzie low frequency station, the *relative bearing* (angle between the nose of the aircraft and the L/MF station) on the ADF indicator will be 080°. The magnetic heading of the aircraft (200°) is added to the relative bearing on the ADF indicator (080°), and the resultant *magnetic bearing* (280°) to the station is determined.

Fig. 8-19. Nondirectional Radio Beacon

Fig. 8-20. Standard Broadcast Station

BEARING INDICATOR

ON/OFF VOLUME CONTROL KNOB

FREQUENCY SELECTION KNOBS

FUNCTION SELECTOR KNOB

Fig. 8-21. ADF Receiver and Indicator

If the pilot of the aircraft in figure 8-22 wanted to fly to the station, the aircraft would be turned to a heading of 280°.

After the turn, the ADF indicator needle would point to zero, indicating that the station is on the nose of the aircraft. In a no-wind situation, the pilot could *home* to the station by keeping the ADF indicator needle on zero.

TRACKING

Through a procedure known as *tracking*, the aircraft may be flown to or away from a radio station on any desired course. This procedure involves a

directed trial-and-error method of determining the wind correction angle. The aircraft in figure 8-23 is flying to a station on a 360° bearing and has established a wind correction angle of 15°. Note that the heading of the aircraft is 015° and the ADF indicator is pointing to the station and showing the 15° wind correction angle on the ADF azimuth.

HOMING

Figure 8-24 illustrates a procedure called *homing to a station*. This procedure is simple since all the pilot has to do is continually change the heading so

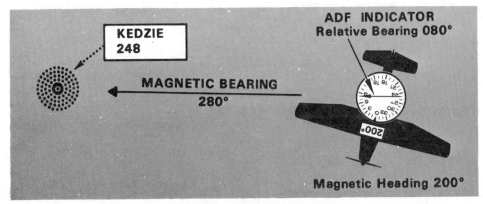

Fig. 8-22. Determining Magnetic Bearing

Fig. 8-23. "Inbound" ADF Wind Correction

Fig. 8-25. "Outbound" ADF Without Wind Correction

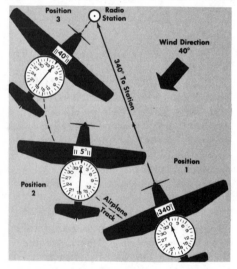

Fig. 8-24. Homing to Station Without Compensations for Wind

that the ADF indicator remains on zero. If there is a crosswind, however, the aircraft will actually drift slightly downwind from the station rather than flying a direct course to the station. *This procedure should never be used for flying away from a station.* If a pilot used the ADF to fly away from the station and did not allow for wind correction, the result would be as shown in figure 8-25, positions B or C. Position A shows the no-wind track.

SECTION D - RADAR AND TRANSPONDERS

RADAR

The term *radar* is derived from *radio detection and ranging.* Radar combines radio and television in that radio signals obtain data which is displayed on a scope similar to a television tube.

Radar works on an *echo* principle. (See Fig. 8-26.) The radar set transmits a high energy radio signal. The metal structure on aircraft reflects or *echoes* the radio signal back to the radar antenna. The object that reflects the signal is often referred to as a *target.*

Fig. 8-26. Radar Echo

The distance to a target is determined by measuring the time required for the radar signal to reach the object or target and return to the radar antenna. The radar signal, traveling at the speed of light, makes the round trip in microseconds as shown in figure 8-27.

Normal radar reflects terrain features, buildings, traffic on a nearby highway, and clouds or precipitation, as well as aircraft. For use in air traffic control, a device known as a moving target indicator automatically eliminates stationary and very slow moving targets.

The use of radar in air traffic control has become a valuable tool because it serves two basic functions: separation of air traffic and pilot navigational assistance. The FAA provides radar coverage to

most of the nation's airway system and provides traffic separation to en route traffic on instrument flight plans.

Radar is also used at terminal facilities by the tower, approach control, and departure control. Approach control normally uses *airport surveillance radar* (ASR) for the separation of traffic, but can assist a pilot in making an approach in instrument weather conditions if the pilot's own navigational equipment is inadequate or inoperative.

At selected locations, approach control also uses *precision approach radar* (PAR) which has very accurate range, azimuth, and glide path information used to bring the pilot right down to the touchdown zone area of the instrument runway. It is interesting to note that precision approach radar was first used during the famous Berlin Airlift after World War II.

Fig. 8-27. Timing of Transmitted and Reflected Signal

TRANSPONDERS

The *transponder* is the airborne portion of the *air traffic control radar beacon system* (ATCRBS), otherwise known as *secondary radar.* Ordinary radar, or *primary* radar, operates by originating radio waves which are reflected back from a target such as an aircraft, to an antenna on the ground. Some of the disadvantages of primary radar are that these reflected waves cannot penetrate high terrain, heavy precipitation, or certain other atmospheric phenomena, and are not effective at great distances. The effectiveness of radar, therefore, has been greatly increased by placing companion equipment, referred to as the *transponder*, in the aircraft itself.

A coded interrogation signal is transmitted by the ground radar, and any aircraft within line of sight and equipped with a transponder that is set to the same code responds automatically by sending back a coded signal. This causes the aircraft to appear as a distinct pattern on the radar controller's scope. The main advantages of the secondary radar system are:

1. Radar target reinforcement — The beacon reinforces the normal radar return on the ground radarscope.
2. Radar target identification — By having the pilot set a specific code on the transponder, the aircraft can be positively identified.
3. Extended radar coverage — Through use of special codes, more aircraft can receive radar guidance over a greater area, and their signals can be received at much greater distances than by primary radar.
4. Vertical separation of aircraft by altitude assignment is easier because special codes can be assigned to aircraft flying at specified altitudes.
5. Emergency codes can be used for rapid identification of aircraft in distress.
6. A transponder signal can penetrate extensive clouds or heavy precipitation.

In the United States, ATC uses Mode A and 4,096 separate codes in combinations such as ONE TWO ZERO ZERO for traffic control. Mode C is also used to add automatic altitude reporting capability.

Fig. 8-28. "Targets" on Radar Screen

The controller sees *beacon targets*, as illustrated in figure 8-28, on the scope only for aircraft which have been instructed to reply on the code on which the controller is interrogating. Since it is important for ATC personnel to know the transponder capability of all aircraft operating in the radar environment, a transponder notation is marked on the flight plan if the aircraft is so equipped.

Figure 8-29 shows a typical transponder. The following functions can be selected.

1. STANDBY — Allows the set to warm up and be ready for immediate use.
2. ON — Turns set on and transmits Mode A reply pulses.
3. ALT — Transmits either Mode A reply pulses or Mode C (altitude reporting) pulses selected automatically by the interrogating signal.

In addition, the IDENT button has a monitor light which blinks each time the set is interrogated by the ground station and when the TST position is selected. When depressed, the IDENT feature transmits a special pulse to effect immediate identification of the aircraft on the ground controller's scope. The code selector knobs are used to select the assigned reply code.

Fig. 8-29. Typical Transponder

TRANSPONDER PHRASEOLOGY

Air traffic controllers use the following phraseology to indicate to the pilot the type of radar beacon transponder operation required by ATC. Mode A or Mode C operations are the only operations to which ATC refers. ATC will not specify other modes on the transponder.

SQUAWK (NUMBER) — Operate radar beacon transponder on designated code number in Mode A.

IDENT — Push the ident button for identification purposes only upon controller's request. Release the button immediately after engaging, since the ident signal transmits for 20 seconds after the button is released.

SQUAWK (NUMBER AND IDENT) — Operate transponder on specified code number and Mode A, then engage the ident feature.

SQUAWK STANDBY — Switch transponder to standby position.

SQUAWK ALTITUDE — Actuate Mode C with automatic altitude reporting.

STOP ALTITUDE SQUAWK — Turn off Mode C.

STOP SQUAWK (MODE IN USE) — Switch the specified mode off.

STOP SQUAWK — Switch transponder to the "OFF" position.

SQUAWK MAYDAY — Operate transponder in emergency position (Mode A Code 7700).

TRANSPONDER CODES

Under no circumstances are civil airplanes permitted to operate on code 0000 as this code is reserved for Air Defense Command use.

Some of the more common codes used by ATC are:

   1200 — VFR flight
* 7600 — Two-way communications loss
   7700 — Emergency

* Squawk 7700 for 1 minute; then 7600 for 15 minutes. Repeat cycle as required.

ATC will state the code number which is needed for their operations if codes other than those listed above are required.

VFR RADAR PROGRAMS

Approach and departure control are intended primarily to serve the instrument pilot transitioning from the enroute portion of a flight to the terminal area or vice versa. At many air terminals, the services of approach and departure control are also available to the VFR pilot. The VFR pilot is not required to use these services; however, when available, their use is highly recommended.

RADAR TRAFFIC INFORMATION SERVICE

Pilots receiving radar traffic information service are advised of any radar "targets" which are near the route of flight. The purpose of this service is very simple; it alerts the pilot to possible conflicting traffic. However, this service is not intended to relieve the pilot of responsibility for continual vigilance to *see and avoid* other aircraft.

When operating in a terminal area, many times the altitude of the reported traffic is unknown. Therefore, the traffic may be well above or below the flight path of the aircraft.

It is important to remember that when operating VFR, this service is available on a "workload permitting" basis. The controller's first responsibility is to serve the needs of aircraft flying on IFR flight plans.

STAGE I SERVICE

Stage I service provides the pilot with *traffic information and limited vectoring* on a workload permitting basis. The pilot of an arriving aircraft should contact approach control on the frequency given over ATIS or listed in the *Airport/Facility Directory*, then provide a position, altitude, transponder code (if so equipped), and destination, followed by a request for traffic information. As the pilot continues toward the terminal, approach control specifies the time or

place to contact the tower, and radar service is automatically terminated.

STAGE II SERVICE

When pilots use Stage II radar, the additional service of *sequencing* aircraft into the traffic pattern is provided. As an arriving aircraft reaches the area in which Stage II service is provided, the pilot should contact approach control and state, *"Request radar service."*

After radar contact is established, the pilot is directed to fly specific headings, either to intersect the appropriate leg of the traffic pattern or to position the flight behind preceding aircraft in the approach sequence. When the aircraft is correctly positioned and the pilot is told to contact the tower, radar service is terminated automatically. A landing sequence number will be issued by the tower unless previously issued by approach control.

The pilot of a *departing* VFR aircraft desiring Stage II service should state, *"Request radar traffic information,"* on initial contact with ground control and advise the controller of the proposed direction of flight. Following takeoff, the tower will advise the pilot when to contact departure control and which frequency to use.

STAGE III SERVICE

In addition to radar vectoring and sequencing, *separation service* is provided with Stage III radar. It is designed to provide separation between participating VFR aircraft and all IFR aircraft operating within the airspace described as the *terminal radar service area* (TRSA). The availability of Stage III service is indicated by the designation Stage III SVC under Communications in the *Airport/Facility Directory*. Also, a graphic of each TRSA can be found in the publication, *Graphic Notices and Supplemental Data.*

chapter 9

FLIGHT PUBLICATIONS

INTRODUCTION

In recent years, use of the nation's airspace has increased at an extremely high rate. In keeping pace with the dynamic and rapidly growing aviation industry, the Federal government is constantly changing regulations and procedures to provide more efficient utilization of the national airspace system and its associated airways, airports, and facilities located throughout the country. Increased control of air traffic and stricter pilot discipline are necessary as airports open and close, navigation facilities change status, new techniques and procedures develop, and new aspects of safety are recognized. Updating and disseminating aviation information on a recurring basis is essential to safe flight operations. This is the task of the Federal Aviation Administration.

The FAA provides many aeronautical information publications for study and flight planning purposes. Use of these publications assures that pilots are supplied with current aviation data.

This chapter will present a brief summary of the *Airman's Information Manual*, the *Airport/Facility Directory, Notices to Airmen, Graphic Notices and Supplemental Data*, and *Advisory Circulars* — all published by the FAA. An informative reference book called the *Jeppesen J-AID* also will be covered. The information contained in these publications will help the pilot operate an aircraft safely, and with confidence, understanding, and professionalism in today's complex aviation environment.

SECTION A — AIRMAN'S INFORMATION MANUAL

The *Airman's Information Manual* (AIM) provides basic flight information and ATC procedures. It furnishes a comprehensive description of the national airspace system and the procedures for operating within that system.

The AIM, shown in figure 9-1, covers the components and operation of navigation aids of all types. A thorough explanation of airspace is also given, as well as the air traffic control rules and procedures which must be followed. Additionally,

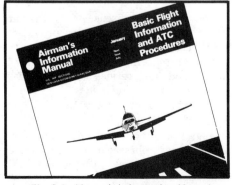

Fig. 9-1. Airman's Information Manual

items pertaining to flight safety and good operating practices are presented. The supplement contains a glossary of standard terms commonly used between the pilot and the ATC controller to assist in effective communication.

NAVIGATION AIDS

The section on air navigation radio aids discusses, in detail, the various types of navaids available, their purpose, and use. Components, operations, and procedures for each kind of navaid are explained, including radar, transponder and approach aids used by both civil and military aircraft.

The AIM also presents a comprehensive discussion of all types of airport lighting, approach lighting aids, and runway and taxiway markings. It is extremely important to become familiar with the material given in this chapter.

AIRSPACE

The discussion on airspace includes controlled, uncontrolled, and special use areas. A review of required cruising altitudes also is presented, along with a description of control areas, positive control areas, control zones, airport traffic areas, and related subjects. The pilot should review this information often in order to be familiar with the operational requirements of the various airspace segments.

AIR TRAFFIC CONTROL

A comprehensive discussion of the air traffic control system is also provided. This includes such services as air route traffic control centers (ARTCCs), control towers, and flight service stations. Radar services are explained in detail, especially transponder operations.

One section is devoted to radio communications, phraseology, and techniques. This critical link in the ATC

system should be studied thoroughly and reviewed periodically. Other portions of the AIM contain information on airport operations; ATC clearance/separation procedures; preflight, enroute, and arrival operations; and emergency procedures.

Pilot/controller roles and responsibilities are outlined briefly. However, for effective participation in the ATC system, several other documents should be consulted and studied. These include the *Federal Aviation Regulations* (FARs), *ATC Handbook, Notices to Airmen, FAA Advisory Circulars,* and *aeronautical charts.*

SAFETY OF FLIGHT

A section on safety of flight explains weather services available and outlines pilot reporting of in-flight weather conditions (PIREPs). Information concerning altimeter setting procedures and errors; wake turbulence; safety, accident, and hazard reports; and bird hazards also is presented.

GOOD OPERATING PRACTICES

The portion on good operating practices should be studied closely. Good judgment in following these suggested practices will greatly enhance the safety of every flight. A brief summary outlines some of the hazards from a medical standpoint.

PILOT/CONTROLLER GLOSSARY

The pilot/controller glossary is intended to promote a common understanding of terms used in the air traffic control system. Terms intended for pilot/controller communications are printed in bold italics; international terms that differ from FAA definitions are italicized.

SECTION B — AIRPORT/FACILITY DIRECTORY

The *Airport/Facility Directory* is a civil flight information publication, revised and distributed by the National Ocean Survey. It contains separate lists of airports, heliports, and seaplane bases which are open to the public. The directories are divided into regions as depicted on the front cover of each volume. (See Fig. 9-2) Other items which are covered include special notices, FSS-CS/T and National Weather Service telephone numbers, VOR/VOT receiver checkpoints, air route traffic control centers, preferred IFR routes, parachute jumping areas, and enroute flight advisory service (Flight Watch) stations.

A legend is printed in the front of each volume clarifying airport information including location, runway data, ground services, communications facilities, and navigation aids. An excerpt of this legend is shown in figure 9-3. The item numbers in the following discussion correspond to the numbered callouts in the illustration.

Fig. 9-2. Airport/Facility Directory

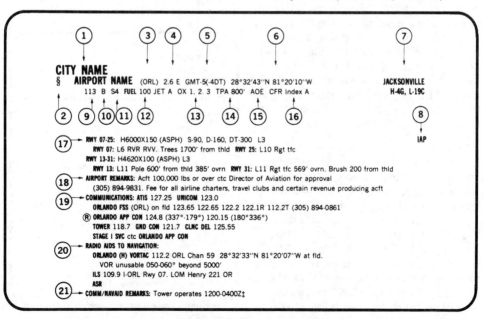

Fig. 9-3. Directory Legend

Each airport is listed alphabetically by state and city (item 1). A symbol preceding the airport name (item 2) indicates availability of NOTAM service. The airport identifier code (item 3) follows the airport name. These identifiers are used by ATC in flight plans instead of the airport name. Item 4 indicates the airport location in nautical miles and general direction from the center of the associated city.

The number of hours to be subtracted from Greenwich Mean Time (GMT), to obtain local standard or daylight savings time is also provided (item 5). The coordinates for geographic position of the airport are shown (item 6), as well as the name of the sectional chart and numbers of the high and low altitude enroute chart panels on which the facility is located (item 7).

The letters "IAP" (item 8) mean that an FAA-approved instrument approach procedure has been published for public use at this airport. The field elevation is shown in feet above mean sea level (item 9). At sea level this will be "00," while below sea level, elevations will be preceded by a minus sign. The letter "B" (item 10) indicates a rotating beacon is installed at this airport. The airport remarks section (item 18) will indicate time of operation if other than dusk to dawn. Aircraft servicing (item 11), fuel (item 12), and oxygen (item 13) are coded as shown in figure 9-4.

If the airport does not have a 24-hour operating control tower, the traffic pattern altitude is shown in feet above ground level (AGL), as shown by figure 9-3, item 14. "AOE" (item 15) indicates this is an airport of entry. If this were a landing rights airport, the letters "LRA" would be shown. U.S. customs officials must be notified of an arrival at these airports. The letters "CFR" and an index code (item 16) show availability of crash, fire, and rescue equipment.

Runway information (item 17) is printed on two lines. If the information is common to the entire runway, it is shown on the first line; otherwise, it will be shown on the second line. Runway direction (number), surface, length, width, weight bearing capacity, gradient (over 0.3 percent), and remarks are shown for each runway. Lengthy information is footnoted and explained in airport remarks (item 18). The remarks concern data affecting the operational status and usability of the airport. Examples are additional runway information, obstructions, restrictions, and landing fees. Availability and appropriate frequencies for such facilities as tower, ground control, ATIS, UNICOM, FSS and ATC frequencies are shown in a listing of communications data (item 19). Complete information on all radio aids to navigation by name, frequency, identifier, geographic coordinates, and location in relation to the airport is also provided (item 20). Restrictions, if applicable, are listed here, as well as availability of radar.

A section on comm/navaid remarks (item 21) is the final entry. Pertinent remarks concerning communications and navi-

(11) SERVICING

S1: Minor airframe repairs.
S2: Minor airframe and minor powerplant repairs.
S3: Major airframe and minor powerplant repairs.
S4: Major airframe and major powerplant repairs.

(12) FUEL

FUEL

CODE	
80	Grade 80 gasoline (Red)
100	Grade 100 gasoline (Green)
100LL	Grade 100LL gasoline (low lead) (Blue)
115	Grade 115 gasoline
A	Jet A—Kerosene freeze point—40° C.
A1	Jet A-1—Kerosene, freeze point—50° C.
A1 +	Jet A-1—Kerosene with icing inhibitor, freeze point
B	Jet B—Wide-cut turbine fuel, freeze point—50° C.
B +	Jet B—Wide-cut turbine fuel with icing inhibitor,

(13) OXYGEN

OX 1	High Pressure
OX 2	Low Pressure
OX 3	High Pressure—Replacement Bottles
OX 4	Low Pressure—Replacement Bottles

Fig. 9-4. Servicing, Fuel and Oxygen Codes

gational aids are listed here. An example is the limited operational hours of a control tower.

The back of the volume contains the special notices section, FSS-CS/T and National Weather Service Telephone Numbers, VOR receiver checkpoints and VOR test facilities (VOTs), ARTCC listings and frequencies, preferred IFR routes, parachute jumping areas, FAA office listings, aeronautical chart bulletins, and enroute flight advisory service (Flight Watch) data. This information should be consulted during flight planning.

SECTION C — NOTAMS AND GRAPHIC NOTICES AND SUPPLEMENTAL DATA

NOTAMs

Notices to Airmen, commonly called NOTAMs, contains information considered important for safe flight operations. (See Fig. 9-5.) For example, events such as the Reading Air Show or the Indianapolis 500 Auto Race create special air traffic problems. Such items as changes in weather broadcasting procedures, the addition of special use airspace, or an amendment to a standard instrument departure could create an unsafe situation if the information were not immediately known.

One section contains information that is expected to remain in effect for at least seven days. It deals with such events as airport or runway closings, navigation facilities temporarily out of service, and displaced runway thresholds.

Another section contains Flight Data Center Notices, called FDC NOTAMs. These are regulatory in nature and pertain to items such as changes to instrument approach procedures, standard instrument departures, aeronautical charts, and selected flight restrictions.

The graphic notices are those changes that must be disseminated as soon as possible without waiting for the next issue of the *Graphic Notices and Supplemental Data* publication. These graphics pertain to such items as terminal radar service areas and airports with a high volume of air traffic.

GRAPHIC NOTICES AND SUPPLEMENTAL DATA

The publication called *Graphic Notices and Supplemental Data* is another important part of the flight planning process. (See Fig. 9-6.) This manual contains information on such items as area advisories, area navigation (RNAV) routes, terminal area graphics, and terminal radar service area (TRSA) graphics.

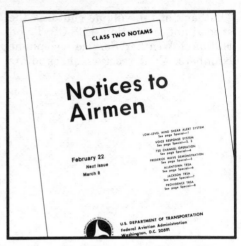

Fig. 9-5. Notices to Airmen

Area advisories contain aeronautical information that is not concerned with a specific airport or navaid, or that fails for some other reason to meet the criteria for inclusion in other flight publications These advisories may appear first in the NOTAMs booklet, but are transferred to *Graphic Notices and Supplemental Data* if they are long term or permanent advisories. Typical subjects are changes in the method of allocating radio frequencies or notices about flights in the vicinity of Wildlife Refuge Areas.

Fig. 9-6. Graphic Notices and Supplemental Data

Area navigation (RNAV) routes, which do not have high enough usage to justify printing on government charts are also tabulated in this publication for flight planning purposes.

New or revised TRSA or terminal area graphic charts may be published first in *Notices to Airmen*. Following an index of terminal area graphic notices are the individual graphics which are intended for the guidance of VFR pilots planning flights in these areas. The charts show concentrations of IFR traffic and suggested VFR routes through or around the terminal areas. The information is strictly "advisory" to inform and guide VFR pilots in the interest of safe flight operations.

Terminal radar service areas are established wherever Stage III radar service is available. Stage III radar service provides vectoring, sequencing, and separation on a full-time basis of both VFR and IFR air traffic landing at the primary airport. Separation service and advisories concerning unknown aircraft are also provided to all participating aircraft not landing at the primary airport but operating within the TRSA. Participating traffic means that an aircraft is in radar and radio contact with approach or departure control. A description of TRSA operational procedures for both pilots and air traffic controllers is included, together with charts of each terminal radar service area in the United States. TRSAs are also depicted on sectional charts.

The procedures for operations conducted in any of these areas should be studied and close reference made to the *Graphic Notices and Supplemental Data* publication before each flight.

SECTION D — SUPPLEMENTAL PUBLICATIONS

ADVISORY CIRCULARS

To provide current aviation information on a recurring basis, the Department of Transportation publishes and distributes *Advisory Circulars*. (See Fig. 9-7.) These circulars provide information and procedures necessary for good operating practice, but which are not binding on the public unless they are incorporated into a regulation.

Advisory Circulars are issued in a numbered subject system corresponding to the subject areas of the FARs. The numbers relate to the FAR subchapter titles and correspond to the FAR parts or sections. Some of the general subject matter areas and related numbers are:

00 General
20 Aircraft
60 Airmen
70 Airspace
90 Air Traffic Control and General Operations
150 Airports

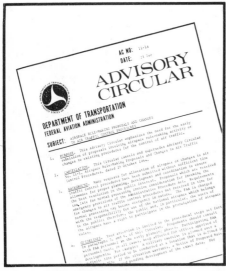

Fig. 9-7. Advisory Circular

When the volume of circulars in a series warrants further breakdown, the general number is followed by a slash and a sub-

subject number. Within the 150 series on airports, for example, 150/5000 denotes Airport Planning.

An *Advisory Circular Checklist*, which is issued periodically as AC-00-2, contains the subjects covered and availability of each circular. This checklist can be requested free of charge from the following address:

> U.S. Department of Transportation
> Publications Section M443.1
> Washington, D.C. 20590

JEPPESEN J-AID

The *Jeppesen Airport and Information Directory (J-AID)* is a collection of the most current aeronautical and airport information available. It includes data for both VFR and IFR flight operations, printed in looseleaf form for ease and promptness of revision. (See Fig. 9-8.)

The *J-AID* is divided into several sections: Introduction, Radio Facilities, Airport Directory, Meteorology, Tables and Codes, Air Traffic Control, and Regulations. The information in these sections is updated on a regular schedule.

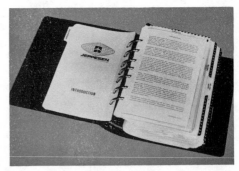

Fig. 9-8. J-AID

Included in the *J-AID* is the material covered in the *Airman's Information Manual* and the *Airport/Facility Directory*, with extensive coverage of many other aeronautical knowledge areas.

Because of the volume of material in the *J-AID* and the frequency of revision, FAR Part 135.81 authorizes the use of the *J-AID* as a substitute for the AIM and the *Airport/Facility Directory* for air taxi and commercial operations. Many airlines and air taxi operations prefer its use.

INTRODUCTION

The Introduction contains a revision record and table of contents. Each time a *J-AID* revision is filed, an entry is made in the revision record. This provides an easy check of whether the latest information has been incorporated.

RADIO FACILITIES

The Radio Facilities section is a complete listing of all radar units; direction finding (DF) stations and procedures; navigation aids by name, frequency and identifier; and commercial broadcast stations. A complete list of VOR check signals and checkpoints, both ground and air, is also provided.

AIRPORT DIRECTORY

A list of public use airports is provided in the Airport Directory. It is divided into three geographical regions: Eastern, Central, and Western. A map of the state showing the location of each airport precedes the alphabetical listings which are arranged by state, city, and airport name.

An airport diagram is provided for each airport with tabular information which includes the name of the airport, elevation, geographical coordinates, manager's name and telephone number, hours of operation, services available, runway information, communications facilities, and the distance and direction from a local navaid. The legend in the front of the directory provides an in-

terpretation of the symbols used in this portion of the *J-AID*.

METEOROLOGY

The Meteorology section provides a list of all National Weather Service offices and flight service stations by region and state and their telephone numbers. It also gives the meanings of symbols and codes used in station models on various weather charts, reports, and forecasts. In addition, all transcribed weather broadcast (TWEB) stations are shown.

TABLES AND CODES

The *J-AID* provides a comprehensive collection of conversion tables and data on commonly used codes. For example, tables for converting temperatures from Fahrenheit to Celsius and for various metric conversions are provided. Tables for wind components and sunrise, sunset, and twilight are provided along with a phonetic alphabet and Morse code listing.

AIR TRAFFIC CONTROL

The information contained in the Air Traffic Control section is basically the same as in the *Airman's Information Manual.* It includes a pilot/controller glossary, data on airspace, services available to pilots, radiotelephone phraseology and techniques, ATC clearances, emergency procedures, information on wake turbulence avoidance, bird hazards, safety of flight, and good operating practices.

REGULATIONS

The last section, Regulations, contains current Federal Aviation Regulations reprinted from Parts 1, 61, 91, 121, 135, 141, HMR 175, and NTSB 830. The regulations, which are updated on a timely basis, may also be purchased separately.

SUMMARY

This section has provided an introduction to several important sources of flight planning information. The pilot should seek out these publications and study them in depth in order to take full advantage of the information they contain.

chapter 10

FLIGHT COMPUTER

SECTION A - CALCULATOR SIDE

THE SCALES

Mathematicians have long used a slide rule as the tool to speed solutions to their problems. The calculator side of the flight computer is basically a circular slide rule with special indices for solving flight problems. The wind side of the computer is merely a device which makes it easy to draw a wind vector. The slide rule part of the calculator side of the computer consists of three scales referred to as A, B, and C as shown in figure 10-1, items 1, 2, and 3.

Fig. 10-1. Flight Computer

The outer scale (A) is fixed to the computer. Scales B and C are printed together on the disc that pivots in the center of the computer. With these three scales, it is a simple matter to establish mathematical ratios which are the basis of problem solving on this side of the computer.

The A scale is used to represent *miles, gallons,* or *true airspeed.* When used to represent miles, the scale provides the distance traveled or speed of the aircraft in knots or miles per hour. Gallons on this scale can represent two values: fuel consumption (gallons per hour), or total quantity of fuel used by the aircraft. TRUE A.S. or TAS on the A scale is an abbreviation for *true airspeed.*

The graduations on the B scale are used for *time* and *minutes* or for *IAS (indicated airspeed)* in either miles per hour or knots. The C scale graduations represent *hours* and *minutes* only.

CHANGING VALUES

In order to accurately read the scales on the calculator side of the computer, it is necessary that the changing values of the graduations of these scales be understood.

When using the A, B, and C scales to solve problems, common sense must be used to determine the value of the number. If a short distance is involved, 25 on the A scale might be read as 2.5 miles. (See Fig. 10-2.) If a long distance is involved, zeros are added to the 25 to get the proper answer. For example, 25 might be 250 or 2,500 miles.

Fig. 10-2. Changing Values

If the number 14 is used as 14, each graduation between 14 and 15 is equal to 0.1. If the 14 is used as 140 each graduation is equal to one. If used as 1,400 and 1,500 each graduation represents 10.

Between the numbers 15 and 16, there are only five graduations as compared to the 10 graduations between 14 and 15. (See Fig. 10-3.) When the numbers are used as 15 and 16 respectively, each graduation between them is equal to 0.2;

Fig. 10-3. Scale Graduations

when used as 150 and 160, each unit represents two.

The changing values on the C scale are somewhat different than those on the A and B scales. (See Fig. 10-4.) These graduations represent minutes and are equal to five or ten minutes as shown by the arrows. For example, between 1:50 and 2:00, the graduations are equal to 5 minutes; between 2:00 and 2:30, the graduations represent 10 minutes.

Fig. 10-4. Minute Graduations

TIME, SPEED, AND DISTANCE

The *speed index* is the large triangle symbol on the B and C scales, and is used as a reference in time and distance problems. (See Fig. 10-5.) The speed index always represents 60 minutes or one hour. In time and distance problems, there are three items for which to solve: time, speed, and distance. Two of these items must be known to work the problem.

Fig. 10-5. Speed Index

SOLVING FOR TIME

If an aircraft is flying at a speed of 100 knots (kts.), how long will it take to fly 132 nautical miles? The steps involved in solving this problem are: (See Fig. 10-6.)

1. Rotate the computer disc until the speed index is located directly under 10, which represents 100 knots.

Fig. 10-6. Time to Fly

2. Look clockwise on the A scale to 132, which is two graduations past 13. Look directly below 132 and find the answer to the problem.
3. It takes 79 minutes, as noted on the B scale, or 1 hour and 19 minutes as noted on the C scale, to travel 132 nautical miles at 100 knots.

SOLVING FOR DISTANCE

In order to solve for distance, another hypothetical problem is shown below. If the aircraft flies at 136 knots for a two-hour period, how many nautical miles will it fly? (See Fig. 10-7.)

1. Place the speed index under 136, which is six graduations to the right of 13 on the A scale. As noted before, this setting denotes the fact that the aircraft is flying at 136 knots.
2. Move clockwise on the C scale to 2:00 (two hours).

Fig. 10-7. Finding Distance

3. Look directly above 2:00 and find 272 on the A scale. The 272 is interpreted by noting that there are five major graduations between 25 and 30 on the A scale. Each one of the major graduations in this case will represent 10 miles. Between each of the major graduations there are five minor graduations which, in this case, will have a value of two miles per graduation. Therefore, the answer is 272 nautical miles.

SOLVING FOR SPEED

In order to find the speed, consider the next hypothetical problem. If an aircraft flies 180 nautical miles in one hour and 10 minutes, what is the speed? To solve this problem, proceed as follows: (See Fig. 10-8.)

1. Position 180 miles on the A scale directly over 1:10 on the C scale.
2. Directly over the speed index, read the answer of 154 knots.

Fig. 10-8. Finding Speed

FUEL CONSUMPTION

Fuel consumption problems are solved in the same manner as time and distance problems except gallons per hour and gallons are used instead of knots or miles per hour and miles.

FINDING ENDURANCE

If an aircraft burns fuel at the rate of eight gallons per hour (g.p.h.) and has 18 gallons of usable fuel on board, the flight endurance of the aircraft may be computed by the following steps: (See Fig. 10-9.)

1. Rotate the computer disc until the speed index is directly under 80, which represents eight gallons per hour in this problem.
2. Look clockwise on the A scale and locate 18 which represents the 18 gallons of usable fuel.
3. Directly under this, combine the B and C scales and interpret the answer as two hours and 15 minutes.

COMPUTING AMOUNT OF FUEL

If an aircraft burns 11 gallons per hour for a period of one hour and 30 minutes, the number of gallons of fuel burned can be computed by the following steps: (See Fig. 10-10.)

1. Place the speed index under 11, the rate of fuel consumption in 60 minutes, or one hour.

Fig. 10-9. Endurance

Fig. 10-10. Fuel Consumed

2. Locate one hour and 30 minutes on the C scale.
3. Look directly over one hour 30 minutes and find the number of gallons burned as computed on the A scale. The answer is 16.5 gallons.

FINDING FUEL CONSUMPTION RATE

The rate of fuel consumption can be determined if the gallons of fuel burned and the total time are known. (See Fig. 10-11.) For example, if an aircraft burns 45 gallons of fuel in two hours and 20 minutes, the rate of fuel consumption per hour may be determined by the following steps:

1. Rotate the calculator disc until 45 on the A scale is directly over two hours 20 minutes on the C scale.
2. Rotate the complete computer and look for the answer on the A scale above the speed index. The

answer to the problem is 19.3 gallons per hour.

AIRSPEED CORRECTIONS

An error in the airspeed instrument occurs in some aircraft due to inherent errors in the position of the static source on the fuselage. The pilot's operating handbook will have a calibration table to show this error if it is significant. The result of the correction is called *calibrated airspeed*. For purposes of this discussion, however, *indicated airspeed*, which is read directly off the airspeed indicator, and calibrated airspeed will be considered synonymous.

TRUE AIRSPEED

The airspeed indicator is a pressure instrument and as such will indicate different values with changes in pressure and temperature. The correction of indicated airspeed to allow for pressure, altitude, and temperature variations results in a value called *true airspeed*.

The computer has a means of converting indicated airspeed to true airspeed. The steps involved are as follows:

1. In the small window labeled "PRESSURE ALTITUDE THOUSANDS OF FEET," place the pressure altitude for the flight under the temperature for the flight on the scale labeled "AIR TEMPERATURE °C" (Celsius). (See Fig. 10-12.)

Fig. 10-11. Rate of Fuel Consumption

Fig. 10-12. Airspeed Scales

2. Without moving any scales, locate the indicated airspeed on the B scale. The B scale is labeled "CAS" (calibrated airspeed) which is considered synonymous with indicated airspeed.

3. Find the true airspeed on the A scale immediately above the indicated airspeed value.

Assume that the aircraft is flying at an altitude of 9,000 feet, the temperature is +10° Celsius, and the indicated airspeed is 150 knots. (See Fig. 10-13.)

1. Rotate the computer disc until +10° Celsius appears over 9,000 feet.

2. Opposite the indicated airspeed of 150 knots, read the true airspeed which is 176 knots.

DENSITY ALTITUDE

Density altitude is used to determine the performance of an aircraft. When taking off at an airport with a temperature of 86° Fahrenheit and a pressure altitude of 6,000 feet (pressure altitude is displayed on an altimeter when it is set to 29.92), the density altitude is computed as follows:

1. Since the temperature is given in degrees Fahrenheit and the computer is scaled in degrees Celsius, the conversion scale on the computer may be consulted to determine the temperature in degrees Celsius. Looking opposite 86°F, find +30°C. (See Fig. 10-14.)

Fig. 10-13. True Airspeed

Fig. 10-14. Temperature Conversion

2. Position +30° Celsius opposite the pressure altitude of 6,000 feet as shown in figure 10-15.

3. The density altitude is read in the density altitude window. In this case, it is approximately 9,000 feet.

In this example, the performance of the aircraft will be equivalent to flying at an altitude of 9,000 feet under standard conditions.

Fig. 10-15. Density Altitude

CONVERSION INDEXES

It is often necessary to convert from one unit of measurement to another; for example, from miles per hour to knots, or from gallons of fuel to pounds of fuel. The flight computer incorporates arrows and scales to perform these common conversions. A brief description of the procedures for making these conversions follows.

To convert statute to nautical miles, or miles per hour to knots, use the two arrows located at 66 and 76 on the outer scale. When a statute value is placed under the arrow marked "STAT" the equivalent nautical value is read under the arrow marked "NAUT." For example, to convert 115 statute miles to nautical miles, place 115 under the "STAT" arrow and read 100 nautical miles under the "NAUT" arrow, as shown in figure 10-16. When converting

a nautical value to a statute value, simply reverse this procedure.

The location of other conversion arrows is listed below with the labels that appear on the computer.

Kilometers (KM.) — near 12 on middle and outer scales
U.S. gallons (U.S. GAL.) — near 13 on middle and outer scales
Imperial gallons (IMP. GAL.) — near 11 on middle and outer scales
Liters (LITERS) — near 50 on middle and outer scales

Fig. 10-16. Knots to Miles Per Hour

Pounds of Fuel (FUEL LBS.) — near 80 on outer scale
Pounds of Oil (OIL LBS.) — near 10 on outer scale
Feet (FT.) — near 14 on outer scale
Meters (METERS) — near 45 on middle scale
Pounds (LBS.) — near 35 on outer scale
Kilograms (KG.) — near 16 on middle scale

To use these conversion arrows, align the two arrows corresponding to the units of measure to be converted, one on the outer scale and the other on the middle scale. Then all values on one scale are directly opposite the converted value on the other. For example, when the "FUEL LBS." arrow on the outer scale is aligned with the "U.S. GAL." arrow on the middle scale, each value of fuel in gallons on the middle scale is opposite its corresponding weight in pounds on the outer scale.

SECTION B — WIND SIDE

In order to understand the wind side of the computer, a brief explanation of how wind affects an aircraft in flight is presented along with related terms and their definitions.

WIND EFFECTS

After a true course is plotted, the effects of wind speed and direction at the planned flight altitude must be considered. Forecast wind information for winds aloft is obtained from the National Weather Service and flight service stations.

Wind is the movement of an air mass over the earth. Its motion is made apparent through blowing trees, choppy water, or the tugging of clothing. If it were a balloon, the aircraft would simply move with the air mass and drift above the terrain. Since the aircraft moves under its own power, however, the speed and direction it travels over the terrain is the result of combining aircraft speed, wind speed, aircraft heading, and wind direction.

WIND SPEED

The National Weather Service reports the speed of the wind in knots, and wind direction is always the direction *from* which it is blowing. Wind speed is the rate or progress of an air mass over the earth. The term *knots*, when referring to speed, means nautical miles per hour. Remember that a nautical mile, which is 6,076 feet long, is equal to one minute of latitude. The term *miles per hour* means statute miles per hour. A statute mile is 5,280 feet long.

AIRSPEED

INDICATED AIRSPEED

An aircraft's speed through the air mass is shown on the airspeed indicator. Only at sea level on a standard day are the indicated airspeed and the aircraft's actual speed through the air the same.

TRUE AIRSPEED

In the thin air of high altitudes, compensations must be made for variances in pressure and temperature to find the actual speed through the air mass. When calculated corrections for temperature and pressure altitude are applied to indicated airspeed, the adjusted airspeed is called *true airspeed* and is expressed in miles per hour or knots.

GROUND SPEED

Another type of speed that affects the aircraft's time in flight is called *ground speed*, because it relates to the aircraft's progress over the ground. If there is no wind, the aircraft's true airspeed and its ground speed will be the same. However, although true airspeed may be constant, the headwind or tailwind affects the ground speed.

For example, an aircraft has a true airspeed of 100 knots. It is flying in an air mass which is moving in the same direction at 20 knots.

The aircraft is considered to have a tailwind, which is assisting its progress over the ground. The aircraft's ground speed is then 120 knots; however, the true airspeed is unaffected by wind. (See Fig. 10-17.)

Reversing this example, assume the aircraft is moving against a 20-knot air mass. Its progress over the ground is determined by subtracting the 20-knot air mass speed from its 100-knot true airspeed. The ground speed is now 80 knots. (See Fig. 10-17.)

DRIFT

In figure 10-18, an aircraft is heading east in an air mass moving from the south at 20 knots, so the aircraft has a

Fig. 10-17. Effect of Wind on Ground Speed

crosswind. At the end of one hour, the aircraft will have drifted 20 nautical miles north of the true course line because of the air mass movement.

When flying from one point to another, the aircraft must not be allowed to drift off course, nor can slow ground speed be permitted to extend time en route beyond fuel endurance. Wind corrections and fuel stops must be determined by careful preflight planning.

Fig. 10-18. Effect of Wind on Track

TRUE HEADING

The direction an aircraft is actually heading, as measured in degrees from true north, is called *true heading*. The path it makes over the ground is called *track*. A specific heading must be maintained to keep the track directly over the planned true course line.

PROBLEM SOLVING

The solution of the effect of wind direction and velocity on the path and speed over the ground is a wind vector triangle. The wind side of the flight computer simplifies the drawing of the vectors of the wind triangle.

The components of the wind side are the *rotating azimuth* and the *sliding grid*. (See Fig. 10-19.) The sliding grid is a section of a graduated circle. The straight lines represent degrees right or left of the centerline and the curved lines represent distance. The sliding grid of this computer has two sides, a high speed side and a low speed side.

The *azimuth circle* rotates freely and is graduated into 360°. The transparent portion is frosted so that it can be written on with a pencil. In the center is a small circle called the *grommet* that is moved directly over the centerline of the grid.

To maintain a specific course, the pilot must determine the *wind correction angle* and adjust the aircraft heading accordingly. The time en route, an important factor in any flight, is influenced by wind as it affects the ground speed. To determine the total effect of wind on a flight, the *true course, true airspeed, wind direction,* and *velocity* must be known.

FLIGHT COMPUTER

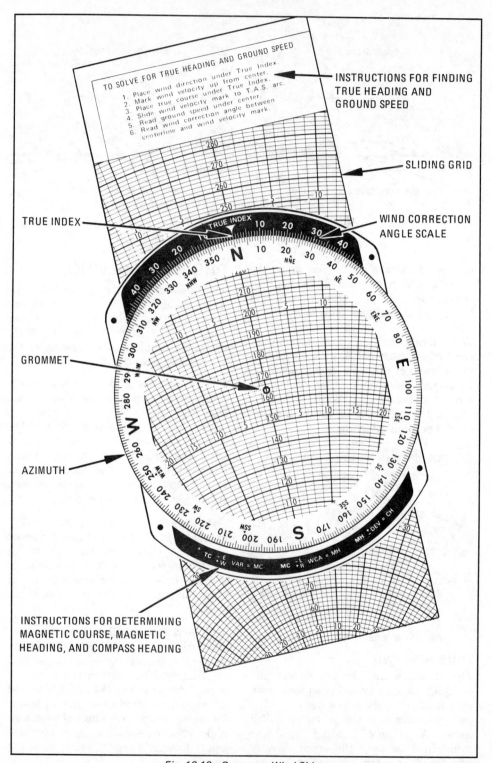

TO SOLVE FOR TRUE HEADING AND GROUND SPEED

1. Place wind direction under True Index.
2. Mark wind velocity up from center.
3. Place true course under True Index.
4. Slide wind velocity mark to T.A.S. arc.
5. Read ground speed under center.
6. Read wind correction angle between centerline and wind velocity mark.

INSTRUCTIONS FOR FINDING TRUE HEADING AND GROUND SPEED

SLIDING GRID

TRUE INDEX

WIND CORRECTION ANGLE SCALE

GROMMET

AZIMUTH

INSTRUCTIONS FOR DETERMINING MAGNETIC COURSE, MAGNETIC HEADING, AND COMPASS HEADING

Fig. 10-19. Computer Wind Side

FINDING TRUE HEADING AND GROUND SPEED

An explanation of how the wind side works is provided with the following example:

Given:

  True course . . . . 084°
  True airspeed . . . . 90 kts.
  Wind direction and
  velocity . . . . . 330° true at 23 kts.

Determine:

  Wind Correction Angle
  True Heading
  Ground Speed

1. Rotate the azimuth until the wind direction of 330° is located directly under the true index. (See Fig. 10-20.)

2. Next, slide the grid through the computer until the grommet is on any one of the heavy curved lines extending from right to left on the grid. For the problem, the 100-mile grid has been arbitrarily chosen.

3. Then place the wind velocity on the azimuth by placing a pencil mark 23 knots above the grommet of the azimuth.

4. Now, place the true course of 084° under the true index. (See Fig. 10-21.)

Fig. 10-20. Plotting the Wind

5. With the true course under the true index, slide the grid until the pencil mark, or wind dot, is positioned on the true airspeed line of 90 knots.

6. Find the wind correction angle

Fig. 10-21. The Solution

by checking the number of vertical lines (degrees) to the right or left (in this case to the left), between the grid center line and the wind dot. The wind correction angle is 13° left.

7. To find true heading, the scales on either side of the true index are used. Since the wind correction angle is 13° left, start at the true index symbol and count 13 units to the left and find the true heading of 071° directly below this graduation. (See Fig. 10-21.) If the wind dot is to the left, count left for true heading; if the wind dot is to the right, count right for true heading.

8. Without moving the computer setting, read the ground speed under the grommet. The ground speed in this problem is 97 knots.

OTHER COMPUTER USES

This chapter has covered the functions of the computer most commonly used by the student pilot. In addition, a flight computer can be used for solving such problems as:

1. short time and distance.
2. finding drift angle (off course).
3. time and distance to a VOR station.
4. multiplication and division.
5. finding unknown winds.
6. finding altitude for most favorable winds.
7. radius of action.
8. metric and other conversions.

chapter 11

MEDICAL FACTORS OF FLIGHT

SECTION A - OXYGEN, ALTITUDE, AND THE BODY

THE ATMOSPHERE

Modern general aviation aircraft are capable of transporting man to altitudes where a knowledge and application of physiological principles is not only desirable, but necessary to sustain life; therefore, the pilot should understand the interrelationships between oxygen, altitude, and the body.

The atmosphere consists of 78% nitrogen, 20.9% oxygen, 1.1% carbon dioxide and other gases. These three main gases are important to the body physiologically. Due to the constant mixing of winds and to other weather factors, the percentages of each gas in the atmosphere are normally constant to 70,000 feet. (See Fig. 11-1.)

Nitrogen, present in a high percentage, is responsible for the major portion of the total atmospheric pressure or weight. Some nitrogen is dissolved in and is carried by the blood, but this gas does not

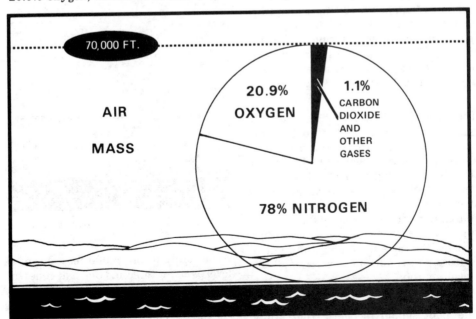

Fig. 11-1. Percentage of Gases in the Atmosphere

enter into chemical combination as it is carried throughout the human body. Each time we breathe, the same amount of nitrogen is exhaled as was inhaled.

Oxygen is a colorless, odorless, tasteless gas and is essential to life. Each time man breathes, approximately 20.9% of that breath is oxygen. In the lungs, a portion of this oxygen is absorbed into the bloodstream and is carried to all parts of the body. It is used to "burn" or oxidize food material and produce energy transformations in the body.

Man can live for weeks without food and for days without water, but only minutes if totally deprived of oxygen. Because he cannot store oxygen in his body, he lives a breath-to-breath existence. He continues to live only as long as he can continually replenish the oxygen consumed by his metabolic processes.

Air is heavy. It weighs 14.7 pounds per square inch at the earth's surface at sea level. Technically speaking, that is the pressure created by a column of air one inch square and about 100 miles high (the approximate thickness of the layer of free air or atmosphere covering the earth). (See Fig. 11-2.) A person normally does not notice this pressure because it presses upon him equally from all directions.

The weight of the atmosphere does not remain the same from top to bottom. Some people like to talk of the atmosphere as an ocean in which the diver finds that the pressure gets greater the deeper he goes. Others picture the air as a haystack because hay packs down at the bottom of the stack and is fairly loose at the top. In the same manner, air always remains the same in composition, but it is denser at the bottom because of all the weight on top.

The pilot should recognize that atmospheric pressure does not diminish at a uniform rate with altitude. Although the atmosphere covers the earth to a height of 100 miles, three-fourths of the molecules of air are packed into a region not much taller than Mt. Everest. (See Fig. 11-3.)

Fig. 11-2. Weight of the Atmosphere

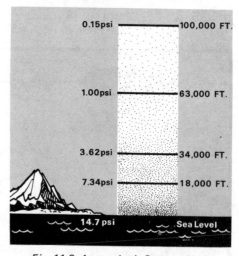

Fig. 11-3. Atmospheric Pressure Varies with Altitude

At an altitude of 18,000 feet above sea level or about three and one-half miles up, the air pressure has been decreased by one-half and is only about seven pounds per square inch. At 34,000 feet, the pressure has been cut in half again to a little more than three and one-half pounds per square inch. At 63,000 feet, there is only one pound of pressure remaining. At 100,000 feet, or nearly 20 miles up, the atmospheric pressure is about 0.15 pounds per square inch. Beyond that, the atmosphere is largely a vacuum.

RESPIRATION

Respiration, which is the exchange of oxygen and carbon dioxide between an organism and its environment, takes place in two phases, internal and external. External respiration is the exchange of gases between the lungs and the surrounding atmosphere. Internal respiration is the exchange of gases across the tissue cell membranes.

The respiratory cycle begins with inhalation of air into the lungs. Inhalation is produced by contraction of the *diaphragm*, the large muscle separating the thoracic and the abdominal cavity.

Ordinarily, a person breathes 12 to 16 times a minute, although the rate will be slower when resting and faster when exercising. The average, quiet, resting man inhales a little more than a pint of air at a time, or from six to eight quarts per minute.

Oxygen used in the body is inhaled through the mouth or nose, passes through the trachea and bronchial tubes, and is directed into the lungs where it transfers to the blood. The blood then carries this oxygen to living cells where energy is obtained for all body processes and functions through the action of oxygen upon compounds in the cells. This transfer of energy produces a waste product gas known as carbon dioxide or CO_2. As carbon dioxide is produced, blood then carries it back to the lungs where it is released to the atmosphere by exhaling through the nose or mouth, completing the respiration cycle. (See Fig. 11-4.)

Fig. 11-4. Oxygen Used in the Body

Fig. 11-5. The Alveoli

Within the lungs, there are millions of tiny air sacs called *alveoli* which inflate like tiny balloons. (See Fig. 11-5.) The number of air sacs in the lungs is estimated to be around 750 million with a surface area between 700 and 800 square feet, or about the size of a tennis court. It is a miracle of human body structure that this large area of gaseous exchange is available within the confines of the chest cavity.

Blood is pumped from the heart through arteries to microscopic *capillaries*, or tiny tubes, through which blood is constantly flowing. The walls of the air sac contain these tiny tubes in which the oxygen is diffused into the blood. The enriched blood then flows through veins back to the heart and ultimately to all parts of the body.

The wall of each air sac consists of a minutely thin membrane, 0.00002 of an inch thick, or about one cell in thickness. This membrane is moist and porous. It is dense enough to retain or hold liquid but is semipermeable enough to permit gas molecules to flow through it.

The tiny capillaries carrying blood through these membranes or walls are so small that the red blood cells are, for the most part, in single file. Thus, a microscopically thin film of blood is exposed to the air in the air sac through the semipermeable membrane. (See Fig. 11-6.)

Fig. 11-6. Blood Exposed to Air
in the Air Sac

GAS TRANSFER

In order to understand how the oxygen can pass through the air sac membrane and into the blood, certain basic information should be examined.

All gases tend to move from high to low pressure areas, and in so doing, are able to pass through thin membranes. These gases will flow from the high to the low pressure side of the membrane until the pressure on both sides equalizes.

For example, in the top portion of figure 11-7, the pressure within the mixture of gases on the left is gas A, 6 pounds per square inch (p.s.i.); gas B, 10 p.s.i.; and gas C, 2 p.s.i. On the right side of the membrane separating the two spaces, gas A has a pressure of 4 p.s.i.; gas B, 10 p.s.i.; and gas C, 4 p.s.i. As shown in the center

portion of figure 11-7, gas A will flow from the left to the right side of the membrane until both sides have equal pressures of gas A. There is no flow of gas B because the pressures were equal at the beginning. Gas C, however, will flow from right to left until the pressures have equalized. The bottom portion of figure 11-7 shows that on both sides of the membrane the pressure of gas A has stabilized at 5 p.s.i.; gas B at 10 p.s.i.; and gas C at 3 p.s.i.

Fig. 11-7. Equalization of Pressures in
a Mixture of Gases Across a Membrane

OXYGEN TRANSFER

This same principle of gas movement to equalize individual pressures on both sides of a membrane takes place in the human body.

Figure 11-8 shows a close-up view of the air sac wall. Since the water vapor and carbon dioxide are added to the air mixture entering the air sac, the percent volumes occupied by oxygen and the other gases are also changed. Less oxygen can enter the air sac due to the pressure of this water vapor and CO_2. The oxygen now occupies a smaller percent of the

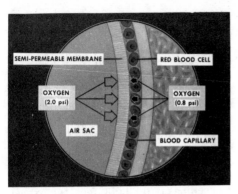

Fig. 11-8. Unequal Oxygen Pressure

total volume, so its pressure is reduced. The oxygen pressure in the air sacs becomes approximately two p.s.i. at sea level.

The pressure of oxygen in the blood as it enters the capillaries around the air sac is only 0.8 p.s.i. Since gases flow from high to low pressure areas, oxygen passes from the air sacs through the semipermeable membrane, through the blood capillary wall, and into the blood where it combines chemically with the *hemoglobin* of the red blood cells. This transfer is accomplished because the oxygen attempts to equalize the pressures on each side of the membrane.

The oxygen-rich blood is pumped by the heart to the cells throughout the body where an oxygen transfer takes place. The cells then use the oxygen to convert carbohydrates, fats, and proteins into new protoplasm or into energy for the life processes.

This energy conversion produces carbon dioxide as a waste product which is released by the body cells and transferred to the plasma of the blood. This exchange of oxygen for carbon dioxide takes place simultaneously as the blood passes through the tissues. The carbon dioxide-rich blood then returns to the heart. From the heart, the carbon dioxide-rich blood is pumped to the lungs where it flows through the tiny capillaries in the minute membranes of the air sacs. Since the air

in the air sacs has a lower carbon dioxide pressure than the carbon dioxide in the blood, the carbon dioxide flows through the blood vessel walls through the semipermeable membranes, and into the air sacs. Exhalation of the air in the lungs expels the carbon dioxide from the body, completing the respiratory cycle.

OXYGEN NEEDS AND AVAILABILITY

The amount of oxygen consumed by the body during the respiratory cycle depends primarily upon the degree of physical or mental activity of the individual. A person walking at a brisk pace will consume about four times as much oxygen as when resting. In the course of an average day, a normal adult male will consume about two and one-half pounds of oxygen. This is approximately equivalent to the weight of food consumed daily. An oxygen supply which might be adequate for a person at rest would be inadequate for the same individual when flying under severe weather conditions or when under mental stress.

Oxygen becomes harder to obtain with altitude because the air becomes less and less dense, and the total pressure decreases. As the total pressure decreases, so does the pressure of oxygen even though the percentage of oxygen in the air remains constant. For example, at 40,000 feet, the total pressure is only 2.7 p.s.i., and the oxygen pressure is 0.56 p.s.i.

As altitude increases and the pressure of oxygen is reduced, the amount of oxygen transfer in the lung air sacs is reduced which results in a decrease in the percentage of oxygen saturation in the blood. This causes a deficiency of oxygen throughout the body, and, for this reason, supplemental oxygen, pressurized cabins, and/or pressurized suits are required if the body is to receive adequate oxygen.

The total effect on an oxygen-deprived person is the result of both altitude and time of exposure. Every cell in the body is affected by the lack of oxygen, but the primary effects are on the brain and the body's nervous system. Above 10,000 feet, deterioration of physical and mental performance is a progressive condition. The curtailment becomes more severe with increased altitude as well as prolonged exposure.

HYPOXIA

The effects of an insufficient supply of oxygen on the body is called *hypoxia.* "Hypo" means "under," and "oxia" refers to oxygen. Some of the common symptoms of hypoxia are:

1. an increased breathing rate.
2. lightheaded or dizzy sensation.
3. tingling or warm sensation.
4. sweating.
5. reduced visual field.
6. sleepiness.
7. blue coloring of skin, fingernails, and lips.
8. behavior changes.

Subtle hypoxic effects begin at 5,000 feet at night. In the average individual, night vision will be blurred and narrowed. Also, dark adaptation will be affected, and at 8,000 feet, night vision is reduced as much as 25% without supplemental oxygen. Little or no effects will be noticed during daylight at these altitudes.

At 10,000 feet, the oxygen pressure in the atmosphere is approximately two p.s.i. Accounting for the dilution effect of water vapor and carbon dioxide in the air sacs, this is not enough to deliver a normal supply of oxygen into the lungs, but is enough to keep the blood about 90% saturated.

This mild deficiency is ordinarily of no great consequence. However, flying in the vicinity of 10,000 feet for over four hours may result in fatigue. Pilots report experiencing difficulty in concentrating, reasoning, solving problems, and making precise adjustments of aircraft controls under prolonged flight conditions at this altitude.

At 15,000 feet, drowsiness, a headache, weariness, fatigue, and a false sense of well-being will normally be experienced in two hours or less. Most important and less evident to the individual is the psychological impairment which could cause judgment errors, poor coordination, and difficulty in performing important tasks.

Proceeding up to 20,000 feet, the oxygen pressure in the air drops to 1.38 p.s.i., or less than half that at sea level. Oxygen saturation of the blood drops to 64% at this altitude. Collapse or convulsions will result within 15 minutes.

An atmospheric pressure reading at 34,000 feet altitude will show 3.6 p.s.i. The oxygen pressure is only 0.76 p.s.i. This is less than the constant pressures of water vapor and carbon dioxide that exist in the lung air sacs and about the same as the oxygen pressure in the blood entering the air sacs. Blood saturation with oxygen is only 30% at this altitude. Little or no oxygen will transfer from the air sacs to the blood because of the small pressure differential across the membrane. Unconsciousness will occur in less than four minutes.

It is true that susceptibility to hypoxia varies, and there are some who can tolerate altitudes well above 10,000 feet without any significant effects. It is equally true that there are those who develop hypoxic effects below 10,000 feet. As a general rule, individuals who do not exercise regularly or who are not in good physical condition will have less resistance to oxygen deficiency.

Also, those persons who have recently overindulged in alcohol, who are moderate to heavy smokers, or who take certain drugs will be more susceptible to hypoxia. Susceptibility can also vary in the same individual from day to day, or from morning to evening.

Because it affects the central nervous system, the general effects of hypoxia are, in many respects, very similar to alcoholic intoxication. A typical individual suffering from hypoxia, induced by exposure between 15,000 and 20,000 feet, will be comparable to an individual who has consumed five to six ounces of whiskey.

The most hazardous feature of hypoxia, as it may be encountered in general aviation aircraft, is its gradual and insidious onset. Its production of a false feeling of well-being called euphoria is particularly dangerous. Since it obscures a person's ability and desire to be critical of himself, he generally does not recognize the symptoms. (See Fig. 11-9.) The hypoxic individual commonly believes things are getting progressively better as he nears total collapse.

Fig. 11-9. Euphoria Often is Experienced by the Hypoxic Individual

While not all of the symptoms mentioned occur in each individual, any given person will develop the same symptoms in the same order each time he becomes hypoxic. For this reason, a person, having once experienced hypoxia under careful supervision is better prepared to recognize his condition if hypoxia occurs again. Such a controlled experience is available in what is known as an altitude chamber. Figure 11-10 shows the progressive hypoxia of a pilot from initial removal of his oxygen mask until total collapse occurred at simulated high altitudes.

There are some false indicators of a hypoxic condition which should be considered. The color of the fingernails has been suggested by some as a guide to determine the degree of hypoxia, depending upon their blueness, but this approach is invalid because when hypoxic, an individual should consider himself as "looking through the optimistic eyes of an alcoholic." Another unreliable clue is shortness of breath. As enlarged upon later, the breathing rate is controlled primarily by carbon dioxide accumulation. When carbon dioxide is exhausted adequately, the individual does not get this ordinarily useful clue to hypoxia.

TIME OF USEFUL CONSCIOUSNESS

The term "time of useful consciousness" refers to the maximum length of time an individual has to perform the purposeful tasks necessary for his survival, such as putting on an oxygen mask. Although the hypoxic individual may remain conscious for a longer period, he has a *limited* time in which his brain receives sufficient oxygen to make decisions and perform useful acts.

Fig. 11-10. Progressive Hypoxia

The table shown in figure 11-11 lists the times of useful consciousness for various altitudes. The times shown represent the average times for flying personnel. Note that the times vary from 10 minutes at 22,000 feet to 1 minute at 30,000 feet. For example, if the pressurization equipment fails in an aircraft flying at 28,000 feet, the pilot and passengers have only two and one-half to three minutes to get the oxygen mask on before they exceed their time of useful consciousness.

ALTITUDE	TIME OF USEFUL CONSCIOUSNESS
22,000 FT.	5 TO 10 MINUTES
25,000 FT.	3 TO 5 MINUTES
28,000 FT.	2½ TO 3 MINUTES
30,000 FT.	1 TO 2 MINUTES

Fig. 11-11. Time of Useful Consciousness vs. Altitude

RECOVERY FROM HYPOXIA

Recovery from hypoxia is rapid, usually within 15 seconds after oxygen is administered. Transient dizziness may occur during the recovery. The severely hypoxic individual recovering from moderate or severe hypoxia is usually quite fatigued and may suffer measurable deficiency in mental and physical performance for many hours.

PREVENTION OF HYPOXIA

Aircrew members have found that a good way to protect themselves from hypoxia is to be constantly aware of the problem and use the altimeter as the primary guide for the use of oxygen. It is recommended that oxygen be used by pilots when they' fly at altitudes over 10,000 feet during the day and altitudes of over 5,000 feet at night. Night vision is reduced and dark adaptation is affected above 5,000 feet. Passengers are urged to use supplemental oxygen above 10,000 feet if the cabin is not pressurized. (See Fig. 11-12.) The pilot should also be aware of the Federal Aviation Regulations requiring use of supplemental oxygen.

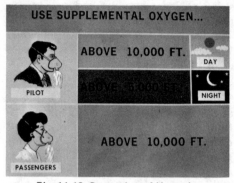

Fig. 11-12. Prevention of Hypoxia

Paraphrasing FAR 91.32: at cabin pressure altitudes above 12,500 feet MSL through 14,000 feet MSL, the pilot is required to use supplemental oxygen for any portion of his flight of over 30 minutes duration at that altitude. If he is above 14,000 feet MSL, he must use supplemental oxygen continuously; above 15,000 feet MSL, the passengers must have supplemental oxygen available.

The chart in figure 11-13 shows the percentage of oxygen needed to maintain sea level and 10,000 foot equivalents. Flying at 15,000 feet, 39% oxygen is needed to maintain a sea level atmosphere. If it is desired to maintain a 10,000 foot atmosphere while flying at 15,000 feet, only

INHALED AIR --- % OXYGEN REQUIRED		
I ALTITUDE	II S.L. EQUIV.	III 10,000 FT. EQUIV.
40,000 FT.		100
36,000 FT.		81
33,000 FT.	100	67
30,000 FT.	84	56
25,000 FT.	63	42
20,000 FT.	49	33
15,000 FT.	39	26
10,000 FT.	31	20.9
5,000 FT.	25	
S.L.	20.9	

Fig. 11-13. Percent of Oxygen Required vs. Altitudes

26% oxygen is required. Notice that above 33,000 feet, even 100% oxygen will no longer provide inhaled air with oxygen equal to that in sea level air. At 40,000 feet, the best that 100% oxygen will do is maintain a 10,000 foot atmosphere.

AIRCRAFT OXYGEN SYSTEMS

Figure 11-14 pictures one of the most common systems used in general aviation aircraft to supply supplemental oxygen. This type of equipment may be permanently installed or may be portable.

The operation of the re-breather continuous-flow oxygen mask, as it is called, is quite simple. (See Fig. 11-15.) First, oxygen flows into the accumulator bag at a continuous rate, filling the bag. A flow indicator in the tubing to the oxygen mask informs the pilot that oxygen is flowing. The rate can be adjusted for the flight altitude by opening or closing the flow control valve, or in most cases, atmospheric pressure is used to control an automatic regulator. (See Fig. 11-14.)

Fig. 11-15. Mask Assembly

pressurized resulting in less outside air entering the mask during inhalation.

The major portion of the oxygen used by the body is from the lower two-thirds of the inhaled air/oxygen volume in the lungs. The upper one-third of the gas mixture, trapped in the bronchial passages and throat cavities, remains relatively concentrated in oxygen.

The oxygen-rich top one-third of the air/oxygen volume in the lungs is exhaled first, passing into the mask and partially re-filling the accumulator bag. Because the bag becomes pressurized by the incoming oxygen from the oxygen system and the initial exhalation air from the lungs, the remaining two-thirds volume of exhaled air is forced out of the tiny holes into the outside air. The small opening, leading from the mask to the accumulator bag, provides a restriction that helps force the majority of the exhaled air out of the mask.

Fig. 11-14. Typical General Aviation Oxygen System

As the user inhales, the oxygen is sucked out of the bag and into the lungs. As the bag collapses, outside air is also drawn into the face mask through several tiny holes in the mask nose piece. This air then mixes with pure oxygen drawn from the bottle. The amount of outside air that is inhaled depends on the rate of oxygen flowing into the mask. The higher the flow rate, the more the bag and mask are

This cycle is repeated during each breath. The higher the altitude, the more the accumulator bag expands due to the lower outside air pressure around the bag. Thus, the inside of the bag receives an expanded volume of oxygen as the outside air pressure diminishes. Since the oxygen inside the bag has a larger volume, less outside air can be drawn into the mask during inhalation.

An advantage of this type of system is the conservation of oxygen by using the re-breather bag. However, at higher altitudes, systems which supply larger volumes of undiluted oxygen upon inhalation and which exhaust the exhaled air more effectively become necessary.

CARBON DIOXIDE

The respiratory center of the brain reacts to the amount of carbon dioxide found in the bloodstream. When a person is in a physically-relaxed state, the amount of carbon dioxide in the blood stimulates the respiratory center, and the breathing rate is stabilized at about 12 to 16 breaths per minute.

When physical activity occurs, the body cells use more oxygen, and more carbon dioxide is produced. Excessive carbon dioxide enters the blood, and through reflex action, the respiratory center responds to this excess. This center reacts, and breathing increases in depth and rate to remove the excess carbon dioxide. When the excess is removed, the respiratory center changes the breathing rate back to normal.

HYPERVENTILATION

"Hyper" means "over or above," and "ventilation" refers to breathing. Thus, *hyperventilation* is defined as excessive ventilation of the lungs from breathing too rapidly and too deeply with resulting loss of too much carbon dioxide from the body. This excessive loss of carbon dioxide causes the blood to become more alkaline.

Over-ventilation of the lungs in pilots or passengers is usually caused by anxiety or apprehension. When this condition occurs, the respiratory center would normally compensate by adjusting the breathing rate. However, persons who are anxious frequently override the respiratory signal, continue the forced breathing, and aggravate the carbon dioxide wash-out.

The resulting chemical imbalance may produce symptoms that are often mistaken for hypoxia. The symptoms associated with hyperventilation are:

1. dizziness.
2. tingling of the fingers and toes.
3. muscle spasms.
4. increased sensation of body heat.
5. nausea.
6. rapid heart rate.
7. blurred vision.
8. finally, loss of consciousness can occur.

A person may induce such symptoms experimentally by simply breathing deeply and rapidly over a period of time. Caution is advised, however, and such breathing should be limited to a period of a minute or two. By this time, a number of the symptoms will be experienced by the individual.

After becoming unconscious, the body's respiratory signals will take over, and the breathing rate will be exceedingly low until carbon dioxide is increased to a normal level. Hyperventilation symptoms can be relieved by voluntarily reducing rate and depth of breathing, allowing the body to build up a normal carbon dioxide level. Pilots are sometimes advised to rebreathe from a paper bag to hasten the return to normal carbon dioxide levels. This procedure artificially increases the percentage of carbon dioxide in the available air supply. (See Fig. 11-16.)

Fig. 11-16. Rebreathing Technique

SECTION B - VERTIGO AND VISION

In day-to-day life, the ability of the human body to function correctly and precisely depends partly upon a person's ability to correctly determine his position relative to the earth. This ability to correctly orient himself is especially important to the pilot. The sensations used by a person to maintain balance are primarily from:

1. the eyes.
2. the nerve endings in the muscles and about the joints (commonly called the "seat-of-the-pants" sensation).
3. certain tiny balance organs which are part of the inner ear structure.

A pilot who has entered clouds and can no longer perceive ground references will literally not be able to tell "which end is up" from his "seat-of-the-pants" sensations and from his balance organs' signals. This is because these nerve endings and balance organs depend, for the most part, upon a correct orientation to the pull of gravity and yet, these forces may not be oriented in the same direction as gravity. The brain struggles to decipher signals sent from the senses, but without the clue normally supplied by vision, incorrect or conflicting interpretations may result.

VERTIGO

The results of such sensory confusion is a dizzy, whirling sensation termed *vertigo*, sometimes referred to as *spacial disorientation*. Vertigo may take a variety of forms and may be produced by a number of different flight situations.

For example, a pilot conducting a night flight above an inclined cloud bank which is well-illuminated by moonlight might experience sensory confusion. The reason for this confusion is that most people naturally assume a cloud layer to be parallel to the surface of the earth. If the cloud bank, however, is inclined, the pilot might attempt to align the aircraft with the cloud bank, thereby flying with a wing-low attitude or gradually increasing rate of climb or descent. (See Fig. 11-17.)

Fig. 11-17. Flying on Top of a Sloping Cloud Deck

In turbulence, if an aircraft is rolled abruptly right or left and then slowly resumes straight-and-level flight, the pilot may be aware of the roll, but not the recovery. On the other hand, if the aircraft rolls very slowly to the left, the pilot might still believe the aircraft to be in straight-and-level flight. A pitch change of 20° from the horizontal, if done slowly and without visual reference, may go unnoticed.

Also, in a banked turn, the acceleration tends to force the body into the seat much the same as when the aircraft is entering a climb or leveling off from a descent. Without visual reference, a banked turn may be interpreted as a climb. When completing a turn, the reduction in pressure gives the pilot the same sensation as going into a dive and may be interpreted this way.

INSTRUMENT CONDITIONS

A very serious, but common type of sensory illusion may occur when a non-instrument rated pilot continues flight into instrument conditions. When this occurs, the pilot has lost outside visual reference.

Often the aircraft will enter a very slight bank at a rate undetectable to the sense of balance. Generally, this bank will increase until there is a noticeable loss of altitude. The pilot, noting the decrease in altitude and still believing the aircraft is in level flight, may pull back on the wheel and perhaps add power in an attempt to regain the lost altitude. This maneuver only serves to tighten the spiral, unless the pilot first corrects the bank attitude.

Once the spiral has started, the pilot will suffer an illusion of turning in the opposite direction when trying to stop the turning motion of the aircraft. Under these circumstances, it is unlikely the appropriate corrective action will be taken. Rather, the spiral will continue to tighten until a possibly dangerous situation develops. (See Fig. 11-18.) This unfortunate situation all too often occurs when pilots without instrument training mistakenly believe they can maintain their orientation in clouds.

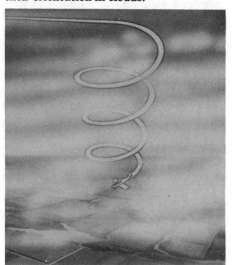

Fig. 11-18. Power Spiral Resulting from Vertigo

GROUND LIGHTS VS. STARS

A common problem associated with night flying is the confusion of ground lights with stars. (See Fig. 11-19.) Many incidents are recorded in which pilots

have put their aircraft into very unusual attitudes in order to keep some ground lights above them, having mistaken them for stars. Some pilots have misinterpreted the lights along the seashore as the horizon, and have maneuvered their aircraft dangerously close to the sea while under the impression they were flying straight and level.

Fig. 11-19. Confusion of Ground Lights with Stars

FLICKER VERTIGO

There are other special causes of vertigo in addition to spacial disorientation (balance organ confusion). Among them is the imposition of a flickering light or shadow at a constant frequency. *Flicker vertigo* can result from a light flickering 4 to 20 times a second and may produce unpleasant and dangerous reactions in some persons. These reactions include dizziness, nausea, unconsciousness, or even reactions similar to an epileptic seizure. They are especially insidious because the subject is often not aware of the cause of distress.

In a single-engine airplane flying toward the sun, the propeller can cause a vertigo-producing flickering effect, especially when the engine is throttled for a landing approach. The flickering shadows of helicopter blades and the bounceback from rotating beacons or strobe lights when they are operated in or near the clouds at night also have been known to cause flicker vertigo. Pilots who are operating under instrument conditions are advised to turn off the rotating beacon or strobe lights in order to avoid this effect. Slight changes in propeller or rotor r.p.m. usually will produce relief when the effect cannot be avoided otherwise.

It should be clear from the previous discussion that instrument training is a valuable asset to any pilot, whether or not he actually flies in instrument conditions.

VISION IN FLIGHT

Since the earliest days of aviation, a pilot's vision has been regarded as a most vital part of his physical equipment for flight. In flying, constant demands are made on the vision in order to avoid obstacles, to judge distances or interpret air traffic control light signals, to read flight instruments inside the cockpit, and to study the terrain.

The pilot's vision may be adversely affected by such diverse factors as dietary deficiencies, hypoxia, and "G" forces.

NIGHT VISION

The ability to see at night can be greatly improved by understanding and applying certain techniques. The pilot's night visual ability can actually be increased by practice. If the eyes are exposed to strong light even briefly, a substance called visual purple is bleached from the nerve cells of the retina and night vision is temporarily destroyed. For this reason, avoidance of strong light must begin well in advance of a night flight, since several minutes are required to regain night vision after it is lost.

After the visual purple has been bleached by the exposure to light, the period during which the substance is resynthesized is known as the period of dark adaptation. A significant portion of dark adaptation is accomplished rather quickly,

usually within a few minutes. When one enters a darkened motion picture theater, within a few minutes the seats or aisles may be seen more clearly. Dark adaptation is usually complete after approximately 30 minutes.

Physiologists have found that dark adaptation is destroyed most quickly and completely by exposure to white light while dark red light has been found to be the least detrimental.

DIET AND NIGHT VISION

Vitamin A is a chemical factor essential to good night vision. Each individual should know which foods contain Vitamin A and eat them regularly. Foods high in Vitamin A content are eggs, butter, cheese, liver, apricots, peaches, carrots, squash, spinach, peas, and all types of green vegetables. Cod liver oil and green vegetables are richest in Vitamin A. Persons who normally eat well-balanced meals should have no difficulty in receiving enough Vitamin A for normal night vision.

CARBON MONOXIDE AND NIGHT VISION

Hypoxia resulting from carbon monoxide poisoning affects visual sharpness, brightness, discrimination, and dark adaptation in the same way and extent as does hypoxia resulting from high altitudes. As an example, it has been shown that five percent saturation of carbon monoxide in the red blood cells has the same effect as an altitude increase of 8,000 to 10,000 feet. Smoking three cigarettes can cause a carbon monoxide saturation of four percent with an effect on visual sensitivity equal to that of an altitude increase of 8,000 feet. These facts stress the seriousness of minor concentrations of carbon monoxide in the cockpits of aircraft involved in night flying.

SECTION C - FLIGHT EFFECTS, DRUGS AND ALCOHOL

Once man lifts himself off the earth's surface, his body is suddenly subject to many motions and conditions to which it may not be accustomed. New references or lack of references may cause the body to grope for stabilization. Most persons adapt to new environments easily and quickly as evidenced by the world's many space flights which are now routine. It is the purpose of this section to explain how the body may react to the various conditions associated with flight.

For new flyers, flight means a new freedom. The body experiences sensations of movement which may be strange to those experienced in routine, earthbound existence. Some persons, however, are more sensitive to motion than others and are the ones most likely to get airsick. After repeated flights, these people usually become accustomed to their new environment and thereafter are not disturbed. Many times, ignorance and fear of the unknown are the main culprits, and a simple explanation of what is happening and what causes it will often cure the problem.

AIRSICKNESS

Airsickness, like seasickness or any other motion-induced disturbance, is primarily the result of the brain receiving conflicting messages from the eyes, organs of balance, and muscle receptors. Thus, a person gets dizzy and feels nauseated, and because the stomach is very sympathetic to nervous or mental fatigue, it reacts to these stimuli.

The airlines have found that the overall rate of motion discomfort in passengers is one percent or less, and that there are marked differences in sex and age. Adult men are the least susceptible. The incidence in women is five times as great as in men, and the incidence in children is nine times as great.

Many factors enter into the cause of motion discomfort and one or all can play a part in any given individual. There are three primary factors which can be involved: physical, environmental, and mental.

PHYSICAL FACTORS

The physical factors are those that are directly related to the organs in the body that perceive motion such as stimulation of the organs of balance in the inner ear, visual response to unusual motions, sensations in the internal organs, the position of the head, illness, and fatigue.

Motion discomfort can be caused in most people by continuous up and down motion, either slow or fast. Specific individuals also vary greatly in susceptibility. The up and down motion of short duration and frequent occurrence is the most common cause. This is true particularly in rough air and turbulence.

POSITION

The position of the head with respect to the direction of the motion is also important. Up-and-down motion with the head back is tolerated more readily than with the head erect. (See Fig. 11-20.) This is why people have less motion-induced distress when reclining or feel better after reclining. The same is true in ocean travel.

Fig. 11-20. Head in Back Position Tolerates Up and Down Motion

ILLNESS

Good sense dictates that a person who is ill should not fly except in emergencies. Illness makes the body less able to withstand discomfort or unusual experiences of any type. People who are ill should not act as pilot in command or accept responsibility as a required crewmember. For example, the common cold could mean trouble for a pilot. A cold may contribute to hypoxia, vertigo, impaired vision, or ear, tooth, or abdominal pain.

ENVIRONMENTAL FACTORS

The environment surrounding the person also contributes to the susceptibility of motion distress. Many things can cause a person to subconsciously tense up because they are uncomfortable or feel different. This feeling can then trigger a chain reaction that results in airsickness.

One of the external factors affecting the body is temperature. Excessive heat is frequently encountered in flying, particularly in light aircraft at low altitudes in the summer. In the winter, excessive cold is sometimes experienced. Either may increase sensitivity to motion.

Noise and vibration can contribute to increased discomfort, fatigue, and anxiety, particularly in people who are apprehensive and unfamiliar with flying.

MENTAL FACTORS

The mental factors associated with motion discomfort are hard to define, but one of these factors is fear. For people new to flying, the anticipation of flight may be enough to generate uncertainty that can develop motion discomfort. Also, some people have a definite fear of becoming airsick, and sure enough, they talk themselves into it. Impressionable people who have heard tall tales about air travel may be very susceptible.

PREVENTATIVE AIDS

What can be done to minimize the problem? If a pilot should become ill and does not have a co-pilot, his safest action is to land as soon as possible.

Student pilots who experience symptoms of motion discomfort are afforded special consideration in the beginning phase of flight instruction. The best approach emphasizes careful flight planning, provides a thorough briefing, restricts practice to gentle maneuvers, and avoids turbulence. Starting with extremely short flights and slowly increasing the length of each training flight sometimes overcomes the tension associated with these sessions. These measures will usually help the pilot to gain confidence and experience that will eliminate motion-induced disturbance after the first few flights.

Since motion distress may be encountered by pilots and passengers, it is helpful to know some of the things that can be done to avoid or relieve the causes and symptoms. (See Fig. 11-21.)

1. Look for distant landmarks and discuss their relative positions, distances, and features. This minimizes concentration on nearby landmarks which may emphasize motion.
2. An explanation of the trip before takeoff and keeping passengers advised during the flight helps to reduce apprehensions. Information concerning changes in direction, altitude, power changes, engine noise, time en route, and points of scenic interest tend to keep passengers from becoming bored. It also increases their understanding and reduces anxiety.
3. Secure medication prior to flight. Dramamine may be useful, especially in persons who are susceptible to motion discomfort. The advice of a physician, preferably an Aviation Medical Examiner, should be sought regarding dosage and desirability of the use of drugs in adults and children.
4. Take a position as near as possible to the center of gravity where there is a minimum of up-and-down or swaying motion.

MEDICAL FACTORS OF FLIGHT

Fig. 11-21. Methods Used to Relieve Motion Discomfort

5. Lie back if possible. This keeps the head reclined and increases the body tolerance to up-and-down motion.

6. Use ear plugs to reduce noise.

7. Provide all the ventilation possible. This reduces cabin odors and keeps air fresh.

8. Flight at higher altitudes in smoother air is helpful. Flying at night may be very useful since it reduces visual stimulation and turbulence is usually at a minimum.

9. Avoid steep banks and sudden attitude changes. Gentle maneuvers insure greater passenger comfort.

10. Use oxygen at high altitudes. Oxygen may be useful when high altitudes are unavoidable. Of course, supplemental oxygen should be available for passengers and pilots for flights above 10,000 feet.

DRUGS

Pilots are normal people who have common, everyday ailments. They also get fatigued and may even be overweight and nervous. Dozens of drug prescriptions and medicines are available for each of these conditions. Many persons think that most commonly used remedies are harmless items which can be used routinely to add to daily well-being. This may not be so, and pilots should know the possible pitfalls and their tolerance to some common medications.

DRUG SIDE EFFECTS

Almost all drugs have side effects detrimental to the body, and the severity of the effects is often increased by flying. Major side effects of common medications can include drowsiness, mental depression, decreased coordination, reduced sharpness of vision, diminished function of the organs of balance, increased nervousness, decreased depth perception, and impaired judgment. Any medical condition for which drugs are necessary is sufficient cause for the pilot not to fly at all.

ASPIRIN

Most headache remedies contain aspirin, which is one of the few drugs normally accepted as having little or no adverse effect on people who are not allergic to it. However, many headache preparations contain pain relievers other than aspirin which reduce tolerance to altitude. Aspirin alone is considered safe for flyers.

NOSE DROPS AND INHALERS

In general, nose drops and inhalers cause little effect on the body other than the nose, if used on occasion. Excessive use of either or both could lead to rapid heartbeat and increased nervousness, either of which may decrease the performance of the flyer.

ANTIHISTAMINES

Antihistamines are used for almost everything, including colds, motion sickness, allergies, hay fever, and as sleeping pills. But they also may have dangerous side effects, such as drowsiness, decreased coordination, mental depression, reduced sense of balance, and diminished alertness. It is recommended that persons not pilot an aircraft for 24 hours after the administration of a usual dose of antihistamines.

COUGH MEDICINE

Cough medicines usually contain a substance which depresses the brain and cough center, a good-tasting syrup, an antihistamine, and a decongestant. It may decrease mental functions. The antihistamine decreases secretions and adds side effects. Decongestant side effects often cause increased heart rate and nervousness. In flight, all the side effects contribute to reduced pilot performance. Cold pills, which contain antihistamines, can also produce these side effects.

TRANQUILIZERS

The pilot who is taking tranquilizers will react abnormally and poorly when under stress, such as when flying on instruments, in marginal weather, at night, or in crowded traffic situations. A tranquilized pilot is a sluggish pilot. His alertness, judgment, reaction time, and perception are all affected adversely.

The FAA recommends that pilots not fly for a 24-hour period after taking a tranquilizer. Stomach soothers, heartburn preparations, and ulcer medications also have a depressant or tranquilizing effect. The same rule would apply to these drugs.

PEP PILLS

Pep pills are an artificial and harmful means of increasing energy and fighting fatigue. Pep pills may cause blurred vision, nervousness, irritability, impaired judgment, and loss of coordination. Reducing pills are essentially pep pills with sedatives or tranquilizers and are also undesirable for pilots.

MOTION SICKNESS DRUGS

Motion sickness drugs, while useful for passengers, should not be used by pilots unless prescribed for a student who experiences airsickness early in flight training. In this case, he should have a qualified instructor pilot at the dual controls, and the entire operation should be under the guidance of a physician and with the knowledge and consent of the instructor. Motion sickness drugs are basically antihistamines which have already been discussed.

Although the drugs which have just been discussed are the most common causes of impaired pilot performance, it should be pointed out that any form of medicine may have adverse effects if the pilot is sensitive to that particular drug. A pilot should not take any drugs or medicines before or during flight unless he is completely familiar with his reaction to the medication. If there is any doubt, he should consult his aviation medical examiner.

Probably the best general recommendation for flying personnel and others di-

rectly associated with flight control is abstinence from all drugs. However, some illnesses and symptoms may not preclude flying or ground traffic control work, but may be benefited by appropriate drugs. The question, therefore, arises as to whether use of the required drugs in such instances may be safe and, in fact, advantageous. This led to the preparation of *Drug Hazards in Aviation Medicine* for Aviation Medical Examiners. It lists drugs, the toxic effects relevant to aviation that they may produce, and a conservative estimate of their allowable use. This book may be purchased from the U.S. Government Printing Office. (See Fig. 11-22.)

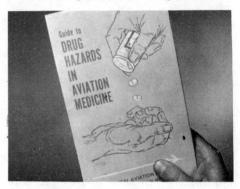

Fig. 11-22. FAA Booklet on Drug Hazards

ANESTHETICS

Following local and general dental and other anesthetics, a period of at least 48 hours should be spent on the ground. If any doubt remains concerning the right time to resume flying, seek appropriate medical counsel.

BLOOD DONATION

It should also be noted that blood donation and flying are not compatible. Blood circulation following a donation takes several weeks to return to normal and, although effects are slight at ground level, there are risks when flying during this period. It is recommended that pilots do not volunteer as blood donors when actively flying, but if blood has been given, an appropriate medical source should be consulted before flying.

CARBON MONOXIDE

The pilot must be aware of carbon monoxide as a threat, especially since most single-engine aircraft are heated by air which has passed over exhaust manifolds. Flying with a defective heat exchanger could be dangerous just as driving a car with a defective muffler is dangerous.

Carbon monoxide is a colorless, odorless, tasteless product of an internal combustion engine and is always present in exhaust fumes. The onset of carbon monoxide symptoms is insidious with "blurred thinking," a possible feeling of uneasiness, and subsequent dizziness. Later a headache may occur. For biochemical reasons, carbon monoxide has a greater affinity for the hemoglobin of the blood than oxygen. Furthermore, once carbon monoxide is absorbed in the blood, it "sticks like glue" to the hemoglobin and actually prevents the oxygen from attaching to the hemoglobin. (See Fig. 11-23.)

Fig. 11-23. Carbon Monoxide (CO) Affinity

The hemoglobin of the blood has 200 times more affinity for carbon monoxide than for oxygen. Thus, if there is only one part of carbon monoxide to 200 parts of oxygen in the cabin air, the hemoglobin will pick up about the same amount of each. More than this amount of carbon monoxide tends to block out the oxygen completely.

An individual exposed to hypoxia alone recovers quickly when oxygen is added to his inhaled air. In fact, recovery occurs usually within the circulation time of the blood, which is just a few minutes. However, an individual affected by carbon monoxide poisoning may be affected for 24 to 48 hours as carbon monoxide remains tenaciously attached to the hemoglobin molecule.

Inexpensive carbon monoxide detectors are available for cabin use. If carbon monoxide is suspected in the cabin, it is important that cabin heat be turned off immediately and a window be opened. An oxygen mask should be used with the oxygen turned to maximum if the aircraft is so equipped. Of course, a landing should be made as soon as a suitable airport is available.

ALCOHOL

Alcohol has effects similar to tranquilizers and sleeping tablets and may remain circulating in the blood for a considerable time, especially if taken with food. FAR's require that a pilot must allow eight hours between the consumption of alcoholic beverages and flying an aircraft. Common sense dictates that large amounts would require an even longer recovery period. A good rule is to allow 24 hours between the last drink and take-off time.

The following physiological and psychological effects of alcohol have been substantiated by research and are considered to be extremely detrimental to piloting an aircraft.

1. A dulling of critical judgment
2. A decreased sense of responsibility
3. Diminished skill reactions and co-ordination
4. Decreased speed and strength of muscular reflexes (even after one ounce of alcohol)
5. Efficiency of eye movements decreased 20% during reading (after one ounce of alcohol)
6. Significantly increased frequency of errors (after one ounce of alcohol)
7. Constriction of visual field
8. Decreased ability to see under dim illumination
9. Loss of efficiency of sense of touch

10. Decrease of memory and reasoning ability
11. Increased susceptibility to fatigue and decreased attention span
12. Decreased relevance of responses in free association test, with an increase in nonsensical reactions
13. Increased self-confidence with decreased insight into immediate capabilities and mental and physical status

PSYCHOLOGICAL CONSIDERATIONS

The psychological effect of desire may drive a person to be overmotivated to achieve a goal, perhaps to the extent judgment is impaired. A pilot may become so intent on getting home, he may attempt to fly through weather that demands skill beyond his experience. (See Fig. 11-24.)

Fig. 11-24. Negative Effect of Desire

Ironically, some pilots who are in professions requiring a high degree of knowledge sometimes place themselves in undesirable situations because of an overpowering desire to fulfill an ambition or goal. An ambitious or aggressive person who lives daily with challenge must continually examine his motives carefully and avoid flying beyond his experience and ability levels.

ANXIETY AND STRESS

Since a pilot in his aviation environment, is required to continually evaluate information, perform complex tasks, and make decisions, aviation psychology deals with a pilot's performance during various emotional states. Two of these states—stress and anxiety—may have adverse effects on a pilot's performance. The causes of emotional stress are many and varied. They can be divided into two categories. The first includes those situations not specifically related to flying such as family problems, financial or business considerations, or the demands of a pressing schedule.

The second category includes situations directly related to flight: for instance, apprehension about adverse weather conditions, malfunctioning equipment, or lack of confidence on the part of the pilot.

Fear is a normal, protective emotion which can build from stress or anxiety. Fear progressing to panic, however, is certainly undesirable. Panic can be avoided or overcome by forcibly maintaining or re-establishing self-control. A person who completely understands a situation can maintain control of his emotions, think more clearly, and reason properly. Once reason and logic are applied to the facts, the proper decision can be made and appropriate action taken.

If a pilot becomes lost or disoriented and panics, for instance, he may wander around aimlessly and compound his problem. If, however, he maintains self-control, he can follow a logical means of evaluating his situation, re-orienting himself, and taking proper corrective action.

As man has created more complex, faster, and higher flying aircraft, his physiological and psychological characteristics have become increasingly important. Although these characteristics create some limitations, man's adaptability and his capacity to design a protective environment have permitted aeronautical exploration undreamed of a few short years ago. It is expected that aviation physiology will become an even greater aspect of the total flight environment of the future.

chapter 12

CROSS-
COUNTRY
FLYING

INTRODUCTION

This chapter applies principles and techniques from chapters on weather, aeronautical charts, aeronautical information publications, navigation, communications, performance, and regulations to cross-country planning and flight. Essentially, it is an exercise in the practical application of knowledge and skills presented in the *Private Pilot Manual.*

The first section outlines the detailed planning which should be associated with a typical cross-country flight. It includes a practical discussion concerning the use of sectional charts and aeronautical information publications, obtaining weather information, and filing a VFR flight plan. The second section describes how the planned flight might actually be conducted and also shows how a flight may need to be altered because of weather considerations.

Although cross-country planning and flight involve a series of complex activities, these tasks become second nature as the basics are mastered and experience is gained. One of the keys to safe cross-country flight is thorough preflight planning. A student who is well prepared on the ground will approach cross-country flying with confidence and will move closer to meeting the requirements of the private pilot certificate.

SECTION A - FLIGHT PLANNING

SELECTING THE CHARTS

The first step in planning a trip is to select the course. In this instance, a direct course will be flown from Jefferson County Airport, southeast of Beaumont, Texas, to Rusk County Airport near Henderson, Texas.

The next step is to locate the departure and destination airports on the appropriate sectional chart. In this example, both airports are on the same side of the chart. If this were not the case, the procedure shown in figure 12-1 should be used to plot the course from

one side of the chart to the other. Sectional charts are folded in accordion-

Fig. 12-1. Continuing Course Line on Reverse Side

pleated fashion for convenient reference to any point on one side, and also to make it easy to refer back to the legend in the margin.

Since Rusk County Airport is very close to the northern edge of the Houston Sectional Chart, the sectional chart diagram printed on the index margin should be checked for the names of bordering charts. (See Fig. 12-2.) The Dallas-Fort Worth and the Memphis Sectionals border the northwest area of the Houston Sectional and will be valuable in addition to the Houston chart. It is wise to carry bordering charts when flying over an area near the edge of a chart because they may be needed to navigate to another airport in the event of bad weather.

DRAWING THE COURSE

Now, the true course is drawn from Jefferson County Airport to Rusk County Airport in a color that can be seen easily. (See Fig. 12-3.) If the trip is over 100 miles long, as in this example, a long straightedge is needed to draw the true course. A yardstick is very good for this purpose; however, if one is not available, the edge of another sectional chart can be used.

CHECKPOINTS

After the true course has been drawn, prominent checkpoints are selected along the course and circled with a color that can be seen easily. These checkpoints will be needed during the flight to verify positions and to make checks on ground speed. The reasons for choosing these checkpoints will be discussed during the VFR flight in the second section of this chapter.

To help in planning a trip, a navigation log should be used to record all pertinent data. An example of such a log is shown in figure 12-4. Once the checkpoints are selected, they are recorded in the navigation log so they can be referred to during pretrip planning and in flight. (See Fig. 12-5, item 1.)

The next element in planning is the measurement of distances using the sectional chart scale of the navigation plotter. Then the distance between each checkpoint is recorded in the nav log. (See Fig. 12-5, item 2.) The total distance of 138 n.m. is also entered in the log. (See Fig. 12-5, item 3.) Now the "distance remaining" column can be filled in. This

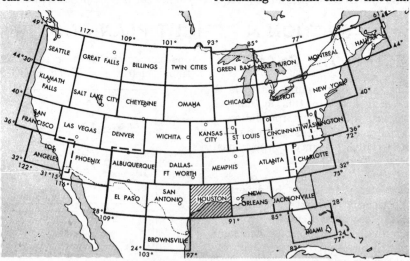

Fig. 12-2. Sectional Chart Diagram

Fig. 12-3. Planning the Course (Sheet 1 of 2)

Fig. 12-3. Planning the Course (Sheet 2 of 2)

Fig. 12-4. Navigation Log

will allow the pilot to recompute his destination ETA over any checkpoint in the event of a *change* in ground speed.

MEASURING THE TRUE COURSE

With the plotter positioned so that the small hole in the plotter is centered over the intersection of the course line and a line of longitude, the true course can be read directly from a semicircular scale. The correct semicircular scale is the one that has the arrow pointing in the same direction as the course. (See Fig. 12-6, item 1.) In this case, the inner scale is the correct one. The true course is 342°. (See Fig. 12-6, item 2.) This means that

Check Points (Fixes)	VOR Ident	Course	Altitude	Wind Dir.	Vel.	CAS	TC		WCA		Dist. Leg	GS Est	Time Off	GPH	Air Departure
	Freq.	(Route)		Temp.	TAS		Var.		MH	CH	Rem. Act.		ETE / ATE	Fuel / Rem.	
Jefferson County						118	342	336	-8	+5	138 8	123	4+5	8.5	
Island in River	⊕→	2500		230 20	17				-6		328 333 130				
Silsbee									328	333	17 123 113	8			
Woodville											29 84	123	14		
Huntington											30 54	123	15		Depart
Nacogdoches											19 35	123	9		ATIS / Cpt
Rusk County											35 0	123	17+5		Grnd / Tower / Dep. / FSS / NiCOM / Field Elev.
										Totals	138	1:17	(17.0) 17	Block In / Block Out

Fig. 12-5. Navigation Log Excerpt

the true course is 342° clockwise from a line projected through true north. The true course is recorded in the navigation log. (See Fig. 12-5, item 4.)

Fig. 12-6. True Course

MAGNETIC VARIATION

The next item to be determined is the *magnetic course* which is nothing more than the true course corrected for *magnetic variation.* As noted in Chapter 7, variation is the angular difference between true north and magnetic north. The True (or geographic) North Pole is the point where all the lines of longitude converge. The Magnetic North Pole is the point where the lines of force of the earth's magnetic field converge. It is approximately 1,000 miles south of the True North Pole. Because of this difference in location, lines drawn from a position on the earth's surface to the True North Pole and to the Magnetic North Pole can show an angular difference which must be considered in navigation problems.

In review, figure 12-7 shows three aircraft with their *noses* pointing toward true north. The aircraft to the left has its compass pointing 10° to the east. The center aircraft is flying on a line of no variation, called the agonic line. True north and magnetic north are in direct alignment in this area. The aircraft on the right has its compass pointing 10° to the west of true north. This means there is a 10° westerly variation in this area. Variation is added to or subtracted from the true course to compensate for this phenomenon.

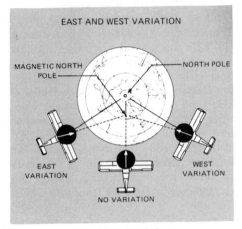

Fig. 12-7. Variation

A helpful memory aid for use when computing magnetic course is the saying *east is least and west is best*. This means that east variation is subtracted and west variation is added to the true course to obtain the magnetic course, as shown in the following formula:

$$TC - \text{East Var.} = MC$$
$$TC + \text{West Var.} = MC$$

Sectional charts show variation by dashed magenta lines called isogonic lines. There is an isogonic line labeled 6°30'E near Rusk County Airport. (See Fig. 12-8.) Since the airport is located between the 6° and 6°30' lines of variation, the value can be rounded to 6°E for easier computation.

If a course crosses many isogonic lines, as on a long east-west flight, the pilot must compensate for the changing variation. On a short east-west flight, the

Fig. 12-8. Magnetic Variation

variation halfway between the departure and destination is normally used.

MAGNETIC COURSE

The magnetic course is computed by taking the true course of 342° and subtracting the 6° easterly magnetic variation in this area. This gives a magnetic course of 336°, which must be flown to make good a true course of 342°. Now, the magnetic course of 336° is recorded in the navigation log. (See Fig. 12-5, item 5.)

OBTAINING WEATHER INFORMATION

Flight service stations and National Weather Service offices are the principal sources of aviation weather for preflight planning. It is best to obtain a weather briefing in person because a clearer picture of the weather can be obtained by personally examining the reports, charts, and forecasts. If this is impossible, a telephone briefing is the next best method. The weather briefing telephone numbers of flight service stations and Weather Service offices are found in the *Airport/Facility Directory*.

The caller should first identify himself as a pilot, then provide the weather briefer with the following data.

1. Aircraft identification and type
2. Departure airport

3. Destination airport
4. Estimated time of departure
5. Estimated time en route
6. Proposed route and flight altitude
7. Probable stops en route
8. Instrument flight rules or visual flight rules

With this information, the weather briefer will normally supply all the essential weather concerning the flight, which should include:

1. Weather at departure and destination airports
2. En route weather
3. Weather for a proposed alternate route, if necessary
4. Precipitation, sky cover, and visibility for all points along the route and alternate route
5. Frontal activity
6. Winds and temperatures aloft forecasts
7. Teletype NOTAMs

A limited amount of weather information may also be obtained by calling the pilot's automatic telephone weather answering service (PATWAS). The telephone numbers for PATWAS are listed in the *Airport/Facility Directory*. They also may be listed in the telephone directory; however, some Weather Service telephone numbers are unlisted.

Many remote locations post teletypewriter printouts which are available to the pilot for "serve-yourself" preflight weather briefings. To use these facilities effectively, a thorough knowledge of weather symbols and codes is needed.

As a last resort, a weather briefing may be obtained by two-way radio; however, due to frequency congestion, this should not be considered standard practice.

While en route, the pilot has several sources of weather information available. First, using the VHF radio, information may be requested at any time from any flight service station within radio range.

In addition, at 15 minutes past each hour, flight service stations regularly broadcast hourly weather reports for their stations, and for reporting points within approximately 150 miles of the broadcast station. In addition, SIGMETs affecting the area are broadcast at 15-minute intervals (on the hour and at 15, 30, and 45 minutes past the hour); AIRMETs are broadcast at 30-minute intervals (at 15 and 45 minutes past the hour).

Transcribed weather broadcasts (TWEBs) are prepared by selected flight service stations, recorded on tape, and broadcast continuously over specified low frequency navigational aids (200-450 kHz) and VOR's. This broadcast identifies the station, gives general weather forecast conditions in the area, PIREPs available, and weather reports at selected locations within a 400-mile radius of the broadcasting station. As changes occur, they are transcribed onto the tape.

With all this available weather information and a minimum of effort, the pilot can become well briefed for flight. A basic knowledge of meteorology and the ability to obtain a weather briefing will enable the pilot to decide whether to continue with the flight or try another day.

WEATHER BRIEFING

To obtain weather information for this cross-country flight, the pilot uses the telephone number listed in the *Airport/Facility Directory*, and calls the flight service station at Lake Charles. The following information is furnished: (See Fig. 12-9.)

1. Lufkin Flight Service Station is reporting high scattered clouds with visibility of more than 10 miles.
2. A few isolated thunderstorms near Lufkin are moving northeast.

```
FDUS2 KWBC 170545
DATA BASED ON 170000Z

VALID 171800Z FOR USE 1500-2100Z. TEMPS NEG ABV 24000

FT   3000    6000    9000    12000   18000   24000  30000  34000  39000

DAL 2211 2414+10 2714+02 2820-06 2832-14 2940-25 294535 295545 295055
HOU 2010 2015+09 2115+01 2120-07 2220-15 2429-25 253532 264240 265045
LFK 2317 2722+12 2723+04 2725-02 2835-16 2840-30 285444 287050 288059
MSY 2405 2408+07 2412+01 2518-07 2523-12 2530-18 263734 274540 275049
SHV 2305 2308+08 2312-01 2420-09 2422-15 2530-25 263530 264035 264540


        SA23  171500
LFK 150 SCT 10+ 146/75/58/2215/998/FEW ISOLD TSTMS MVG NE
BPT 100 SCT 15+ 145/86/60/2015/005
→BPT 06/004 BPT 16-34 CLSD UFN

TX 171505
GGG CLR  15+ 145/89/60/2110/000/FEW CU SE
LCH 120 BKN 12 143/78/65/1805/987
TYR 200 SCT 12 140/82/65/1710/980
```

BPT   Beaumont, TX (Jefferson County Airport)
DAL   Dallas, TX
HOU   Houston, TX
LCH   Lake Charles, LA (Lake Charles Municipal Airport)
GGG   Longview, TX (Gregg County Airport)
LFK   Lufkin, TX (Angelina County Airport)
MSY   New Orleans, LA
SHV   Shreveport, LA
TYR   Tyler, TX (Pounds Field)

Fig. 12-9. Weather Information

3. Winds and temperatures aloft are:
   a. surface to 3,000 feet — 230°, 17 knots.
   b. 6,000 feet — 270°, 22 knots, +12°C.
   c. 9,000 feet — 270°, 23 knots, +04°C.

A weather log should be used to insure that all appropriate information has been received and recorded. Figure 12-10 shows a completed log for this trip.

After receiving the wind information, the pilot selects an altitude for the flight, remembering that a cruising altitude which is more than 3,000 feet above the surface must be selected according to the guidelines set in FAR Part 91.109. Since the best wind is forecast to be from the

WEATHER LOG						
	Ceiling, Visibility, and Precipitation		Winds Aloft	Icing and Freezing Level	Turbulence and Cloud Tops	Position of Fronts, Lows, and Highs
	Reported	Forecast				
LFK Departure	HIGH SCATTERED CLOUDS VIS. 10+		3000' 230°-17KTS			
En Route	TSTMS Moving NE		↓			
Destination	CLEAR (GGG) 15+ (FSS)		↓			
Alternate						

Fig. 12-10. Listing Weather Conditions on Log

surface to 3,000 feet, this regulation does not apply to this trip, and any flight altitude within this range may be used.

An altitude of 2,500 feet above mean sea level is chosen because, at this altitude, the aircraft will maintain about 2,000 feet above the ground throughout the trip. This is low enough to easily observe checkpoints and high enough to be well above any terrain or obstacles.

The winds and temperatures aloft forecast does not provide information on temperature at the selected cruising altitude; however, since Lufkin is approximately the midway point on the flight, the standard lapse rate and the surface temperature at Lufkin can be used to estimate the temperature at 2,500 feet. Figure 12-9 shows that the surface temperature at Lufkin is 75°F (24°C). The difference between the cruising altitude of 2,500 feet and the ground elevation of approximately 300 feet is 2,200 feet. Using the standard lapse rate of 2°C/1,000 feet, the decrease in temperature is estimated to be approximately 4°C and the temperature at 2,500 feet to be 20°C (24°C − 4°C = 20°C). The wind and temperature information is now entered in the navigation log. (See Fig. 12-5, item 6.)

DETERMINING TRUE AIRSPEED

For VFR planning purposes, true airspeed can be obtained either by referring to the performance charts in the pilot's operating handbook or by computer calculations. The variables in the cruise performance chart are outside air temperature, pressure altitude, and power setting. A TAS of 118 knots can be obtained by referring to the chart.

For the alternate method of calculating true airspeed, the 20°C temperature already calculated for 2,500 feet, a calibrated airspeed of 113 knots (based

on previous experience), and a pressure altitude of 2,500 feet should be used. With the flight computer and the above data, a TAS of approximately 118 knots can be computed. This value is entered in the navigation log for use in determining magnetic heading and ground speed. (See Fig. 12-5, item 7.)

FINDING MAGNETIC HEADING AND GROUND SPEED

True course, true airspeed, and wind direction and velocity are the values which are needed to solve the ground speed and magnetic heading problems on the wind side of the computer.

Magnetic heading is computed as follows:

1. Place 230°, the wind direction, under the true index on the wind side of the flight computer. (See Fig. 12-11, item 1.)
2. Plot up from the grommet 17 knots, which is the wind velocity, and place a dot on the centerline. It should be remembered that each minor graduation up and down the scale is equal to 2 knots. (See Fig. 12-11, item 2.)
3. Rotate the azimuth until the true course of 342° is directly under the true index. (See Fig. 12-12, item 3.)
4. Now, slide the grid through the computer until the wind dot rests on the 118-knot true airspeed line. (See Fig. 12-12, item 4.)
5. Note the wind correction angle of 8° left. (See Fig. 12-12, item 5.) Each graduation to the left and right of the centerline below 150 knots is equal to 2°.
6. After noting that the wind correction angle is to the left 8°, subtract 8° from the magnetic course of 336° previously determined (See Fig. 12-5, item 5)

Fig. 12-11. Setting Wind Direction and Velocity

Fig. 12-12. Finding Groundspeed and Magnetic Heading

and arrive at a magnetic heading of 328° which, together with the wind correction angle, is recorded in the log. (See Fig. 12-5, item 8.) Always remember that, if the wind correction is to the left, subtract it from the magnetic course; if it is to the right, add it to the magnetic course.

7. The ground speed can be determined by referring to the wind side of the computer and checking the grommet position. In this problem, the grommet is on 123 knots, which is the estimated ground speed. (See Fig. 12-12, item 6.) The 123 knots is now recorded in the navigation log. (See Fig. 12-5, item 9.)

TIME REQUIRED TO FLY THE TRIP

The time to make the trip can now be solved since the ground speed of 123 knots and distance of 138 n.m. are known. The time for the trip is worked out on the calculator side of the computer as follows: (See Fig. 12-13.)

1. Rotate the disc until the black speed index is directly under 123 knots.
2. Then, move along the "A" scale and locate 138 n.m., the distance from Jefferson County Airport to Rusk County Airport.
3. Look directly under "138" and find the time of 67 minutes on the "B" scale, or 1 hour and 7 minutes.

Normally, additional time is allowed for departing the traffic pattern and for the climb to cruising altitude. Time also should be allotted for entry into the traffic pattern at the destination airport.

For this cross-country, five minutes will be allowed for climb and five minutes for descent and landing. This adds an additional 10 minutes to the trip. (See Fig. 12-5, item 10.)

The calculated time between checkpoints, arrival and departure allowance, and the total time for flying the trip are entered in the nav log. (See Fig. 12-5, item 11.)

The pilot's operating handbook lists the fuel consumption rate of the aircraft as 8-1/2 gallons per hour. This is recorded in the nav log. (See Fig. 12-5, item 12.)

Now, with the above information and the time required to fly the trip, the computer can be used to find the total amount of fuel burned. (See Fig. 12-14.)

1. First, rotate the disc on the calculator side of the computer until the speed index is directly under the fuel consumption rate of 8-1/2 gallons per hour. (Remember, the speed index represents 60 minutes, or 1 hour.)
2. Next, locate 1 hour and 17 minutes on the "C" scale, which is the same as 77 minutes on the "B" scale.
3. Look directly over this time to find 10.9 gallons on the "A"

Fig. 12-13. Time for the Trip

Fig. 12-14. Fuel Consumption

scale. This is rounded off to 11 gallons.

This amount, however, does not provide any reserve fuel. Enough fuel must be carried on a VFR flight to fly to the first point of intended landing and, at normal cruising speed, fly after that for 30 minutes during the day and 45 minutes at night. A fuel reserve of 30 minutes is equal to approximately four gallons. The pilot's operating handbook recommends an allowance of two gallons of fuel for engine warm-up and climb to 2,000 feet; therefore, the aircraft should have at least 17 gallons (to the nearest gallon) of fuel on board at takeoff. This amount is entered in the nav log. (See Fig. 12-5, item 13.) Since the aircraft will be carrying 38 gallons, there will be plenty of fuel for the trip.

COMPASS HEADING

One of the last flight planning steps is the determination of the compass heading. The information needed to determine the compass heading is found on the compass correction card, mounted in the aircraft. This card is a means of recording the compass deviation caused by the magnetic interference of the aircraft parts, such as radio, engine, instruments, or anything in the aircraft that would disturb the compass.

Figure 12-15 shows the compass correction card for the aircraft used in this flight. Since the magnetic heading is 328°, the pilot can locate the *nearest* value on the card which is 330°. A 330° magnetic heading requires a compass heading of 335°, which is a +5° deviation.

The formula for compass heading is:

MH ± Deviation = Compass Heading

Adding the +5° deviation to the magnetic heading of 328° gives a compass heading of 333° for the trip. The deviation and compass heading of

333° are recorded in the navigation log. (See Fig. 12-5, item 14.)

Any metal (such as notebooks, ring binders, tools, or other objects) that would affect the compass should be kept well clear of the instrument panel area because it can contribute to erroneous compass readings.

FOR	STEER
N	002
30	031
60	060
E	090
120	120
150	150
S	180
210	210
240	240
W	272
300	303
330	335
RADIO ON	☒
NO RADIO	☐

Fig. 12-15. Compass Correction Card

FLIGHT PLAN

After the completion of the navigation log, the FAA flight plan should be filled out and filed with the FSS, preferably in person. If a personal visit cannot be made, a telephone call is the next best method. Use of the radio for filing flight plans while en route results in unnecessary frequency congestion. After the flight plan has been filed, it is not *activated* until the pilot is airborne and calls the flight service station to inform FSS personnel of the actual time of departure. If the flight plan is not activated within an *hour* of the proposed departure time, the FSS will *cancel* the flight plan. Any trip that is canceled after the flight plan is filed should be canceled by calling the FSS.

After the flight plan is activated, the flight service station sends a flight notification message to the FSS nearest the destination. At the destination airport, the flight plan *must be closed*. The pilot may elect to close the flight plan with a flight service station other than the destination station; however, this decision should be relayed to the departure FSS when the flight plan is filed. An aircraft is considered overdue on a VFR flight plan when no communications have been received or when it fails to arrive at the destination within 30 minutes after the ETA. If a flight plan is not closed, ATC begins a telephone search to locate the overdue aircraft. If ATC is unable to locate the aircraft, costly search and rescue procedures are started.

When the estimated time of arrival has changed significantly, it is important for a pilot to extend the flight plan with any flight service station within radio range. It is also extremely important to close the flight plan by contacting the destination flight service station when the flight is complete. This can be done by radio or by telephone after landing. In any event, the pilot must remember to CLOSE THE FLIGHT PLAN.

The FAA flight plan is to be filled in as follows: (See Fig. 12-16.)

1. TYPE OF FLIGHT PLAN: Check the type of flight plan. Check both the VFR and IFR blocks if it is a composite VFR/IFR. IFR flight plans can only be filed by qualified instrument pilots flying IFR equipped aircraft.

2. AIRCRAFT IDENTIFICATION: The full identification number of the aircraft should be used; e.g., N17356.

3. AIRCRAFT TYPE AND SPECIAL EQUIPMENT: Enter the designator for the aircraft; for example, Clipwing 23. If the designator is unknown, use the manufacturer's name followed by a slant (/) and the transponder/DME code letter. These code letters can be found in the *Airman's Information Manual* and at the bottom of the Sanderson flight plan form.

4. TRUE AIRSPEED: This figure is to be given in *knots* based on the estimated TAS at the planned flight altitude.

5. POINT OF DEPARTURE: Enter the departure point/airport identifier code, or the name if the identifier is unknown. Identifier

Fig. 12-16. Flight Plan Form

codes are listed in the *Airport/Facility Directory*.

6. DEPARTURE TIME: This time is to be stated in Greenwich Mean Time, also referred to as Zulu (Z) time. The use of Zulu time eliminates any confusion resulting from differences in local time along the route of flight. After departure, the pilot will activate the VFR flight plan and give the FSS the actual time of departure. When the flight plan is filed in the air, the actual or proposed departure time is given.

7. INITIAL CRUISING ALTITUDE: On a VFR flight plan, enter the appropriate VFR altitude to assist briefers in providing weather and wind information.

8. ROUTE OF FLIGHT: Define the route of flight by using navaid identifier codes or names, airways, and waypoints. Radials and bearings can also be used to define routes or, when appropriate, simply enter the word "DIRECT."

9. DESTINATION: Enter the destination airport identifier code, or the name if the identifier code is unknown. Include the city and state, if the airport name alone might be confused with another.

10. ESTIMATED TIME EN ROUTE: The total estimated time from takeoff to landing should be entered in hours and minutes based on the latest forecast winds.

11. REMARKS: Enter only remarks that clarify other flight plan information or that are pertinent to air traffic control.

12. FUEL ON BOARD: Total usable fuel on board the aircraft in hours and minutes should be entered.

13. ALTERNATE AIRPORT(S): Specify an alternate airport if desired or required.

14. PILOT'S NAME, ADDRESS, TELEPHONE NUMBER, AND AIRCRAFT HOME BASE.

15. NUMBER OF PERSONS ABOARD.

16. COLOR OF AIRCRAFT: The major color or colors should be listed.

OTHER FLIGHT LOG COLUMNS

The frequency box on the navigation log should also be filled in prior to departing on the cross-country flight. The departure and destination airport frequencies may be found in the *Airport/Facility Directory*. (See Figs. 12-17 and 12-18.) The pertinent information is entered in the frequency box. (See Fig. 12-19.)

BEAUMONT PORT ARTHUR

§ **JEFFERSON COUNTY** (BPT) 8.7 SE GMT-6(-5DT) 29°57'03"N 94°01'12"W   **HOUSTON**
    16   B   S4   **FUEL** 100, JET A   LRA   CFR Index B   **H-4F, L-17B**
    RWY 11-29: H6751X150 (CONC) S-90, D-170, DT-230   **IAP**
        HIRL. Standard plastic grooving entire length & width
    RWY 11: SSALR
    RWY 16-34: H5072X150 (CONC-ASPH) S-90, D-170, DT-230 MIRL. Currently being overlaid
    RWY 16: REIL, VASI   **RWY 34:** VASI
    RWY 02-20: H4992X150 (CONC-ASPH) S-30, D-50 MIRL. Closed to jet acft
    COMMUNICATIONS: ATIS 126.3 **UNICOM** 122.95
      LAKE CHARLES FSS (LCH) LC 722-0288 NOTAM FILE BPT
      BEAUMONT LRCO 122.1R, 122.2, 114.5T (LAKE CHARLES FSS)
    Ⓡ **BEAUMONT APP CON** 124.85 (NORTH/EAST) 121.3 (WEST)
      TOWER 119.5 **GND CON** 121.9
    Ⓡ **BEAUMONT DEP CON** 124.85 (NORTH/EAST) 121.3 (WEST)

Fig. 12-17. Airport/Facility Directory — Jefferson County Listing

HENDERSON

§ **RUSK COUNTY** (F12) 2.6 W GMT-6(-5DT) 32°08'35"N 94°51'05"W
441 S4 **FUEL** 80, 100

MEMPHIS
L-13D, -17B
IAP

RWY 12-30: H3000X100 (ASPH) S-22
   RWY 30: Trees 2000' from thld
RWY 16-34: H3000X150 (ASPH) S-22 MIRL
COMMUNICATIONS: UNICOM 122.8
   SHREVEPORT FSS (SHV)
   GREGG CO LRCO 122.2 122.1R 112.4T (SHREVEPORT FSS)
   LONGVIEW APP & DEP CON 125.3
RADIO AIDS TO NAVIGATION:
   GREGG COUNTY (L) BVORTAC 112.4 GGG Chan 71 32°25'03"N 94°45'11"W 190° 17.3 NM to fld. 320/07E
   HENDERSON NDB (MHW) 371 HNO 32°11'16"N 94°51'39"W 164° 2.4 NM to fld.

Fig. 12-18. Airport/Facility Directory — Rusk County Listing

			Airport Frequencies		
			Departure	Destination	
			Jefferson Co	*Rusk Co.*	
			ATIS *126.3*	ATIS	
			Cpt		
			Grnd *121.9*	Apch	
			Tower *119.5*	Tower	
			Dep.	Grnd	
			FSS *122.2*	FSS *122.2*	
			UNICOM *122.95*	UNICOM *122.8*	
			Field Elev. *16*	Field Elev. *441*	

Fig. 12-19. Frequency Box

The navigation log is used for two distinctly different operations. First, it is used to organize and record all the preflight planning information including the course, distance, weather briefing, estimated time en route, and the fuel required for the flight. The blank columns and blocks of information on the navigation log are completed during the actual flight. The following section explains the second use of the flight log — its function during the course of a flight as a flight record.

SECTION B - FLYING A VFR TRIP

BEFORE TAKEOFF

Before takeoff, the pilot should review the items to be accomplished during the flight; specifically these are:

1. Note the time off the ground at takeoff.
2. Open the flight plan as soon as practical after leaving the traffic pattern at the point of departure.
3. Climb to altitude, pick up the first checkpoint, and establish the compass heading that is listed on the navigation log.
4. Determine the ETA (estimated time of arrival) by adding time en route to time off.
5. Determine the time between checkpoints and, using distance between these points as listed in the navigation log, determine ground speed with the computer.
6. When the actual ground speed is known, readjust the ETA as necessary.

EN ROUTE

After takeoff and departure from the traffic pattern, the pilot contacts Lake Charles Flight Service Station to activate the flight plan. The time off the ground is 9:56 Central Daylight Time. Smoke can be seen coming from the oil refinery next to the island identified as the first checkpoint. The pilot heads directly for this smoke.

Now the pilot can determine the estimated time of arrival at the first checkpoint, as well as at Rusk County Airport. Since the estimated time en route to the first checkpoint is 9 minutes, this is added to the time off to get an ETA of 10:05. (See Fig. 12-20, item 1.) Since the estimated total time en route is 1:17, the estimated time of arrival is 11:13 Central Daylight Time. This time is entered in the navigation log. (See Fig. 12-20, item 2.)

Fig. 12-20. Navigation Log

Fig. 12-21. First Checkpoint

Fig. 12-23. Checkpoint at Silsbee

The first circled checkpoint is the island located near the oil refinery. (See Fig. 12-21.) As the aircraft passes over this point, the time of 10:05 is recorded over the island. (See Fig. 12-22). It is always good practice to record the time over checkpoints on the navigation log (see Fig. 12-20, item 3), or on the chart near the checkpoint. These times are used to make ground speed checks. Then, if the ground speed varies from the computed

The pilot finds the time required to fly 17 nautical miles at 123 knots using the calculator side of the computer. In figure 12-24, item 1 shows the index is set at 123, the predicted ground speed. Item 2 points to 17, the distance. Below 17, the pilot reads 8.3, which can be rounded off to 8 minutes. This time, added to 10:05 (the time over the first checkpoint) is 10:13 (the estimated time over Silsbee). (See Fig. 12-20, item 4.)

The chart shows two tower symbols with the word "CAUTION" printed next to them. (See Fig. 12-25.) The symbol represents tall towers supporting

Fig. 12-22. Island in River

value recorded in the navigation log, the estimated time of arrival can be changed.

Now the aircraft is turned to a heading of 333°, which is the estimated compass heading for the trip. The next checkpoint is Silsbee, 17 nautical miles from the first checkpoint. If the compass heading is correct, the aircraft should pass just east of the city. (See Fig. 12-23.)

Fig. 12-24. Computing Time
Between Checkpoints

Fig. 12-25. Powerline Symbol

powerlines that cross the stream. Figure 12-26 is a view of the powerlines crossing the stream as seen from the aircraft. The path cleared of trees marks the powerline location and is easily visible from the air. However, the wires and towers are almost invisible from the air. This powerline crossing is a hazard to a float-equipped airplane that attempts to land or take off on this stream.

Fig. 12-26. Powerlines Crossing Stream

At Silsbee, the pilot checks for the railroad going through the city from the west to the east. (See Fig. 12-27.) Then, looking to the left as the aircraft passes over the tracks on the east side of Silsbee, the railroad track is visible as it approaches Silsbee from the west. (See Fig. 12-28.) It makes a bend in the city and then proceeds in an easterly direction.

Railroads provide excellent means of identifying communities. Very often,

their patterns are visible for miles. However, railroad tracks as well as roads can be hidden easily by trees and buildings.

The time, as the aircraft passes over the railroad tracks, is 10:13, as estimated. This time is recorded for the next ground speed check. (See Fig. 12-20, item 5.)

Fig. 12-27. Railroad Symbol

Checking the chart, the pilot notices the dashed line running east and west labeled "underground pipeline." (See Fig. 12-29.) Although the pipeline cannot be seen, the right-of-way should be clearly visible. Looking east from over the area marked with the dashed line, the cleared

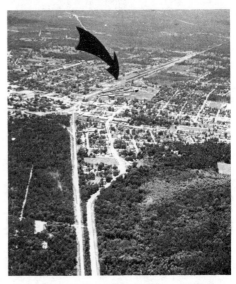

Fig. 12-28. Railroad Passing Through Silsbee

Fig. 12-29. Underground Pipeline Symbol

right-of-way that marks the location of the underground pipeline is visible. (See Fig. 12-30.) This is a *good* landmark, however, the pilot should be careful not to confuse this with a powerline right-of-way, since powerlines and their supporting towers are very difficult to see from the air.

Fig. 12-30. Underground Pipeline

Referring to the chart, it looks as if the aircraft is almost over the tower represented by the symbol shown in figure 12-31. Figure 12-32 shows a close-

up view of the tank towers and radio tower that were shown on the chart with an obstruction symbol. The arrow points out the almost invisible radio tower which is taller than the tank towers. The guy-wires supporting this tower are completely invisible.

Very often, radio towers are located in areas lacking prominent landmarks. This makes them even more difficult to find. Because of this, pilots are urged to use caution when flying low, such as during takeoffs or landings near radio towers. At night these towers are lighted with flashing red lights.

Progress of the flight to this point has been as planned. The next checkpoint is Woodville. It is important to hold a good compass heading since the course passes over a primary road rather than directly over Woodville.

At this point, the pilot can estimate the time of arrival at Woodville using the known ground speed of 123 knots. The time to fly 29 n.m., the distance between Silsbee and Woodville, is approximately 14 minutes. Adding this time to the time over the last checkpoint (Silsbee at 10:13), the estimated time of arrival over the primary road east of Woodville is 10:27. (See Fig. 12-20, item 6.)

Fig. 12-31. Obstruction Symbol

Fig. 12-32. Towers at Silsbee

The symbol shown in figure 12-33, to the left of the course, represents a lookout tower. However, since the tower is 1-1/2 miles from the course, it is difficult to see. Figure 12-34 shows the lookout tower from the closest point along the course. This tower would be a poor choice as a checkpoint. When choosing checkpoints, the pilot should remember that all features shown on a sectional chart are not always easily seen from the air. Whenever possible, items selected as checkpoints should be visual references that are easily seen and identified from information on the chart.

Fig. 12-35. Position Abeam Woodville

item 1) and the reservoir to the east (item 2). The sighting of these landmarks confirms the position. The time of 10:27 is recorded. (See Fig. 12-20, item 7.)

From this point in the flight to its termination, additional references will be made regarding the recording of time, ground speed, etc. This is good operational practice; however, for clarity, these entries will not be shown on the flight log for the remainder of the trip.

On 122.6 MHz, Lufkin Flight Service Station reports a band of thunderstorm activity from the east through the southeast quadrant, with the heaviest activity centered over Manning. Movement of the storm activity is reported to be northeast at about 10 knots. Lufkin also advises that the wind from the surface to 3,000 feet is from 230° at 17 knots.

Fig. 12-33. Lookout Tower Symbol

Fig. 12-34. Lookout Tower

WEATHER DETOUR

As the flight approaches Woodville, the next checkpoint, the pilot notices that the thunderstorm activity reported in the preflight weather briefing covers a wide area ahead and to the left of the course. After confirming the aircraft's position at Woodville, the pilot calls the Lufkin Flight Service Station for a check on the current weather. The time is now 10:27 and the aircraft should be over the road crossing the course line, with Woodville to the west (see Fig. 12-35,

After studying the chart, it appears that the best choice is to fly behind the storm by way of Corrigan and north via the dual-lane highway to East Texas Regional Airport near Nacogdoches. The dual-lane highway will provide a continuous checkpoint. (See Fig. 12-36.)

A check with the plotter shows that a line from the present location to Corrigan is 50° to the left of the present true course line of 342°. (See Fig. 12-37.) The pilot changes course to head for the place where the powerlines make an

Fig. 12-36. Course Alteration

Fig. 12-37. Plotting New Course

abrupt change in direction. (See Fig. 12-38.) The magnetic compass reads 280° as the airplane passes over the powerlines. Continuing on a heading of 280°, the aircraft arrives over the road and the railroad, which curves away from the road. (See Fig. 12-39.) The time of 10:30 is noted and recorded. This will be important at Chester when checking ground speed.

Fig. 12-38. Change in Direction of Powerline

Fig. 12-39. Road and Railroad

Approaching Chester, the track made by the road and powerline right-of-way leading to Corrigan can be plainly seen. (See Fig. 12-40.) At this point, the aircraft is slightly to the right of the expected position. (See Fig. 12-41.) By correcting the heading of the aircraft to the left, the aircraft arrives directly over Chester at 10:35, 5 minutes and 10 nautical miles from the last checkpoint.

Fig. 12-40. Parallel Road and Powerline

Fig. 12-41. Position Right of Course

The pilot records the time over Chester and then checks the ground speed for this leg. Using the flight computer, 50 (representing 5 minutes) on the B scale is set beneath 10 on the outer scale. Opposite the speed index is 12, which represents 120 knots, the present ground speed. (See Fig. 12-42.) Now the estimated time of arrival over Corrigan, which is approximately 13 nautical miles from Chester, can be calculated.

Fig. 12-42. Finding Groundspeed

Fig. 12-44. Powerline and Road Symbols

Using the computer, the pilot sets the speed index at 12 (see Fig. 12-43, item 1) representing 120 knots, then proceeds to the right to 13 (item 2), the distance between Chester and Corrigan. Under 13 on the B scale is 6.5 minutes, which is rounded off to 7 minutes. By adding 7 to the time over Chester, 10:35, the ETA for Corrigan is 10:42.

Fig. 12-45. Powerline and Road

is the place on the chart where the powerline changes direction. (See Fig. 12-46.)

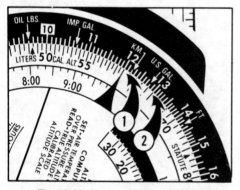

Fig. 12-43. Finding ETA at Corrigan

Fig. 12-46. Change in Direction of Powerline

As shown on the chart, the powerline right-of-way and the highway provide a prominent, continuous checkpoint to Corrigan. At this time, the flight is seven n.m. from Corrigan. (See Fig. 12-44.) The highway and the powerline as they appear from the air can be seen in figure 12-45. By looking ahead, it appears that the powerline right-of-way has been extended and continues ahead to Corrigan. However, there is evidence of a powerline right-of-way going north. This

The road and the cleared right-of-way marking the location of the powerline between Chester and Corrigan has provided a continuous checkpoint to follow directly to Corrigan. The chart shows another such continuous checkpoint — the dual-lane highway leading from Corrigan (See Fig. 12-47, item 1) north to Nacogdoches (item 2).

Fig. 12-47. Dual-Lane Highway

As the pilot approaches from the east, the north-south highway is barely visible because of the trees and buildings. However, as the flight reaches Corrigan, it becomes visible. The pilot turns north to follow the highway, then notes and records the time of 10:43. The log shows the time over Chester as 10:35 and over Corrigan as 10:43. The time en route was eight minutes and the distance between these two points is 13 nautical miles.

This information is used to compute the ground speed between Chester and Corrigan. As shown by item 1 in figure 12-48, the time en route of eight minutes (represented by the 80 on the B scale) is set under the distance traveled, 13, on the A scale. Then, over the speed index pointed out by item 2 in figure 12-48, the ground speed is indicated by the number 9.8 or 98 knots.

Fig. 12-48. Ground Speed Between Chester and Corrigan

The ground speed has dropped 22 knots from the previous check, which indicates a change in the wind. Information on winds aloft should be requested from the Lufkin Flight Service Station on 122.6 MHz.

Lufkin relays PIREP information that indicates the winds from the surface to 3,000 feet are from approximately 330° at 32 knots. This information is recorded for later reference.

Proceeding north, Diboll can be seen in the distance. By making minor heading adjustments, Diboll can be kept in a steady position relative to the nose of the airplane. This trial and error method can be used to correct for wind drift. The magnetic compass should be referenced from time to time to maintain a straight course. The magnetic compass now reads 348°.

The pattern of the dual-lane highway and the railroad can be seen as they pass through the city of Diboll. (See Fig. 12-49.) To the west of the dual-lane highway, there should be evidence of the powerlines running almost parallel to the highway.

Fig. 12-49. Railroad and Highway Through Diboll

Just prior to reaching Diboll, the pattern of the dual-lane highway and railroad are easily recognized, as in figure 12-50, item 1. To the west, the area cleared for the powerline is seen (item 2).

Fig. 12-50. Pattern of Railroad, Highway, and Powerline

Fig. 12-51. Curves in Highway

From this position almost over Diboll, the curves in the highway shown in figure 12-51 can be identified. The curves appear as sharp bends due to the aircraft's distance and angle from the highway. (See Fig. 12-52.)

Fig. 12-52. Curves Appear as Sharp Bends

In a few minutes, the airport can be seen. The airport symbol on the chart helps to identify the runway pattern of Angelina County Airport. (See Figs. 12-53 and 12-54.) The time abeam Angelina County Airport is 10:53.

Fig. 12-53. Airport Symbol

It has taken 10 minutes to cover 15 nautical miles, the distance between Corrigan and Angelina County Airport. The ground speed is computed to be 90 knots. This is a good time to compute a new ETA at Rusk County Airport. With a ground speed calculated at 90 knots, it will take 37 minutes to cover the remaining distance. When 37 minutes are added to 10:53, the time over Angelina County Airport, the new estimated time of arrival at Rusk County is 11:30. This is well within the airplane's fuel range. Lufkin radio should be advised of the new ETA.

Fig. 12-54. Angelina County Airport

The next major visual reference point is East Texas Regional Airport, southwest of Nacogdoches. Just north of Lufkin are some oil tanks. (See Fig. 12-55.) They are valuable in helping to establish a position. The notation on the chart identifies the solid round dots. (See Fig. 12-56.)

Fig. 12-55. Oil Tanks

Fig. 12-56. Oil Tank Depiction

to follow. It should take six minutes to reach East Texas Regional Airport. During this time, the pilot plans a course from East Texas Regional to Rusk County Airport.

This final segment has few good checkpoints. (See Fig. 12-57.) However, careful planning at this time will result in a compass heading that will take the aircraft direct to the destination.

The road and powerline leading to Nacogdoches provide an excellent path

By using the wind information received from Lufkin Flight Service Station and

Fig. 12-57. Final Leg of Trip

applying the appropriate compass correction, the compass heading is computed to be 342°. The predicted ground speed is 87 knots and the estimated time en route is 24 minutes.

The time is 11:07 as the flight passes over East Texas Regional Airport. The pilot records this time in the navigation log. By adding the en route time of 24 minutes, the pilot obtains the Rusk County ETA of 11:31. Then the aircraft is turned to 342° which is the computed compass heading from East Texas Regional to Rusk County Airport.

In eight minutes, a road and railroad are sighted. (See Fig. 12-58.) To the right of course, the small town of Trawick is seen. Figure 12-59 shows that the railroad makes a turn just east of Trawick (item 1), and the secondary road joins a primary road (item 2).

Fig. 12-60. Road and Railroad
as Seen from Airplane

When the airplane is directly over the railroad, the tracks disappear behind the trees as they make the first turn east of Trawick. (See Fig. 12-60, item 1.) The road continues into the distance where it seems to stop (item 2). Actually, it joins a primary road running north and south, as indicated on the chart. That point is five nautical miles away from the present position.

To the northwest, Cushing, with the road and railroad almost converging can be identified. (See Fig. 12-61, item 1.) Also, the powerline right-of-way is visible in the distance, as pointed out in figure 12-61, item 2.

Fig. 12-58. Road and Railroad
Symbols at Trawick

Fig. 12-59. Road and Railroad
Symbols East of Trawick

Fig. 12-61. Landmarks near Cushing

As the airplane continues north, the pilot notices the pattern of roads near Laneville, as shown by the arrow in figure 12-62. This unique road pattern makes Laneville easily identifiable. Figure 12-63 shows that the east-west road through the town can be seen clearly.

LANDING

There is one final landmark to be checked prior to reaching the destination. This is the highway that cuts across the flight path from southwest to northeast. The airport should be visible in the background. (See Fig. 12-64.) As the airplane approaches the highway (see Fig. 12-65), the pilot begins to prepare for the landing. As the flight nears the destination (see Fig. 12-66), the time is 11:26, five minutes ahead of the ETA which was computed as the flight passed over East Texas Regional Airport.

Fig. 12-62. Pattern of Roads Near Laneville

Fig. 12-64. Road and Airport Symbols

Fig. 12-63. Laneville

Fig. 12-65. Road and Destination Airport

Fig. 12-66. Rusk County Airport

The pilot may choose to close the flight plan by radio prior to landing or by telephone when the flight is complete. Using the radio method, Shreveport FSS can be contacted through the Gregg County limited remote communications outlet (LRCO) on 122.2 MHz. For telephone contact, the number listed in the *Airport/Facility Directory* should be used. This telephone number may also be posted at the airport. Whichever method is selected, this very important step in cross-country flying should not be overlooked.

ALPHABETICAL INDEX

(Note: The Federal Aviation Regulations are not indexed in this section.
See page 6-2 for the index to the FAR's.)

a

b

c

g

m

n

o

OBSCURED, 5-17

OBSTRUCTIONS TO VISION, 5-28

OCCLUDED FRONT, 5-21

OIL PRESSURE GAUGE, 2-33

OIL TEMPERATURE GAUGE, 2-34

OLEO STRUT, 1-6

OROGRAPHIC LIFTING, 5-22

OUTSIDE AIR TEMPERATURE GAUGE, 2-10

OXYGEN, 11-1, 11-2

p

PAYLOAD, 4-3

P-FACTOR, 1-28, 1-29

PARACHUTE JUMPING AREAS, 9-3, 9-5

PARALLELS, 7-2

PARKING AREA, 3-6

PARTIAL OBSCURATION, 5-18

PEP PILLS, 11-18

PHANTOM STATION (WAYPOINT), 8-14

PILOT/CONTROLLER GLOSSARY (AIM), 9-2

PIREPs, 5-37

PITCH AXIS, 2-2

PITOT-STATIC INSTRUMENTS
airspeed indicator, 2-10, 2-11
altimeter, 2-13
vertical speed indicator, 2-16

PITOT-STATIC SYSTEM, 2-11

PITOT TUBE, 2-10

PLAIN FLAPS, 1-19

PLANFORM, 1-17

PLOTTER, 7-25

POLAR EASTERLIES, 5-4

POSITIVE CONTROL AREA, 7-14

POSITIVE STATIC STABILITY, 1-25

POWERPLANT, 1-9

PRECESSION, GYROSCOPIC, 2-18

PRECISION RUNWAY MARKINGS, 3-3

PRE-IGNITION, 2-30

PRESSURE ALTITUDE, 2-14

PRESSURE GRADIENT, 5-13

PRESSURE LAPSE RATE, 5-10

PRESSURE SYSTEMS
characteristics, 5-13
definition, 5-13
gradient, 5-13
types of, 5-11

PREVAILING WESTERLIES, 5-4

PRIME MERIDIAN, 7-2

PROHIBITED AREA, 7-21

PROPELLERS
climb prop, 2-37
constant-speed, 2-39
cruise, 2-37
fixed-pitch, 2-37
principles of operation, 1-10, 2-36

PROTRACTOR, 7-25

PSYCHOLOGICAL CONSIDERATIONS
anxiety, 11-20
stress, 11-20

r

RADAR
AIM, 9-2
airport surveillance, 8-19
echo, 8-19
explanation of abbreviation, 8-19
general principles of operation, 8-19
precision approach, 8-19
primary, 8-19
programs for VFR aircraft, 8-22
secondary, 8-19
traffic information service, 8-22

RADAR SUMMARY CHARTS, 5-41

RADIALS, VOR, 8-2

RADIATION FOG, 5-15

RADIO COMMUNICATIONS, 3-13

RADIO NAVIGATION
Victor airways, 8-2

RADIO PHRASEOLOGY, 3-15

RADIUS OF ACTION, 10-12

RAIN-INDUCED FOG, 5-16

RECEIVER, 3-13

RED BEACONS, 3-9

REFERENCE DATUM, 4-4

REFUELING, 2-47

RELATIVE BEARING, 8-16

S